Strive for a 5: Preparing for the AP® Statistics Examination

to accompany
The UPDATED Practice of Statistics, **Sixth Edition**
Daren Starnes • Josh Tabor

Jason Molesky
Michael Legacy
Erica Chauvet
Jeff Eicher

bedford, freeman & worth
high school publishers

ISBN -13: 978-1-3192-8309-4
ISBN-10: 1-3192-8309-8

W.H. Freeman and Company
Bedford, Freeman & Worth High School Publishers
One New York Plaza
Suite 4500
New York, NY 10004-1562
Highschool.bfwpub.com/catalog

Table of Contents

Preface

Strive for a 5: Preparing for the AP® Statistics Examination is designed for use with *The UPDATED Practice of Statistics, Sixth Edition* by Daren Starnes and Josh Tabor. It is intended to help you evaluate your understanding of the material covered in the textbook, reinforce the key concepts you need to learn, develop your conceptual understanding and communication skills, and prepare you to take the AP® Statistics Exam. This book is divided into two sections: a study guide and a test preparation section.

THE STUDY GUIDE SECTION

The study guide is designed for you to use throughout your course in AP® Statistics. As each chapter is covered in your class, use the study guide to help you identify and learn the important statistics concepts and terms. For each section, this guide provides learning targets, checks for understanding, practice problems, and hints to help you master the material and verify your understanding before moving on to the next section.

This guide is designed to help you clearly identify what it is you need to learn, whether or not you have learned it, and what you need to do to close any gaps in your understanding. That is, it will help you answer the questions:

"Where am I going?".
"Where am I now?"
"How can I close the gap?"

For each chapter, the study guide is organized as follows.
- **Overview**: The chapter content is summarized to provide a quick overview of the material covered. The material is broken down into the specific learning targets to help you answer the question "Where am I going?"

- **Chapter Sections:** Each section includes a presentation of the important content to help guide your learning. The section content includes the following.
  - **Learning Targets**: These "I can…" statements provide a guide for you to keep track of your learning. Check these off as you become confident with each of the concepts.
  - **Vocabulary**: Space for you to record and study definitions of important terms.
  - **Concept Explanations**: Important concepts are explained further to aid you in your study of the key points of each section.
  - **Checks for Understanding**: Mini assessments for each learning target help you answer the question "Where am I now?"

- **Chapter Summary**: The key concepts of the chapter are briefly reviewed and a summary of all of the learning targets is provided to help you check your learning

- **Multiple Choice Questions**: These multiple-choice questions focus on the key concepts that you should grasp after reading the chapter and are designed for quick exam preparation. After checking your answers, you should reflect on the big ideas from the chapter and identify the concepts you may need to study more.

- **FRAPPY!:** A "Free-Response AP Problem, Yay!" is provided after each chapter. Each FRAPPY is modeled after actual AP Statistics Exam questions and provide an opportunity for you to practice your communication skills to maximize your score. These problems are meant to help you determine what further work is needed to address the question "How can I close the gap?"

- **Vocabulary Crossword Puzzle**: These puzzles provide a fun way for you to check your understanding of key definitions from the chapter.

Answers to all questions and problems in the study guide are available in the back of the book. Checking your answers will help you determine whether or not you need additional work on specific learning targets.

THE TEST PREPARATION SECTION

The "Preparing for the AP Statistics Examination" section of this guide is meant to help you better understand how the exam is constructed and scored, how best to study for the exam, and how to make sure you highlight what you have learned when answering exam questions. Two full-length exams and answer modeled on the actual Advanced Placement Exam (40 multiple-choice questions, 5 free response questions, and an investigative task) are included to help you get a feel for the actual test. Try to simulate the actual exam conditions as much as possible when taking these practice tests!

We hope that your use of "Strive for a 5: Preparing for the AP® Statistics Examination" will assist you in your study of statistical concepts, help you earn as high a score as possible on the exam, and provide you with an interest and desire to further your study of statistics.
Jason, Michael, Erica, and Jeff

About the Authors

Jason M. Molesky
Northfield, MN

Jason served as an AP® Statistics Reader and Table Leader since 2006. After teaching AP® Statistics for 8 years and developing the FRAPPY system for AP® Statistics exam preparation, Jason served as the Director of Program Evaluation and Accountability for the Lakeville Area Public Schools. He has recently settled into his dream job as an educational consul-tant for Apple. Jason maintains the "Stats Monkey" website, a clearinghouse for AP® Statistics resources.

Michael Legacy
Greenhill School, Dallas, TX

Michael is a past member of the AP® Statistics Development Committee (2001-2005) and a former Table Leader at the Reading. He currently reads the Alternate Exam and is a lead teacher at many AP® Summer Institutes. Michael is the author of the 2007 College Board AP® Statistics Teacher's Guide and was named the Texas 2009-2010 AP® Math/Science Teacher of the Year by the Siemens Corporation.

Erica Chauvet
Waynesburg University, Waynesburg, PA

Erica has more than 15 years of experience in teaching high school and college statistics and has served as an AP® Statistics Reader for the past 10 years. Erica famously hosts the two most highly anticipated events at the Reading: the Fun Run and the Closing Ceremonies. She has also worked as a writer, consultant, and reviewer for statistics and calculus textbooks for the past 10 years.

Jeff Eicher, Jr.
Classical Academy High School, Escondido, CA

Jeff has taught AP Statistics for 9 years and been an AP reader for 3 years. He has served on the AP® Statistics Instructional Design Team, creating resources for students and teachers. Jeff is also a NMSI consultant, mentoring teachers and hosting Saturday study sessions.

CHAPTER 1: Data Analysis

"Statistical thinking will one day be as necessary for efficient citizenship as the ability to read and write." H.G. Wells

CHAPTER OVERVIEW

Statistics is the science of data. We begin our study of the subject by mastering the art of examining and describing sets of data. This chapter introduces you to the concept of exploratory data analysis. You will learn how to use a variety of graphical tools to display data as well as how to describe data numerically.

By the end of this chapter, you should understand the difference between categorical and quantitative data, how to display and describe these two types of data, and how to move from data analysis to inference. These skills are the basis for our entire study of Statistics. Use this guide to help ensure you have a firm grasp on these concepts!

Sections in this Chapter
Introduction: Data Analysis: Making Sense of Data
Section 1.1: Analyzing Categorical Data
Section 1.2: Displaying Quantitative Data with Graphs
Section 1.3: Describing Quantitative Data with Numbers

PLAN YOUR LEARNING

Use the following *suggested* guide to help plan your reading and assignments in "The Practice of Statistics, Updated 6th Edition." Put a check mark in the last column when you are done. Note: your teacher may schedule a different pacing or assign different problems. Be sure to follow his or her instructions!

Read	Do	Done!
Ch1 Introduction	1, 3, 5, 7, MC 9-10	
Section 1.1: p. 9-16	13, 15, 17, 19, 21, 23	
Section 1.1: p. 17-23	27, 29, 33, 35, MC 40-43	
Section 1.2: p. 30-34	45, 49, 51, 59, 63	
Section 1.2: p. 34-47	55, 65, 69, 77, MC 80-85	
Section 1.3: p 54-65	87, 89, 91, 95, 97, 101, 103, 105, 121	
Section 1.3: p 65-74	109, 111, 113, 115, MC 123-126	
Chapter Summary	Review Exercises FRAPPY!	

Use this "Strive Guide" to help identify learning targets for each section, summarize key concepts, practice additional problems, and check your understanding as you read the text.

Introduction - Statistics: The Science and Art of Data

Before You Read: Section Summary

In this section, you will learn the basic terms and definitions necessary for our study of statistics. You will also be introduced to the idea of moving from data analysis to inference. One of our goals in statistics is to use data from a representative sample to make an inference about the population from which it was drawn. In order to do this, we must be able to identify the type of data we are dealing with, as our choice of statistical procedures will depend upon that distinction.

Learning Targets:

_____ I can identify individuals and variables in a set of data.
_____ I can classify variables as categorical or quantitative.

While You Read: Key Vocabulary and Concepts

statistics:
individuals:
variable:
categorical variable:
quantitative variable:
discrete variable:
continuous variable:
distribution:
inference:

After You Read: Check for Understanding

Concept 1: Individuals and Variables

Sets of data contain information about individuals. The characteristics of the individuals that are measured are called variables. Variables can take on different values for different individuals. It is these values and the variation in them that we will be learning about in this course.

Concept 2: Types of Variables

Variables can fall into one of two categories: categorical or quantitative. When the characteristic we measure places an individual into one of several groups, we call it a categorical variable. When the characteristic we measure results in numerical values for which it makes sense to find an average, we call it a quantitative variable. This distinction is important, as the methods we use to describe and analyze data will depend upon the type of variable we are studying. In the rest of this chapter, we'll learn how to display and describe the distribution of a variable.

Check for Understanding:

_____ *I can identify individuals and variables in a set of data.*

Mr. Bush gathered some information on 6 students in his class and organized it in a table.

Student	Gender	ACT Score	Favorite Subject	Height (in)
James	M	34	Statistics	70
Jen	F	35	Biology	51
DeAnna	F	32	History	67
Jonathan	M	28	Literature	69
Doug	M	33	Algebra	71
Sharon	F	30	Spanish	68.5

1) Who are the individuals in this dataset?

2) What variables were measured? Identify each as quantitative (discrete), quantitative (continuous) or categorical.

3) Could we infer from this set of data that students who prefer math and science perform better on the ACT? Explain.

Section 1.1: Analyzing Categorical Data

Before You Read: Section Summary

In this section, you will learn how to describe and analyze categorical variables. You will learn how to display data with pie charts and bar graphs as well as how to describe these displays. You will also learn how to analyze the relationship between two categorical variables using marginal and conditional distributions.

Learning Targets:

_____ I can make and interpret bar graphs for categorical data.
_____ I can identify what makes some graphs of categorical data misleading.
_____ I can calculate marginal and joint relative frequencies from a two-way table.
_____ I can calculate conditional relative frequencies from a two–way table.
_____ I can use bar graphs to compare distributions of categorical data.
_____ I can describe the nature of the association between two categorical variables.

While You Read: Key Vocabulary and Concepts

frequency table:
relative frequency table:
bar graph:
pie chart:
marginal relative frequency:
joint relative frequency:
conditional relative frequency:
segmented bar graph:
mosaic plot:
association:

After You Read: Check for Understanding

Concept 1: Displaying Categorical Data

A frequency table (or a relative frequency table) displays the counts (or percentages) of individuals that take on each value of a variable. Tables are sometimes difficult to read and they don't always highlight important features of a distribution. Graphical displays of data are much easier to read and often reveal interesting patterns and departures from patterns in the distribution of data. We can use pie charts and bar graphs to display the distribution of categorical variables. Note, when constructing graphical displays, we must be careful not to distort the quantities. Beware of pictographs and watch the scales when displaying or reading graphs!

Check for Understanding:
_____ *I can make and interpret bar graphs for categorical data.*

A local business owner was interested in knowing the coffee-shop preferences of her town's residents. According to her survey of 250 residents, 75 preferred "Goodbye Blue Monday", 50 liked "The Ugly Mug", 38 chose "Morning Joe's", 50 said "One Mean Bean", 25 brewed their own coffee, and 12 preferred the national chain.

1) Construct a bar graph to display the data. Describe what you see.

2) Construct a pie chart to display the data. How does this display differ from the bar chart?

Concept 2: Two-Way Tables

Bar graphs and pie charts are helpful when analyzing a single categorical variable. However, often we want to explore the relationship between two categorical variables. To do this, we organize our data in a two-way table with a row variable and a column variable. The counts of the individuals in each intersecting category make up the entries in the table.

When exploring a two-way table, you should start by describing each variable separately. This can be done by describing the marginal distribution of the row or column variable. To explore the relationship between the variables, study the conditional distributions by graphing each distribution of one variable for a fixed value of the other. If there is no association between the two variables, the graphs of the conditional distributions will be the same. If there is an association between the two variables, the graphs of the conditional distributions will be different.

Check for Understanding:

_____ *I can describe the nature of the association between two categorical variables.*

A survey of 1000 randomly chosen residents of a Minnesota town asked "Where do you prefer to purchase your daily coffee?" The two-way table below shows the responses.

Coffee preference by gender

Preference	Male	Female	Total
National Chain	95	65	160
One Mean Bean	15	85	100
The Ugly Mug	145	25	170
Goodbye Blue Monday	170	90	260
Home-brewed	100	160	260
Don't drink coffee	10	40	50
Total	535	465	1000

Based on the data, can we conclude that there is an association between gender and coffee preferences? Use appropriate graphical and numerical evidence to support your conclusion.

Section 1.2: Displaying Quantitative Data with Graphs

Before You Read: Section Summary

In this section, you will learn how to display quantitative data. Like categorical data, we are interested in describing the distribution of quantitative data. Dotplots, stemplots, and histograms are helpful tools for revealing the shape, center, and variability of a distribution of quantitative data. These basic plots will come in very handy throughout the course, so be sure to master them in this section!

Learning Targets:

_____ I can make and interpret dotplots, stemplots, and histograms of quantitative data.

_____ I can identify the shape of a distribution from a graph.

_____ I can describe the overall pattern (shape, center, and variability) of a distribution and identify any major departures from the pattern (outliers).

_____ I can compare distributions of quantitative data using dotplots, stemplots, and histograms.

While You Read: Key Vocabulary and Concepts

dotplot:
stemplot:
histogram:
shape:
center:
variability:
outliers:
symmetric:
skewed to the right:
skewed to the left:

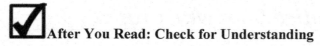

After You Read: Check for Understanding

Concept 1: *Statistical Opinions Can Vary!*

The reason we construct graphs of quantitative data is so that we can get a better understanding of it. Constructing a plot helps us examine the data and identify its overall pattern. When examining the distribution of a quantitative variable, start by looking for the overall pattern and then describe any major departures from it. Note its shape. Is it symmetric? Is it skewed? How many peaks does it have? What is its center? How variable are the data? Are the values bunched up around the center, or are they spread out? Finally, are there any outliers? Do any values fall far away from the rest of the distribution? The answers to each of these questions are very important when describing a set of data. Be sure to address all of them as you explore data sets throughout this course. As you explore data, don't forget Statistical Opinions Can Vary (Shape, Outliers, Center, Variability)!

Concept 2: *Dotplots and Stemplots*

Dotplots and stemplots are the easiest graphs to construct, especially if you have a small set of data. These plots are helpful for describing distributions because they keep the data intact. That is, you can determine the individual data values directly from the plot. When comparing two sets of data, we can construct back-to-back stemplots or dotplots that share the same scale. Remember, when constructing plots, always label your axes and provide a key!

Check for Understanding:

_____ *I can make and interpret dotplots and stemplots.*

A recent study by the Environmental Protection Agency (EPA) measured the gas mileage (miles per gallon) for 30 models of cars. The results are below:

EPA-Measured MPG for 30 Cars

36.3	32.7	40.5	36.2	38.5	36.3	41.0	37.0	37.1	39.9
41.0	37.3	36.5	37.9	39.0	36.8	31.8	37.2	40.3	36.9
36.7	33.6	34.2	35.1	39.7	39.3	35.8	34.5	39.5	36.9

1) Construct a dotplot to display this data and describe the distribution.

2) Construct a stemplot to display this data.

Concept 3: Histograms

When dealing with larger sets of data, dotplots and stemplots can be a bit cumbersome and time-consuming to construct. In these cases, it may be easier to construct a histogram. Instead of plotting each value in the data set, a histogram displays the frequency of values that fall within equal-width classes. Be sure not to confuse histograms with bar graphs. Even though they look similar, they describe different types of data!

Check for Understanding:

_____ *I can make and interpret a histogram.*

The EPA expanded its study to include a total of 50 car models. The results are below.

EPA-Measured MPG for 50 Cars

36.3	32.7	40.5	36.2	38.5	36.3	41.0	37.0	37.1	39.9
41.0	37.3	36.5	37.9	39.0	36.8	31.8	37.2	40.3	36.9
36.7	33.6	34.2	35.1	39.7	39.3	35.8	34.5	39.5	36.9
36.9	41.2	37.6	36.0	35.5	32.5	37.3	40.7	36.7	32.9
42.1	37.5	40.0	35.6	38.8	38.4	39.0	36.7	34.8	38.1

1) Construct a histogram for these data by hand. Describe the distribution.

2) Use your calculator to construct a histogram. Do you get the same graph? If not, how can you make your calculator match the histogram you constructed in part (a)?

Section 1.3: Describing Quantitative Data with Numbers

Before You Read: Section Summary

In this section, you will learn how to use numerical summaries to describe the center and variability of a distribution of quantitative data. You will also learn how to identify outliers in a distribution. Being able to accurately describe a distribution and calculate and interpret numerical summaries forms the foundation for our statistical study. By the end of this section, you will want to make sure you are comfortable selecting appropriate numerical summaries, calculating them (by hand or by using technology), and interpreting them for a set of quantitative data.

Learning Targets:

_____ I can calculate and interpret measures of center (mean and median) for a distribution of quantitative data.

_____ I can calculate and interpret measures of variability (range, IQR, and standard deviation) for a distribution of quantitative data.

_____ I can explain how outliers and skewness affect measures of center and variability.

_____ I can identify outliers using the $1.5 \times IQR$ Rule.

_____ I can make and interpret boxplots of quantitative data.

_____ I can use boxplots and numerical summaries to compare distributions of quantitative data.

While You Read: Key Vocabulary and Concepts

mean:
median:
range:
standard deviation:
quartiles:
interquartile range (IQR):
five-number summary:
boxplot:

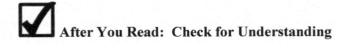**After You Read: Check for Understanding**

Concept 1: Exploratory Data Analysis

Statistical tools and ideas can help you examine data in order to describe their main features. This examination is called an *exploratory data analysis (EDA)*. To organize our exploration, we want to:

- **Examine each variable by itself**...then move on to study relationships among the variables.
- **Always, always, always, always, *plot your data*....** always.
- **Begin with a graph or graphs**...construct and interpret an appropriate graph of the data.
- **Add numeric summaries**...for quantitative data, calculate and interpret appropriate measures of center and measures of spread.
- **Don't forget your SOCV!** Shape, Outliers, Center, Variability...for quantitative data, note these important features!

Concept 2: Measures of Center

The mean and median measure the center of a set of data in different ways. While the mean, or average, is the most common measure of center, it is not always the most appropriate. Extreme values can "pull" the mean towards them. The median, or middle value, is resistant to extreme values and is sometimes a better measure of center. In symmetric distributions, the mean and median will be approximately equal, while in a skewed distribution the mean tends to be closer to the "tail" than the median. Always consider the shape of the distribution when deciding which measure to use to describe your data!

Check for Understanding:

_____ *I can calculate and interpret measures of center.*

Consider the following stemplot of the lengths of time (in seconds) it took students to complete a logic puzzle. Use it to answer the following questions. Note: 2 | 2 = 22 seconds.

```
1 | 58
2 | 23
2 | 677778888999
3 | 2344
3 | 68
4 | 011223
4 | 6
5 | 00
```

1) Based only on the plot, how does the mean compare to the median? How do you know?

2) Calculate and interpret the mean.

3) Calculate and interpret the median.

4) Which measure of center would be the more appropriate summary of the center of this distribution? Why?

Technology: Use your calculator to find the mean and median for this set of data and verify that you get the same results as (2) and (3).

Concept 3: Measures of Variability and Boxplots

Like measures of center, we have several different ways to measure variability for distributions of quantitative data. The easiest way to describe the variability of a distribution is to calculate the range (maximum − minimum). However, extreme values can cause this measure to be much greater than the variability of the majority of values. A measure of variability that is resistant to the effect of outliers is the interquartile range (*IQR*).

> To find the *IQR*, arrange the observations from smallest to largest and determine the median. Then find the median of the lower half of the data. This is the first quartile. The median of the upper half of the data is the third quartile. The distance between the first quartile and third quartile is the interquartile range.

Not only does the *IQR* provide a measure of variability, it also provides us with a way to identify outliers. According to the $1.5 \times IQR$ rule, any value that falls more than $1.5 \times IQR$ above the third quartile or below the first quartile is considered an outlier. The minimum, maximum, median, and quartiles make up the "five-number summary". This set of numbers describes the center and variability of a set of quantitative data and leads to a useful display – the boxplot (box and whisker plot).

Another measure of variability that we will use to describe data is the standard deviation. The standard deviation measures roughly the average distance of the observations from their mean. The calculation can be quite time-consuming to do by hand, so we'll rely on technology to provide the standard deviation for us. However, be sure you understand how it is calculated!

When describing data numerically, always make sure to note a measure of center AND a measure of variability. If you choose the median as your measure of center, it is best to use the *IQR* to describe the variability. If you choose the mean to describe center, use the standard deviation to measure the variability.

Check for Understanding:
_____ *I can calculate and interpret measures of variability.*

The length (in pages) of Mrs. Molesky's favorite books are noted below

242   346   314   330   340   322   284   342   368   170   344   318   318   374   332

1) Use these data to construct a boxplot. Describe the center and variability using the five-number summary.

2) Calculate and interpret the mean and standard deviation for these data.

Chapter Summary: Data Analysis

In this chapter, we learned that statistics is the art and science of data. When working with data, it is important to know whether the variables are categorical or quantitative, as this will determine the most appropriate display for the distribution. For categorical data, the display will help us describe the distribution. For quantitative data, the display will help us describe the shape of the distribution and suggest the most appropriate numeric measures of center and variability. Always begin with a graph of the distribution, then move to a numerical description. When exploring quantitative data, we want to be sure to interpret the shape, outliers, center, and variability. Look for an overall pattern to describe your data and note any striking departures from that pattern.

As you study, be sure to focus on *understanding*, not just mechanics. While it may be easy to "plug the data" into your calculator, simply making graphs and calculating values is not the point of statistics. Rather, focus on being able to explain HOW a graph or value is constructed and WHY you would choose a certain display or numeric summary. Get in this habit early…your calculator is a powerful tool, but it cannot replace your thinking and communication skills!

How well do you understand each of the learning targets?

Learning Target	Got It!	Almost There	Needs Work
I can identify individuals and variables for a set of data.			
I can classify variables as categorical or quantitative.			
I can make and interpret bar graphs for categorical data.			
I can identify what makes some graphs of categorical data misleading.			
I can calculate marginal and joint relative frequencies from a two-way table.			
I can calculate conditional relative frequencies from a two–way table.			
I can use bar graphs to compare distributions of categorical data.			
I can describe the association between two categorical variables.			
I can make and interpret dotplots, stemplots, and histograms of quantitative data.			
I can identify the shape of a distribution from a graph.			
I can describe the overall pattern (shape, center, and variability) of a distribution and identify any major departures from the pattern (outliers).			
I can compare distributions of quantitative data using dotplots, stemplots, and histograms.			
I can calculate and interpret measures of center (mean and median) for a distribution of quantitative data.			
I can calculate and interpret measures of variability (range, IQR, and standard deviation) for a distribution of quantitative data.			
I can explain how outliers and skewness affect measures of center and variability.			
I can identify outliers using the $1.5 \times IQR$ Rule.			
I can make and interpret boxplots of quantitative data.			
I can use boxplots and numerical summaries to compare distributions of quantitative data.			

Chapter 1 Multiple Choice Practice

Directions. Identify the choice that best completes the statement or answers the question. Check your answers and note your performance when you are finished.

1. You measure the age (years), weight (pounds), and breed (beagle, golden retriever, pug, or terrier) of 200 dogs. How many variables did you measure?
   (A) 1
   (B) 2
   (C) 3
   (D) 200
   (E) 203

2. You open a package of Lucky Charms cereal and count how many there are of each marshmallow shape. The <u>distribution</u> of the variable "marshmallow" is:
   (A) The shape: star, heart, moon, clover, diamond, horseshoe, balloon.
   (B) The total number of marshmallows in the package.
   (C) Seven—the number of different shapes that are in the package.
   (D) The seven different shapes and how many there are of each.
   (E) Because "shape" is a categorical variable, it doesn't have a distribution.

3. A review of voter registration records in a small town yielded the following table of the number of males and females registered as Democrat, Republican, or some other affiliation.

	Male	Female
Democrat	300	600
Republican	500	300
Other	200	100

   What proportion of males are registered as Democrats?
   (A) 300
   (B) 30
   (C) 0.33
   (D) 0.30
   (E) 0.15

4. For a physics course containing 10 students, the maximum point total for the quarter was 200. The point totals for the 10 students are given in the stemplot below.

   ```
   11 | 6  8
   12 | 1  4  8
   13 | 3  7
   14 | 2  6
   15 |
   16 |
   17 | 9
   ```

   Which of the following statements is NOT true?
   (A) In a symmetric distribution, the mean and the median are equal.
   (B) About fifty percent of the scores in a distribution are between the first and third quartiles.
   (C) In a symmetric distribution, the median is halfway between the first and third quartiles.
   (D) The median is always greater than the mean.
   (E) The range is the difference between the largest and the smallest observation in the data set.

5. When drawing a histogram, it is important to
    (A) have a separate class interval for each observation to get the most informative plot.
    (B) make sure the heights of the bars exceed the widths of the class intervals so that the bars are true rectangles.
    (C) label the vertical axis so the reader can determine the counts or percent in each class interval.
    (D) leave large gaps between bars. This allows room for comments.
    (E) scale the vertical axis according to the variable whose distribution you are displaying.

6. A set of data has a mean that is much larger than the median. Which of the following statements is most consistent with this information?
    (A) The distribution is symmetric.
    (B) The distribution is skewed left.
    (C) The distribution is skewed right.
    (D) The distribution is bimodal.
    (E) The data set probably has a few low outliers.

7. The following is a boxplot of the birth weights (in ounces) of a sample of 160 infants born in a local hospital.

Birth weight (ounces)

About 40 of the birth weights were below what value?
    (A) 92 ounces
    (B) 102 ounces
    (C) 112 ounces
    (D) 122 ounces
    (E) 132 ounces

8. A sample of production records for an automobile manufacturer shows the following figures for production per shift:

          705   700   690   705

What is the variance of this sample?
    (A) 8.66
    (B) 7.07
    (C) 75
    (D) 50
    (E) 20

9. You catch 10 cockroaches in your bedroom and measure their lengths in centimeters. Which of these sets of numerical descriptions are *all* measured in centimeters?
    (A) median length, variance of lengths, largest length
    (B) median length, first and third quartiles of lengths
    (C) mean length, standard deviation of lengths, median length
    (D) mean length, median length, variance of lengths.
    (E) both (B) and (C)

10. A policeman records the speeds of cars on a certain section of roadway with a radar gun. The histogram below shows the distribution of speeds for 251 cars.

    Which of the following measures of center and spread would be the best ones to use when summarizing these data?
    (A) Mean and interquartile range.
    (B) Mean and standard deviation.
    (C) Median and range.
    (D) Median and standard deviation.
    (E) Median and interquartile range.

Check your answers below. If you got a question wrong, check to see if you made a simple mistake or if you need to study that concept more. After you check your work, identify the concepts you feel very confident about and note what you will do to learn the concepts in need of more study.

#	Answer	Concept	Right	Wrong	Simple Mistake?	Need to Study More
1	C	Variables				
2	D	Categorical variables				
3	D	Two-way table				
4	D	Distribution basics				
5	C	Constructing histograms				
6	C	Skewed distributions				
7	B	Interpreting boxplots				
8	D	Variance				
9	E	Summary statistics units				
10	B	Choosing statistics				

FRAPPY! Free Response AP® Problem, Yay!

The following problem is modeled after actual Advanced Placement Statistics free response questions. Your task is to generate a complete, concise response in 15 minutes. After you generate your response, read over the solution and scoring guide. Score your response and note what, if anything, you would do differently to increase your own score.

SugarBitz candies are packaged in 15 oz. snack-size bags. The back-to-back plot below displays the weights (in ounces) of two samples of SugarBitz bags filled by different filling machines. The weights ranged from 14.1 oz. to 15.9 oz.

(a) Compare the distributions of weights of bags packaged by the two machines.

(b) The company wishes to be as consistent as possible when packing its snack bags. Which machine would be *least* likely to produce snack bags of SugarBitz that have a consistent weight? Explain.

(c) Suppose the company filled its bags using the machine you chose in part (b). Which measure of center, the mean or the median, would be closer to the advertised 15oz.? Explain why you chose this measure.

FRAPPY! Scoring Rubric

Use the following rubric to score your response. Each part receives a score of "Essentially Correct," "Partially Correct," or "Incorrect." When you have scored your response, reflect on your understanding of the concepts addressed in this problem. If necessary, note what you would do differently on future questions like this to increase your score.

Intent of the Question

The goals of this question are (1) to determine your ability to use graphical displays to compare and contrast two distributions and (2) to evaluate your ability to use statistical information to make a decision.

Solution

(a) Both distributions are single-peaked. However, Machine A's distribution is roughly symmetric while Machine B's is skewed to the right. The center of the weights for Machine A (median A = about 15) is slightly higher than that of Machine B (median B = about 14.5). There is more variability in the weights produced by Machine B. Machine A has one low value (14.1) that does not fall with the majority of weights. However, it does not appear to be extreme enough to be considered an outlier.

(b) Both machines produce bags of varying weight. However, Machine B has a higher variability as evidenced by a wider overall range. Machine B would be least likely to produce a consistent weight for the snack bags.

(c) The mean would be closer to the advertised 15 oz. weight. This is because in a skewed distribution, the mean is pulled away from the median in the direction of the tail. In Machine B's distribution, the peak is at about 14.5 oz so we would expect the mean to be higher and closer to 15 oz.

Scoring:

Parts (a), (b), and (c) are scored as essentially correct (E), partially correct (P), or incorrect (I).

Part (a) is essentially correct if you correctly identify similarities and differences in the shape, center, and spread for the two distributions.
Part (a) is partially correct if you correctly identify similarities and differences in two of the three characteristics for the two distributions.
Part (a) is incorrect if you only identify one similarity or difference of the three characteristics for the two distributions.

Part (b) is essentially correct if Machine B is chosen using rationale based on its measure of spread of the packaged weights.
Part (b) is partially correct if B is chosen, but the explanation does not refer to the variability in the weights.
Part (c) is incorrect if B is chosen and no explanation is provided OR if A is chosen.

Part (c) is essentially correct if the mean is chosen and the explanation addresses the fact that the mean will be greater than the median in a skewed right distribution.
Part (c) is partially correct if the mean is chosen, but the explanation is incomplete or incorrect.
Part (c) is incorrect if the mean is chosen, but no explanation is given OR if the median is chosen.
NOTE: If Machine A was chosen in part (b) and the solution to part (c) indicates either the mean or median would be appropriate due to the fact that they will be approximately equal in a symmetric, mound-shaped distribution, part (c) should be scored as essentially correct.

4   Complete Response
  All three parts essentially correct

3   Substantial Response
  Two parts essentially correct and one part partially correct

2   Developing Response
  Two parts essentially correct and no parts partially correct
  One part essentially correct and two or one parts partially correct
  Three parts partially correct

1   Minimal Response
  One part essentially correct and no parts partially correct
  No parts essentially correct and two parts partially correct

My Score:
What I did well:
What I could improve:
What I should remember if I see a problem like this on the AP Exam:

Chapter 1 Formula Sheet

Create a one-page summary of important concepts and formulas found in this chapter. This will serve as a valuable resource as you prepare for the AP Exam.

Chapter 1 Crossword Puzzle
DATA ANALYSIS

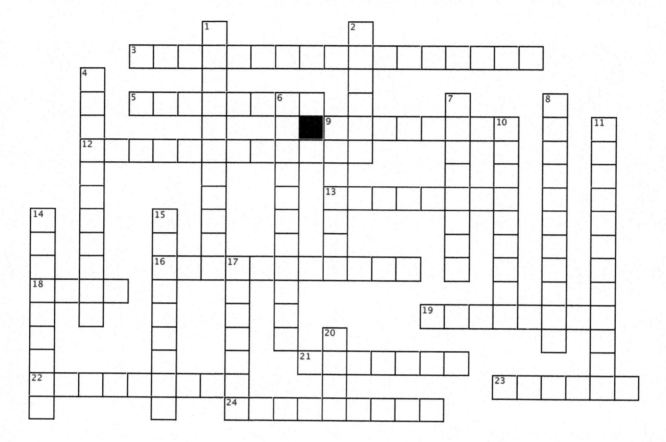

Across

3. The average distance of observations from their mean (two words)
5. The average squared distance of the observations from their mean
9. Displays the counts or percents of categories in a categorical variable through differing heights of bars
12. Tells you what values a variable takes and how often it takes these values
13. Displays a categorical variable using slices sized by the counts or percents for the categories
16. When specific values of one variable tend to occur in common with specific values of another
18. A measure of center, also called the average
19. A graphical display of quantitative data that involves splitting the individual values into two components
21. One of the simplest graphs to construct when dealing with a small set of quantitative data
22. Drawing conclusions beyond the data at hand
23. The shape of a distribution if one side of the graph is much longer than the other
24. What we call a measure that is relatively unaffected by extreme observations

Down

1. The objects described by a set of data
2. The midpoint of a distribution of quantitative data
4. A _____ distribution describes the distribution of values of a categorical variable among individuals who have a specific value of another variable.
6. A variable that places an individual into one of several groups or categories
7. A characteristic of an individual that can take different values for different individuals
8. When comparing two categorical variables, we can orgainze the data in a ___-___ _____.
9. A graphical display of the five-number summary
10. A graphical display of quantitative data that shows the frequency of values in intervals by using bars
11. A variable that takes numerical values for which it makes sense to find an average
14. The shape of a distribution whose right and left sides are approximate mirror images of each other
15. These values lie one-quarter, one-half, and three-quarters of the way up the list of quantitative data
17. A value that is at least 1.5 IQRs above the third quartile or below the first quartile
20. When exploring data, don't forget your _____

CHAPTER 2: Modeling Distributions of Quantitative Data

*"It is not knowledge, but the act of learning, not possession but
the act of getting there, which grants the greatest enjoyment."* Carl Friedrich Gauss

CHAPTER OVERVIEW

In Chapter 1, we built a "toolbox" of graphical and numerical tools for describing distributions of data. We now have a clear strategy for exploring data. This chapter introduces you to a key concept in statistics – describing the location of an observation within a distribution. You will learn how to measure position by using percentiles as well as by using a standardized measure based on the mean and standard deviation. We'll discover that sometimes the overall pattern of a large number of observations is so regular it can be described by a smooth curve. Density curves will be introduced as a model to describe locations without having to rely on every one of the data values. One of the most common density curves, the Normal distribution, will be explored in Section 2.2. You will not only learn the properties of the Normal distributions, but also how to perform a number of calculations with them. The concepts introduced in this section will be revisited throughout the course, so be sure to master them in this chapter!

Sections in this Chapter

Section 2.1: Describing Location in a Distribution
Section 2.2: Density Curves and Normal Distributions

PLAN YOUR LEARNING

Use the following *suggested* guide to help plan your reading and assignments in "The Practice of Statistics, Updated 6th Edition." Put a check mark in the last column when you are done. Note: your teacher may schedule a different pacing or assign different problems. Be sure to follow his or her instructions!

Read	Do	Done!
Section 2.1: p. 90-97	1, 3, 7, 9, 11, 13, 15, 19	
Section 2.1: p. 97-103	21, 25, 29, 31, MC 33-38	
Section 2.2: p. 109-119	41, 45, 47, 49, 51	
Section 2.2: p. 119-130	53, 55, 57, 59, 61, 63	
Section 2.2: p. 131-137	73, 75, 77, 79, 81, MC 85-90	
Chapter Summary	Multiple-Choice FRAPPY!	

Use this "Strive Guide" to help identify learning targets for each section, summarize key concepts, practice additional problems, and check your understanding as you read the text.

Section 2.1: Describing Location in a Distribution

Before You Read: Section Summary

In this section, you will learn how to describe the location of an individual value in a distribution. You have probably encountered measures of location before through the concept of percentiles. In this section, you will learn how to calculate and interpret percentiles as well as how to identify percentiles through a cumulative relative frequency graph. You will also learn a new way to describe location by using the mean and standard deviation that you studied in Chapter 1. Standardized scores, or z-scores, will be introduced as a way to describe location within a distribution and to compare observations from different distributions. Finally, you will be introduced to the concept of a density curve. This smooth curve models the overall shape of a distribution and can be used in place of the actual data to answer questions about the distribution. The concepts you learn in this section will very important throughout the course. Be sure to master these concepts!

Learning Targets:

_____ I can find and interpret the percentile of an individual value in a distribution.
_____ I can estimate percentiles and individual values using a cumulative relative frequency graph.
_____ I can find and interpret the standardized score (z-score) of an individual value in a distribution of data.
_____ I can describe the effect of adding, subtracting, multiplying by, or dividing by a constant on the shape, center, and variability of a distribution of data.

While You Read: Key Vocabulary and Concepts

percentile:
cumulative relative frequency graph (ogive):
standardized score (z-score):
effect of adding (or subtracting) a constant:
effect of multiplying (or dividing) by a constant:

After You Read: Check for Understanding

Concept 1: Measuring Position - Percentiles

A common way to measure position within a distribution is to tell what percent of observations fall at or below the value in question. Percentiles are relatively easy to find – especially when our data is presented in order or in a dotplot or stemplot. To find a percentile, simply calculate the percent of values that fall at or below the value of interest. Cumulative relative frequency graphs, or ogives, provide a graphical tool to find percentiles in a distribution.

Check for Understanding:

_____ *I can find and interpret the percentile of an individual value in a distribution.*
_____ *I can estimate percentiles and individual values using a cumulative relative frequency graph.*

The number of points earned on a Chapter 2 quiz are displayed in the stemplot and ogive below:

```
0 | 0 1 2
1 | 2 2 4 8
2 | 1 1 3 4 5 9 9
3 | 0 0 0 3 6
4 | 4 5 7
5 | 0
```

Key: 5 | 0 = 50 points

1) James earned a score of 33. Calculate and interpret his percentile.

2) Heather earned a score of 14. Calculate and interpret her percentile.

3) Using the cumulative relative frequency graph, at what percentile is a score of 38?

4) Using the cumulative relative frequency graph, estimate and interpret the quartiles of this distribution.

Concept 2: Measuring Position – Standardized Scores

When describing distributions, we learned that measures of center and spread are both very important characteristics. It follows, then, that measuring the position of an observation in a distribution should take into account both the center and the spread of the distribution. After all, saying a particular observation falls 5 points above the average doesn't mean much unless you know how varied the observations are. If the distribution has a small spread, an observation that is 5 points above the average might be an extreme value. However, if the distribution has a large spread, being 5 points above average might not be a big deal. We MUST consider center and spread when describing location. The standardized value, or z-score, of an observation does just that. The z-score simply tells us how many standard deviations a particular observation falls above or below the mean. This method of describing location not only allows us to describe individuals within a distribution, but also allows us to compare the positions of individuals in different distributions. We will be standardizing values A LOT in this course. Master the concept now!

Check for Understanding:

_____ *I can find and interpret the standardized score (z-score) of an individual value in a distribution of data.*

Here are the number of points earned on the Chapter 2 quiz.

```
0 | 0 1 2
1 | 2 2 4 8
2 | 1 1 3 4 5 9 9
3 | 0 0 0 3 6
4 | 4 5 7
5 | 0          Key: 5 | 0 = 50 points
```

1) Calculate the mean and standard deviation.

2) Alyse earned a 45. Calculate and interpret her standardized quiz score.

3) Carl earned a 2. Calculate and interpret his standardized quiz score.

4) The scores on the next quiz had a mean of 32 and a standard deviation of 6.5. Alyse earned a 47 on this quiz. On which quiz did she perform better relative to the rest of the class? Explain.

Concept 3: Transforming Data

When we find *z*-scores, we are transforming our data to a standardized scale. That is, we subtract the mean and divide by the standard deviation, converting the observation from its original units to a standardized scale. Sometimes we transform data to switch between measurement units (inches to centimeters, Fahrenheit to Celsius, etc.). When we do this, it is important to know what happens to the center and spread of the transformed distribution. Adding (or subtracting) a constant to each of the observations in a set of data will have an effect on the center of the distribution, but not on the spread or the shape. Multiplying (or dividing) each of the observations by a positive constant will change the center and the spread of the distribution, but not its shape. Most important, while transforming data in these ways may change the center and spread of a distribution, the locations of individual observations remain unchanged! So, if you had a *z*-score of 1.5 on a quiz and your teacher decided to double everyone's score and give an additional 5 points, your *z*-score would STILL be 1.5!

Check for Understanding:

_____ *I can describe the effect of adding, subtracting, multiplying by, or dividing by a constant on the shape, center, and variability of a distribution of data.*

Here are the number of points earned on the Chapter 2 quiz.

```
0 | 0 1 2
1 | 2 2 4 8
2 | 1 1 3 4 5 9 9
3 | 0 0 0 3 6
4 | 4 5 7
5 | 0              Key: 5 | 0 = 50 points
```

1) Describe the distribution of quiz scores.

2) Suppose the teacher added 5 points to each student's score. How would the new distribution of scores compare to the distribution in question 1?

3) Suppose the teacher decided to double the original scores instead of adding points. How would this new distribution of scores compare to the distribution in question 1?

Section 2.2: Density Curves and Normal Distributions

Before You Read: Section Summary

Sometimes the overall pattern of distribution is so regular that it can described by a smooth curve. Density curves are a handy tool for modeling distributions of data. This section is devoted entirely to the most common type of density curve – the Normal curve. In this section, you will learn the basic properties of the Normal distributions and how to use them to perform a variety of calculations. You will learn how to determine whether or not a distribution of data can be described as approximately Normal. For distributions that can be described by a Normal curve, you will learn how to determine the proportion of observations that fall into given intervals. You will also learn how to find the value corresponding to a specified percentile in a Normal distribution. Throughout this section, a variety of tools and methods will be presented to help you perform Normal calculations by hand and on your calculator. Remember, whenever you perform a calculation by hand or by calculator, it is important to interpret the results in the context of the situation! Make sure you are comfortable with not only performing the calculations in this section but also in describing what your results mean!

Learning Targets:

_____ I can use a density curve to model distributions of quantitative data.

_____ I can identify the relative locations of the mean and median of a distribution from a density curve.

_____ I can use the Empirical Rule to estimate (i) the proportion of values in a specified interval, or (ii) the value that corresponds to a given percentile in a Normal distribution.

_____ I can find the proportion of values in a specified interval in a Normal distribution using Table A or technology.

_____ I can find the value that corresponds to a given percentile in a Normal distribution using Table A or technology.

_____ I can determine whether a distribution of data is approximately Normal from graphical and numerical evidence.

While You Read: Key Vocabulary and Concepts

density curve:
Normal distribution, Normal curve:
Empirical (68-95-99.7) Rule:
standard Normal distribution:
Normal probability plot:

✔️ **After You Read: Check for Understanding**

Concept 1: Density Curves

You have learned that exploring quantitative data requires making a graph, describing the overall shape, and providing a numerical summary of the center and spread. When we have a large number of observations, we can describe the overall pattern using a smooth curve called a density curve. There are two key features of density curves you need to remember. First, since it is describing the distribution of values it is always on or above the horizontal axis. Second, since it is representing the distribution of all of the values, the area underneath it is exactly 1. Since the area under the entire curve is 1, the area under the curve and between any two values on the horizontal axis is the proportion of observations in the distribution that fall in that interval. One other key point is noted in this section. In a symmetric distribution, the mean and median will be the same. However, in a skewed distribution, the mean will be pulled away from the median in the direction of the tail. Make sure you note that fact, it will come in handy on the AP Exam!

Check for Understanding:

_____ *I can use a density curve to model distributions of quantitative data.*

The scores on Ms. Chauvet's Chapter 1 test are displayed in the density curve below:

1) How do you know this is a legitimate density curve?

2) What percent of scores fell between 28 and 40?

3) How does the mean exam score compare to the median? Explain.

4) If 8% of the scores fall below 28, what percent of the scores fall above 40?

Concept 2: Normal Distributions and Normal Distribution Calculations

Normal distributions play an important role in statistics. That's because many distributions of real data and chance outcomes are symmetric, single-peaked, and bell-shaped and can be described by the family of Normal curves. The Empirical Rule allows us to be even more specific, noting that in Normal distributions, approximately 68% of the observations will fall within one standard deviation of the mean, approximately 95% of observations will fall within two standard deviations, and approximately 99.7% of observations will fall within three standard deviations. This fact allows us to perform calculations about the approximate proportion of observations in a distribution that fall into certain intervals without even knowing all of the individual observations!

As we explore situations in statistics, not all observations of interest will fall one, two, or three standard deviations from the mean. That is, we might be interested in knowing what proportion of observations are at least 1.72 standard deviations above the mean. In cases like this, the empirical rule can help us estimate the proportion, but we'll want to be more exact. Because all Normal distributions share the same properties, the standard Normal table and Normal calculations allow us to perform calculations for *any* observation in an approximately Normal distribution.

To perform a Normal calculation, start by expressing the problem in terms of a variable x. Sketch a picture of the distribution and shade the area of interest. Perform calculations by standardizing x and then using Table A or your calculator to find the required area under the Normal curve. Finally, be sure to write your conclusion in the context of the problem.

Check for Understanding:

_____ *I can find the proportion of values in a specified interval in a Normal distribution using Table A or technology.*

Suppose Chapter 2 Test scores in Ms. Chauvet's class were Normally distributed with mean 83 and standard deviation 5.

1) Sketch the density curve that describes the distribution of scores on the quizzes.

2) What percent of scores are between 78 and 93? Use the empirical rule.

3) A score greater than 90 earns an "A." What percent of the Chapter 2 Tests were an "A"?

4) What percent of scores fall between 71 and 95?

5) What score would place a student in the 20th percentile in this class?

Concept 3: Assessing Normality

It is important to note that just because a distribution is symmetric, single-peaked, and bell-shaped, it is NOT necessarily Normal. Normal distributions are handy models for some distributions of data. However, before performing Normal calculations, you should be sure the distribution you are exploring really IS Normal! The Normal probability plot of a distribution of data is a helpful tool in assessing Normality of a distribution of data. If the points on a Normal probability plot fall in a relatively straight line, you have evidence that the data are approximately Normal and Normal calculations are justified. If the points taper off or display other systematic departures from a straight line, a Normal model probably isn't appropriate for the distribution. Make sure you are comfortable constructing Normal probability plots on your calculator and interpreting them in the context of the problem!

Check for Understanding:

_____ *I can determine whether a distribution of data is approximately Normal from graphical and numerical evidence.*

Here are the number of push-ups that the 23 students on the JV and High School basketball teams did in one minute:

15, 19, 20, 22, 23, 26, 27, 27, 28, 28, 28, 28, 31, 32, 34, 35, 38, 39, 41, 42, 44, 45, 50

Use graphical and numerical methods to determine whether these data are approximately Normally distributed.

Chapter 2 Summary: Modeling Distributions of Quantitative Data

In this chapter, we expanded our toolbox for working with quantitative data. We learned how to describe the location of an individual within a distribution by determining its percentile or by calculating a standardized score (z-score) based on the mean and standard deviation of the distribution. We also learned that distributions with a clear overall pattern can be described using a density curve. A common density curve, the Normal curve, is a helpful model for describing many quantitative variables. Knowing how to justify that a distribution is approximately Normally distributed is an important skill. If you can show that a distribution is Normal, you can use the Normal distribution calculations to answer a number of questions about observations within the set of data. The empirical rule and the standard Normal table are both useful tools when performing calculations about observations in Normal distributions.

You should approach data analysis problems using four steps:
- Graph the data
- Look for an overall pattern and departures from this pattern
- Calculate and interpret numerical summaries
- If the data follow a regular overall pattern, describe the distribution with a smooth curve

The concepts introduced in this chapter will form the basis of much of our study of inference later on in the course. Standardizing data, justifying Normality, and performing Normal calculations are critical skills for statistical inference. Be sure to practice them as you will be using them a LOT!

How well do you understand each of the learning targets?

Learning Target	Got It!	Almost There	Needs Work
I can find and interpret the percentile of an individual value in a distribution.			
I can estimate percentiles and individual values using a cumulative relative frequency graph.			
I can find and interpret the standardized score (z-score) of an individual value in a distribution of data.			
I can describe the effect of adding, subtracting, multiplying by, or dividing by a constant on the shape, center, and variability of a distribution of data.			
I can use a density curve to model distributions of quantitative data.			
I can use the Empirical Rule.			
I can find the proportion of values in a specified interval in a Normal distribution.			
I can find the value that corresponds to a given percentile in a Normal distribution.			
I can determine whether a distribution of data is approximately Normal from graphical and numerical evidence.			

Chapter 2 Multiple Choice Practice

Directions. Identify the choice that best completes the statement or answers the question. Check your answers and note your performance when you are finished.

1. The 16th percentile of a Normally distributed variable has a value of 25 and the 97.5th percentile has a value of 40. Which of the following is the best estimate of the mean and standard deviation of the variable?
   (A)   Mean ≈ 32.5; Standard deviation ≈ 2.5
   (B)   Mean ≈ 32.5; Standard deviation ≈ 5
   (C)   Mean ≈ 32.5; Standard deviation ≈ 10
   (D)   Mean ≈ 30; Standard deviation ≈ 2.5
   (E)   Mean ≈ 30; Standard deviation ≈ 5

2. What portion of observations from a standard Normal distribution take values larger than 0.75?
   (A)   0.2266
   (B)   0.2500
   (C)   0.7704
   (D)   0.7764
   (E)   0.8023

3. A study was conducted to determine how long students spend washing their hands in the restroom. A student stood to the side, pretending to be using her phone, and discretely timed 10 students. Here are the number of seconds each student washed their hands: 3, 8, 15, 2, 3, 7, 20, 6, 9, 4. What is the percentile of the student who washed their hands for 4 seconds?

   (A)   10%
   (B)   20%
   (C)   30%
   (D)   40%
   (E)   50%

4. The distribution of the heights of students in a large class is roughly Normal. The average height is 68 inches, and approximately 99.7% of the heights are between 62 and 74 inches. Thus, the standard deviation of the height distribution is approximately equal to
   (A)   2
   (B)   3
   (C)   4
   (D)   6
   (E)   9

5. The mean age (at inauguration) of all U.S. Presidents is approximately Normally distributed with a mean of 54.6. Barack Obama was 47 when he was inaugurated, which is the 11th percentile of the distribution. George Washington was 57. Approximately what percentile is George Washington at?
   (A)   6th
   (B)   65th
   (C)   63rd
   (D)   35th
   (E)   39th

6. Which of the following statements are false?
   I. The standard Normal table can be used with z-scores from any distribution
   II. The mean is always equal to the median for any Normal distribution.
   III. Every symmetric, bell-shaped distribution is Normal
   IV. The area under a Normal curve is always 1, regardless of the mean and standard deviation.

   (A)   I and II
   (B)   I and III
   (C)   II and III
   (D)   III and IV
   (E)   None of the above gives the correct set of true statements.

7. High school textbooks don't last forever. The lifespan of all high school statistics textbooks is approximately Normally distributed with a mean of 9 years and a standard deviation of 2.5 years. What percentage of the books last more than 10 years?
   (A)   11.5%
   (B)   34.5%
   (C)   65.5%
   (D)   69%
   (E)   84.5%

8. The distribution of the time it takes for different people to solve their Strive for a Five crossword puzzle is strongly skewed to the right, with a mean of 10 minutes and a standard deviation of 2 minutes. The distribution of z-scores for those times is

   (A)   Normally distributed, with mean 10 and standard deviation 2.
   (B)   Skewed to the right, with mean 10 and standard deviation 2.
   (C)   Normally distributed, with mean 0 and standard deviation 1.
   (D)   Skewed to the right, with mean 0 and standard deviation 1.
   (E)   Skewed to the right, but the mean and standard deviation cannot be determined without more information.

9. The cumulative relative frequency graph below shows the distribution of lengths (in centimeters) of ears for a sample of adults. The third quartile for this distribution is approximately:

   (A)   6.7 cm
   (B)   7 cm
   (C)   6 cm
   (D)   5.5 cm
   (E)   7.5 cm

10. The plot shown below is a Normal probability plot for the total cost of 120 home renovation projects completed by a large company. Which statement is true for these data?

(A)   The distribution is clearly Normal.
(B)   The distribution is approximately Normal.
(C)   The distribution appears to be skewed.
(D)   The distribution appears to be uniform.
(E)   There is insufficient information to determine the shape of the distribution.

Check your answers below. If you got a question wrong, check to see if you made a simple mistake or if you need to study that concept more. After you check your work, identify the concepts you feel very confident about and note what you will do to learn the concepts in need of more study.

#	Answer	Concept	Right	Wrong	Simple Mistake?	Need to Study More
1	E	Empirical Rule				
2	A	Standard Normal Table				
3	D	Percentile				
4	A	Empirical Rule				
5	B	Standard Normal Calculations				
6	B	Properties of Normal Distributions				
7	B	Standard Normal Calculations				
8	D	Standardized Scores				
9	A	Cumulative Relative Frequency Graph				
10	C	Normal Probability Plots				

FRAPPY! Free Response AP® Problem, Yay!

The following problem is modeled after actual Advanced Placement Statistics free response questions. Your task is to generate a complete, concise response in 15 minutes. After you generate your response, read over the solution and scoring guide. Score your response and note what, if anything, you would do differently to increase your own score.

Final exam grades are determined by the percent correct on the exam. A teacher's records indicate the performance on the exam is Normally distributed with mean 82 and standard deviation 5. The grades on her exam are assigned using the scale below.

Grade	Percent Correct
A	$94 \leq \text{percent} \leq 100$
B	$85 \leq \text{percent} < 94$
C	$76 \leq \text{percent} < 85$
D	$65 \leq \text{percent} < 76$
F	$0 \leq \text{percent} < 65$

(a) Use a sketch of a Normal distribution to illustrate the proportion of students who would earn a B. Calculate this proportion.

(b) Students who earn a B, C, or D are considered to "meet standards". Based on this grading scale, what percent of students will receive a score that places them in a category other than "meets standards"?

(c) What grade would the student who scored at the 25th percentile earn on this chapter? Justify your answer.

FRAPPY! Scoring Rubric

Use the following rubric to score your response. Each part receives a score of "Essentially Correct," "Partially Correct," or "Incorrect." When you have scored your response, reflect on your understanding of the concepts addressed in this problem. If necessary, note what you would do differently on future questions like this to increase your score.

Intent of the Question

The goal of this question is to determine your ability to perform and interpret Normal calculations.

Solution

Final Exam Grades

(a) $P(\text{grade} = B)$
$= P(85 \leq \text{percent} < 94)$
$= P\left(\dfrac{85-82}{5} \leq z \leq \dfrac{94-82}{5}\right)$
$= P(0.6 \leq z < 2.4)$
$= 0.9918 - 0.7257$
$= 0.2661$

Using tech: $P(85 \leq \text{percent} < 94) = \text{Normalcdf(lower: 85, upper: 94, mean: 82, SD: 5)} = 0.2661$

(b) $P(A \text{ or } F) = P(A) + P(F)$
$= P\left(z < \dfrac{65-82}{5}\right) + P\left(z \geq \dfrac{94-82}{5}\right)$
$= P(z < 3.4) + P(z \geq 2.4)$
$= 0.0003 + 0.0082$
$= 0.0085$

Using tech: $P(A \text{ or } F) = \text{Normalcdf(lower: } -1000, \text{ upper: 65, mean: 82, SD: 5)}$
$+ \text{Normalcdf(lower: 94, upper: 1000, mean: 82, SD: 5)}$
$= 0.0085$

(c) A z-score of -0.6745 corresponds to the 25th percentile.
$-0.6745 = \dfrac{x-82}{5}$
$(-0.6475)(5) = x - 82$
$-3.2375 = x - 82$
$x = 78.63$

Scoring:

Parts (a), (b), and (c) are scored as essentially correct (E), partially correct (P), or incorrect (I).

Part (a) is essentially correct if (1) the appropriate probability is illustrated using a labeled Normal curve and (2) the proportion is correctly computed.
Part (a) is partially correct if only one of the above elements is correct

Part (b) is essentially correct if the response (1) recognizes the need to look at grades of A and F and (2) correctly computes the tail probabilities and adds them together.
Part (b) is partially correct if the response considers only an A or an F and calculates the corresponding tail area correctly OR recognizes the need to look at A an F but only calculates one of

the tail areas correctly OR approximates the probabilities using the empirical rule OR computes the proportion that will "meet standards" OR states the correct answer without supporting work.

Part (c) is essentially correct if (a) the correct *z*-score is identified for the 25th percentile and (2) the correct corresponding score is calculated.
Part (c) is partially correct if only one of the above elements is correct.

NOTE: If the student makes an error in part (b) and correctly uses that probability in part (c) to compute a reasonable probability, part (c) is essentially correct.

4   Complete Response
   All three parts essentially correct

3   Substantial Response
   Two parts essentially correct and one part partially correct

2   Developing Response
   Two parts essentially correct and no parts partially correct
   One part essentially correct and one or two parts partially correct
   Three parts partially correct

1   Minimal Response
   One part essentially correct and no parts partially correct
   No parts essentially correct and two parts partially correct

My Score:
What I did well:
What I could improve:
What I should remember if I see a problem like this on the AP Exam:

Chapter 2 Formula Sheet

Create a one-page summary of important concepts and formulas found in this chapter. This will serve as a valuable resource as you prepare for the AP Exam.

Chapter 2 Crossword Puzzle
MODELING DISTRIBUTIONS OF QUANTITATIVE DATA

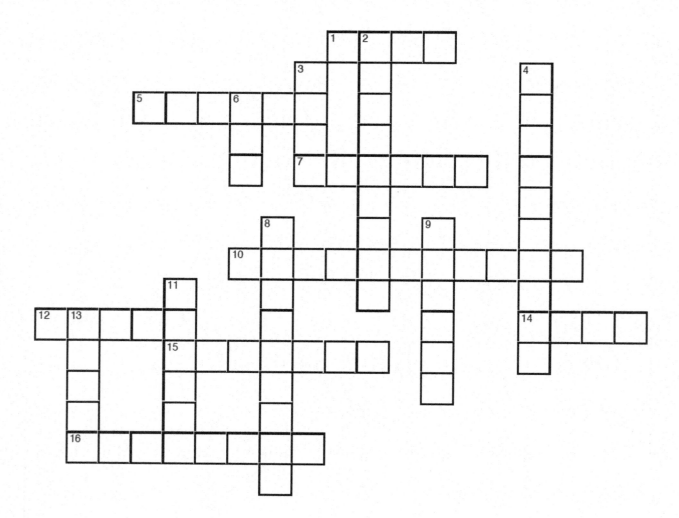

Across

1. The balance point of a density curve, if it were made of solid material
5. The standardized value of an observation
7. These common density curves are symmetric and bell-shaped
10. A Normal _____ plot provides a good assessment of whether a data set is approximately Normally distributed
12. Another name for a cumulative relative frequency graph
14. The standard Normal table tells us the area under the standard Normal curve to the ___ of z
15. A ___ curve is a smooth curve that can be used to model a distribution
16. This Normal distribution has mean 0 and standard deviation 1

Down

2. The _____ rule is also known as the 68-95-99.7 rule for Normal distributions
3. To standardize a value, subtract the ___ and divide by the standard deviation
4. The value with p percent of the observations less than it
6. The area under any density curve is always equal to
8. We ___ data when we change each value by adding a constant and/or multiplying by a constant.
9. If a Normal probability plot shows a _____ pattern, the data are approximately Normal
11. The point that divides the area under a density curve in half
13. This mathematician first applied Normal curves to data to errors made by astronomers and surveyors

CHAPTER 3: Exploring Two-Variable Quantitative Data

"You can only predict things after they've happened." Eugene Ionesco

CHAPTER OVERVIEW

Our statistics toolbox now contains a variety of ways to explore a single quantitative variable. Further, we have learned ways to explore one or more categorical variables. Often in our studies, though, we will need to explore and describe the relationship between two quantitative variables. In this chapter, we will learn how to analyze patterns in "bivariate" relationships by plotting them and calculating summary statistics about them. Also, we will learn how to describe them using mathematical models that can be used to make predictions based on the relationship between the variables. Investigating the relationship between two variables is a key component of statistical study and is the final skill necessary for our data exploration toolbox. Be sure to master the concepts and methods in this chapter!

Sections in this Chapter
Section 3.1: Scatterplots and Correlation
Section 3.2: Least-Squares Regression
Section 3.3: Transforming to Achieve Linearity

PLAN YOUR LEARNING

Use the following *suggested* guide to help plan your reading and assignments in "The Practice of Statistics, Updated 6th Edition." Put a check mark in the last column when you are done. Note: your teacher may schedule a different pacing or assign different problems. Be sure to follow his or her instructions!

Read	Do	Done!
Introduction, Section 3.1: p.152-159	1, 3, 5, 9, 11	
Section 3.1: p. 160-170	13, 15, 17, 19, 23, MC 29-34	
Section 3.2: p.176-182	37, 39, 41, 43, 45	
Section 3.2: p. 183-187	47, 49, 51, 53	
Section 3.2: p.188-193	55, 57, 59, 67	
Section 3.2: p. 194-204	63, 65, MC 71-78	
Section 3.3: p. 213-224	81, 83, 85, 87	
Section 3.3: p. 225-228	89, 91, 93, MC 95-96	
Chapter Summary	Multiple Choice FRAPPY!	

Use this "Strive Guide" to help identify learning targets for each section, summarize key concepts, practice additional problems, and check your understanding as you read the text.

Section 3.1: Scatterplots and Correlation

Before You Read: Section Summary

Many statistical studies examine more than one variable. So far, we have learned methods to graph and describe relationships between categorical variables. In this chapter, we'll learn that the approach to data analysis that we learned for a single quantitative variable can also be applied to explore the relationship between two quantitative variables. That is, we'll learn how to plot our data and add numerical summaries. We'll then learn how to describe the overall patterns and departures from patterns that we see. Finally, we'll learn how to create a mathematical model to describe the overall pattern. This section will focus primarily on displaying the relationship between two quantitative variables and describing its form, direction, and strength. Like the previous chapters, you will find that technology can be used to do most of the difficult calculations. However, be sure you understand *how* the calculator is determining its results and *what* those results mean!

Learning Targets:

_____ I can distinguish between explanatory and response variables for quantitative data.
_____ I can make a scatterplot to display the relationship between two quantitative variables.
_____ I can describe the direction, form, and strength of a relationship displayed in a scatterplot and identify unusual features.
_____ I can interpret the correlation.
_____ I can understand the basic properties of correlation, including how the correlation is influenced by outliers.
_____ I can distinguish correlation from causation.

While You Read: Key Vocabulary and Concepts

explanatory variable:
response variable:
scatterplot:
direction, form, strength, unusual features:
positive association, negative association, no association:
correlation *r*:

After You Read: Check for Understanding

Concept 1: Explanatory and Response Variables

The purpose of many studies involving two quantitative variables is to develop a model so that we can use one variable to make a prediction for the other. Because of that, it is important to clearly identify which variable in a situation is *explanatory* and which is the *response*. The explanatory variable is the one we think explains the relationship or "predicts" changes in the response variable. It is important to know the difference as identifying the explanatory and response variable will determine how we display the data and how we calculate a summary model. Note: you may have learned about *independent* and *dependent* variables in an earlier math or science class. Those are just different names for explanatory and response variables. We'll avoid using independent and dependent here, though, because those terms have a different meaning later in the course.

Check for Understanding:

_____ *I can distinguish between explanatory and response variables for quantitative data.*

Identify the explanatory and response variable in the following situations:

1) How does test anxiety affect test performance? In a recent study, researchers measured students' test anxiety and recorded their subsequent performance on a standardized test.

2) Is brain size related to memory? A 2018 study measured the volume of each subject's hippocampus and then administered a verbal retention assessment.

Concept 2: Scatterplots

As we learned in Chapters 1 and 2, plotting data should always be our first step in a data exploration. The most useful graph for exploring bivariate relationships is the scatterplot. Making a scatterplot is pretty easy. 1) Determine which variable goes on which axis. (Hint: The eXplanatory variable goes on the *x*-axis!) 2) Label and scale the axes. 3) Plot individual data values. Once you have the scatterplot constructed, take some time to describe what you see. What is the overall form of the relationship? Is it linear? Nonlinear? What direction does the relationship take? Is it positive or negative? How strong is the relationship? Do the points follow the pattern closely, or are they widely scattered? Finally, are there any unusual observations?

Check for Understanding:

_____ *I can make a scatterplot to display the relationship between two quantitative variables.*

_____ *I can describe the direction, form, and strength of a relationship displayed in a scatterplot and identify unusual features.*

Use the following data to construct a scatterplot and describe the form, direction, and strength of the relationship between anxiety and exam performance. Note: Higher anxiety scores indicate higher levels of test anxiety.

Anxiety	23	14	14	0	7	20	20	15	21	4
Exam Score	43	59	48	77	50	52	46	60	51	70

Concept 3: Measuring Linear Relationships - Correlation

Scatterplots are great tools for displaying the direction, form, and strength of the relationship between two quantitative variables. Often, we will want to know whether or not the relationship is linear and, if so, how strong the linear relationship is. However, our eyes aren't the most accurate judges of the strength of linear relationships. The correlation r provides a numerical summary of the strength of the linear relationship that can be easily interpreted.

Some key points to remember about r:
- r is always a number between -1 and 1.
- Perfect linear relationships will have a correlation of $r = 1$ or $r = -1$.
- Positive relationships have a positive correlation and negative relationships have a negative correlation.
- Correlation has no units of measurement. It would be incorrect to say that the correlation between age and height is $r = 0.9$ inches/year.
- Finally, the closer $|r|$ is to 1, the stronger the linear relationship between the quantitative variables.

Note, however, just because the linear relationship is strong, it is possible that curvature still exists! Scatterplots that display little to no pattern will have a correlation close to 0.

Here is a summary, showing some values of the correlation coefficient, and appropriate descriptions based on those values:

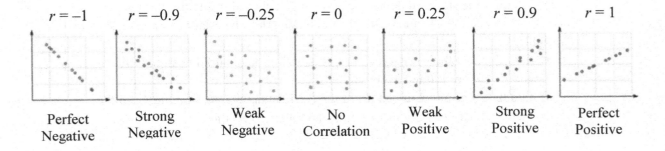

$r = -1$	$r = -0.9$	$r = -0.25$	$r = 0$	$r = 0.25$	$r = 0.9$	$r = 1$
Perfect Negative	Strong Negative	Weak Negative	No Correlation	Weak Positive	Strong Positive	Perfect Positive

Check for Understanding:
_____ *I can interpret the correlation.*

Use the data from the anxiety vs. exam score example to calculate and interpret the correlation coefficient. What does this value tell you about the relationship?

Section 3.2: Least-Squares Regression

Before You Read: Section Summary

In the last section, we learned that we can display the relationship between two quantitative variables using a scatterplot. Further, we can use a scatterplot to describe the direction, form, and strength of the relationship. The correlation coefficient r allows us to describe the situation by telling us how strong the *linear* relationship between the variables is. In this section, we'll learn how to summarize the overall pattern of a linear relationship by finding the equation of the least-squares regression line. This line can be used to not only model the linear relationship, but also to make predictions based on the overall pattern. Like correlation, our calculator will do most of the work for us. Your job is to be able to interpret and apply the results!

Learning Targets:

_____ I can make predictions using regression lines, keeping in mind the dangers of extrapolation.

_____ I can calculate and interpret a residual.

_____ I can interpret the slope and y intercept of a regression line.

_____ I can determine the equation of a least-squares regression line using technology or computer output.

_____ I can construct and interpret residual plots to assess whether a regression model is appropriate.

_____ I can interpret the standard deviation of the residuals and r^2 and use these values to assess how well a least-squares regression line models the relationship between two variables.

_____ I can describe how the least-squares regression line, standard deviation of the residuals, and r^2 are influenced by outliers.

_____ I can find the slope and y intercepts of the least-squares regression line from the means and standard deviations of x and y and their correlation.

While You Read: Key Vocabulary and Concepts

regression line:
extrapolation:
residual:
y intercept:

slope:
least-squares regression line:
residual plot:
standard deviation of the residuals, *s*:
coefficient of determination r^2:
high leverage, outliers, and influential points:
association vs. causation:

 After You Read: Check for Understanding

Concept 1: Least-Squares Regression Line

The main concept in this section is that of the least-squares regression line. When a scatterplot suggests a linear relationship between quantitative explanatory and response variables, we can summarize the pattern by "fitting" a line to the points. This line can then be used to predict values of the response variable for given values of the explanatory variable. Be careful, though. We should use caution not to make predictions too far outside of our observed *x*-values. Extrapolation can be dangerous, as we don't know whether or not the pattern continues outside our observations!

The equation of the least-squares regression line can be calculated by hand, if you know the mean and standard deviation of the variables and the correlation *r*. However, you might want to rely on technology to provide the equation for you. Focus your energy on interpreting the slope and *y*-intercept in context and on using the model to make predictions. The *y*-intercept is often meaningless in the context of our situations. It tells us what response value we'd predict to see if our explanatory value was zero. The slope is the key value of interest in describing the relationship between two quantitative variables. It tells us how much the predicted value of *y* increases (or decrease) for each one-unit increase in the *x*-values. Put that in your long-term memory bank because you will see it again in future chapters!

By the end of this section, you should be able to construct and interpret a least-squares regression model, justify its use, and use it to make predictions. Be sure to focus on interpreting the different components of the model!

Concept 2: Regression Lines-Prediction and Extrapolation

A regression line is a line the models the data. That is, it summarizes the overall pattern and provides an equation that represents the relationship between our explanatory and response variable. This equation can be used to predict the response for a given value of the explanatory variable. Use caution not to extrapolate when making predictions, though, as we do not know if the relationship between the variables extends far beyond the observed values of x!

Concept 3: Least-Squares Regression Line

Chances are any scatterplot you construct or encounter will not display a perfectly straight line. In most cases, the observed points will be, well, scattered. Because most of our observed relationships are not perfectly linear, predictions of y made from our regression line will often be different than observed y values, resulting in a prediction error. That is, there will be some amount of vertical distance between the regression line and the observed value. This vertical difference (actual y – predicted y) is called a residual. The regression line that "best fits" our observed data is the one that minimizes the squared residuals. This "line of best fit" that minimizes that prediction error is called the least-squares regression line.

Familiarize yourself with the formulas that can be used to determine the slope and intercept of the least-squares regression line. We will rely on technology to generate this equation, but you should recognize that we can construct the equation by hand given the mean and standard deviation of x and y as well as the correlation r between them.

Check for Understanding:

_____ *I can make predictions using regression lines, keeping in mind the dangers of extrapolation.*
_____ *I can calculate and interpret a residual.*
_____ *I can interpret the slope and y intercept of a regression line.*
_____ *I can determine the equation of a least-squares regression line using technology or computer output.*

Using the following data, determine the least-squares regression line to predict exam scores from anxiety scores. Note: Higher anxiety scores indicate higher levels of test anxiety.

Anxiety	23	14	14	0	7	20	20	15	21	4
Exam Score	43	59	48	77	50	52	46	60	51	70

1) What is the equation of the least-squares regression line?

2) Interpret the slope of the least-squares regression line in the context of the situation.

3) What exam score can we predict for an anxiety score of 15?

4) What is the residual for an anxiety score of 15?

5) Should you use the least-squares regression line to predict an exam score for a person who had an anxiety score of 35? Why or why not?

Concept 4: Assessing How Well the Least-Squares Regression Line Fits the Data

In Section 3.1, we learned that our eyes aren't always the best judge of linear relationships. While correlation r gives us a better understanding of the strength of the linear relationship, we still need to assess how well the least-squares regression line fits the observed data. If it fits well, it may be a useful prediction tool. If it doesn't fit well, we may want to search for a model that fits it better.

One way to assess how well the least-squares regression line fits our data is to make a residual plot. Plotting the residuals gives us more information about the relationship between quantitative variables and helps us assess how well a linear model fits the data. If the residual plot displays a pattern, a better (perhaps nonlinear) model might exist!

We can also assess the fit of the least-squares regression line by interpreting the coefficient of determination r^2. r^2 is a measure of how well the regression model explains the response. Specifically, it is interpreted as the fraction of variation in the values of y that is explained by the least-squares regression line of y on x. For example, if $r^2 = 0.82$, we can say that 82% of the variation in y is due to the linear relationship between y and x. 18% is due to factors other than x.

Check for Understanding:

_____ *I can construct and interpret residual plots to assess whether a regression model is appropriate.*

_____ *I can interpret the standard deviation of the residuals and r^2 and use these values to assess how well a least-squares regression line models the relationship between two variables.*

Consider the equation of the least-squares regression line of exam score on anxiety.

1) Construct and interpret the residual plot for the least-squares regression line.

2) What is the value of r? What is the value of r^2? Interpret each of these in the context of the problem.

Concept 5: Interpreting Computer Regression Output

As noted already, we will often rely on technology to generate the equation of the least-squares regression line. You are probably familiar with using your calculator to produce the equation. Make sure you can also interpret computer output to identify the slope and intercept of the regression line as well as other important values such as correlation and the coefficient of determination. There is a strong possibility you will need to read computer output on the AP Exam!

Check for Understanding:

_____ *I can determine the equation of a least-squares regression line using technology or computer output.*

A study was performed to determine the effect of temperature on a pond's algae level. Temperature was measured in degrees Fahrenheit, and algae level was measured in parts per million. Consider the computer output below.

```
Predictor     Coef      Stdev     t-ratio   P
Constant      42.8477    5.750     77.40     0.000
Temp          0.47620    0.5911    13.70     0.000

s = 0.4224          R-sq= 91.7%          R-sq(adj)=91.2%
```

1) Write the equation of the least-squares regression line. Identify any variables used.

2) Interpret the slope of the least-squares regression line.

3) Identify and interpret the correlation coefficient.

4) Identify and interpret the standard deviation of the residuals.

Section 3.3: Transforming to Achieve Linearity

Before You Read: Section Summary

In this section, you will learn how to deal with curved relationships. Since you already know how to model a linear relationship, you will learn how to transform data that show a curved relationship so that a linear model would be appropriate. That is, you will apply mathematical transformations to one or both variables to "straighten" out the scatterplot. By finding the linear model for the transformed data, you can make predictions involving the original data. The better the fit of your model, the better your prediction!

Learning Targets:

_____ I can use transformations involving powers, roots, and logarithms to create a linear model that describes the relationship between two quantitative variables, and use the model to make predictions.

_____ I can determine which of several models does a better job of describing the relationship between two quantitative variables.

While You Read: Key Vocabulary and Concepts

transforming data:

power model:

logarithm:

exponential model:

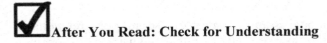

After You Read: Check for Understanding

Concept 1: Transforming with Powers and Roots
When we know or suspect that a nonlinear relationship between two variables can be described by a model
of the form $y = ax^p$ we have two strategies to transform the data to achieve linearity:

1) Raise all of the x values to the p power and plot (x^p, y)
2) Take the pth root of the y values and plot (x, $\sqrt[p]{y}$).

We can then determine the least-squares regression line for the transformed data and use this equation to
make predictions about the original data.

Check for Understanding:
_____ *I can use transformations involving powers, roots, or logarithms to create a model that describes
the relationship between two quantitative variables, and use the model to make predictions.*

The following data represent the lengths (mm) and diameters (mm) of the humerus bones of the
Moleskius Primateum species of monkeys once thought to inhabit Northern Minnesota.

Diameter	17.6	26	31.9	38.9	45.8	51.2	58.1	64.7	66.7	80.8	82.9
Length	159.9	206.9	236.8	269.9	300.6	323.6	351.7	377.6	384.1	437.2	444.7

Previous studies suggest the diameter and length are related by a power model of the form *length* =
a(*diameter*)$^{0.7}$. Transform the original data and use least-squares regression to find an appropriate model
for the transformed data.

You discover a portion of a *Moleskius Primateum* humerus bone with a diameter of 47mm. Use your
model to predict how long the entire bone was.

Concept 2: Transforming with Logarithms

In general, we don't know whether or not a power model is appropriate for describing the relationship between two quantitative variables. Some curved relationships are better summarized using an exponential model. A more efficient method for linearizing curved scatterplots involves using logarithms. To determine an appropriate model, use the following process:

If you are carrying out the transformation from data:

1) Use logarithms to transform your data.
   - Plot $(x, \log y)$
   - Plot $(\log x, \log y)$

2) Determine which transformation is most linear.
   - If $(x, \log y)$ is most linear, an exponential model may best describe (x, y)
   - If $(\log x, \log y)$ is most linear, a power model may best describe (x, y)

3) Find the appropriate linear model.

   - If $(x, \log y)$ is most linear, find the LSRL of the transformed data $\widehat{\log y} = a + bx$

   - If $(\log x, \log y)$ is most linear, find the LSRL of the transformed data $\widehat{\log y} = a + b(\log x)$

4) Use your model to make predictions for the original data.

If you are given graphical displays and summary statistics:

1) Choose the model for which the residual plot has the most random scatter.

2) If it is unclear which residual plot has the most random scatter, choose the model with the greatest value of r^2.

Check for Understanding:

_____ *I can determine which of several models does a better job of describing the relationship between two quantitative variables.*

The following data describe the number of police officers (thousands) and the violent crime rate (per 100,000 population) in a sample of states.

Police	86.2	9.2	45	39.9	6	11.8	2.9	14.6	30.5	12.3	46.2	15.2	10.9
Crime	1090	559	1184	1039	303	951	132	763	635	726	840	373	523

Which of the following models best describes the relationship displayed in the table? Explain.

Equation	n	s	r^2
$\hat{y} = 454.2152 + 9.7164x$	13	233.596	0.512

Equation	n	s	r^2
$\ln \hat{y} = 6.004 + 0.0163x$	13	0.502	0.39

Equation	n	s	r^2
$\ln \hat{y} = 4.886 + 0.5365 \ln x$	13	0.365	0.678

Use your model to predict the violent crime rate for a state with 25,400 police officers.

Chapter Summary: Exploring Two-Variable Quantitative Data

In this chapter, we expanded our toolbox for working with quantitative data. We learned how to analyze and describe the relationship between two quantitative variables. Using scatterplots, we can display the relationship and describe the direction, strength, and form of the overall pattern. Correlation provides a numerical summary of the strength of the linear relationship between the variables and the equation of the least-squares regression line provides a model that can be used to make predictions. Residual plots, the standard deviation of the residuals, and the coefficient of determination help us assess the fit of the least-squares regression line and may suggest whether or not a linear model is appropriate. Finally, we learned that outliers and influential points can affect our interpretations and regression results. Just like we did with a single quantitative variable, we should be able to identify departures from the overall pattern and explain their influence on our analysis. And always remember: Association does not imply causation!

In the event the relationship between two variables is curved, you can use transformations to "straighten" the scatterplot. You can find the least-squares regression line for the transformed data and make better predictions for the original relationship. The most common methods for transforming data involve taking powers, roots, or logarithms of one or both variables. To determine which transformation does a better job of "straightening" the relationship, examine residual plots.

After You Read: What Have I Learned?
Complete the vocabulary puzzle, multiple-choice questions, and FRAPPY. Check your answers and performance on each of the learning targets. Be sure to get extra help on any targets that you identify as needing more work!

Learning Target	Got It!	Almost There	Needs Work
I can distinguish between explanatory and response variables for quantitative data.			
I can make a scatterplot to display the relationship between two quantitative variables.			
I can describe the direction, form, and strength of a relationship displayed in a scatterplot and identify unusual features.			
I can interpret the correlation.			
I can understand the basic properties of correlation, including how the correlation is influenced by outliers.			
I can distinguish correlation from causation.			
I can make predictions using regression lines, keeping in mind the dangers of extrapolation.			
I can calculate and interpret a residual.			
I can interpret the slope and y intercept of a regression line.			
I can determine the equation of a least-squares regression line using technology or computer output.			
I can construct and interpret residual plots to assess whether a regression model is appropriate.			
I can interpret the standard deviation of the residuals and r^2 and use these values to assess how well a least-squares regression line models the relationship between two variables.			
I can describe how the least-squares regression line, standard deviation of the residuals, and r^2 are influenced by outliers.			
I can find the slope and y intercepts of the least-squares regression line from the means and standard deviations of x and y and their correlation.			
I can use transformations involving powers, roots, and logarithms to create a linear model that describes the relationship between two quantitative variables, and use the model to make predictions.			
I can determine which of several models does a better job of describing the relationship between two quantitative variables.			

Chapter 3 Multiple Choice Practice

Directions. Identify the choice that best completes the statement or answers the question. Check your answers and note your performance when you are finished.

1. A study is conducted to determine if one can predict the academic performance of a first-year college student based on their high school grade point average. The explanatory variable in this study is
    (A)   academic performance of the first-year student.
    (B)   grade point average.
    (C)   the experimenter.
    (D)   number of credits the student is taking.
    (E)   the college.

2. Consider the following scatterplot, which describes the relationship between stopping distance (in feet) and air temperature (in degrees Centigrade) for a certain 2,000-pound car travelling 40 mph.

    Do these data provide strong evidence that warmer temperatures actually *cause* a greater stopping distance?
    (A)   Yes. The strong straight-line association in the plot shows that temperature has a strong effect on stopping distance.
    (B)   No. $r \neq +1$
    (C)   No. We can't be sure the temperature is responsible for the difference in stopping distances.
    (D)   No. The plot shows that differences among stopping distances are not large enough to be important.
    (E)   No. The plot shows that stopping distances go down as temperature increases

3. If another data point were added with an air temperature of 0° C and a stopping distance of 80 feet, the correlation would
    (A)   decrease, since this new point is an outlier that does not follow the pattern in the data.
    (B)   increase, since this new point is an outlier that does not follow the pattern in the data.
    (C)   stay nearly the same, since correlation is resistant to outliers.
    (D)   increase, since there would be more data points.
    (E)   Whether this data point causes an increase or decrease cannot be determined without recalculating the correlation.

4. Consider the following scatterplot of amounts of CO (carbon monoxide) and NOX (nitrogen oxide) in grams per mile driven in the exhausts of cars. The least-squares regression line has been drawn in the plot.

Based on the scatterplot, the least-squares line would predict that a car that emits 2 grams of CO per mile driven would emit approximately how many grams of NOX per mile driven?
(A)   4.0
(B)   1.25
(C)   2.0
(D)   1.7
(E)   0.7

5. In the scatterplot shown in problem 4, the point indicated by the open circle
(A)   has a negative value for the residual.
(B)   has a positive value for the residual.
(C)   has a zero value for the residual.
(D)   has a zero value for the correlation.
(E)   is an outlier.

6. A study of the effects of television measured how many hours of television each of 125 grade school children watched per week during a school year and their reading scores. The study found that children who watch more television tend to have lower reading scores than children who watch fewer hours of television. The study report says that, "Hours of television watched explained 25% of the observed variation in the reading scores of the 125 subjects." The correlation between hours of TV and reading score must be
(A) $r = 0.25$.
(B) $r = -0.25$.
(C) $r = -0.5$.
(D) $r = 0.5$.
(E)   Can't tell from the information given.

7. A fisheries biologist studying whitefish in a Canadian lake collected data on the length (in centimeters) and egg production for 25 female fish. A scatter plot of her results and computer regression analysis of egg production versus fish length are given below. Note that number of eggs is given in thousands (i.e., "40" means 40,000 eggs).

```
Predictor      Coef      SE Coef    T        P
Constant      -142.74    25.55     -5.59    0.000
Fish length    39.250    5.392      7.28    0.000

S = 6.75133   R-Sq = 69.7%   R-Sq(adj) = 68.4%
```

Which of the following statements is a correct interpretation of the slope of the regression line?
(A) For each 1-cm increase in the fish length, the predicted number of eggs increases by 39.25 cm.
(B) For each 1-cm increase in the fish length, the predicted number of eggs decreases by 142.74 cm.
(C) For each 1-unit increase in the number of eggs, the predicted fish length increases by 39.25 cm.
(D) For each 1-unit increase in the number of eggs, the predicted fish length decreases by 142.74 cm.
(E) For each 1-cm increase in the fish length, the predicted number of eggs increases by 39,250.

8. Use of the Internet worldwide increased steadily from 1990 to 2002. A scatterplot of this growth shows a strongly non-linear pattern. However, a scatterplot of *ln* Internet Users *versus* Year is much closer to linear. Below is a computer regression analysis of the transformed data (note that natural logarithms are used).

```
Predictor      Coef      SE Coef      T          P
Constant      -951.10    43.45      -21.89     0.000
Year           0.4785    0.02176     21.99     0.000

S = 0.2516    R-Sq = 98.2%   R-Sq(adj) = 98.0%
```

Which of the following best describe the model that is given by this computer printout?
(A) The linear model: $\widehat{users} = -951.10 + 0.4785(\text{year})$

(B) The power model: $\widehat{users} = e^{-951.10}(\text{year})^{0.4785}$

(C) The power model: $\widehat{users} = 10^{-951.10}(\text{year})^{0.4785}$

(D) The exponential model: $\widehat{users} = e^{-951.10}(e^{0.4785})^{\text{year}}$

(E) The exponential model: $\widehat{users} = 10^{-951.10}(10^{0.4785})^{\text{year}}$

9. Suppose the relationship between a response variable y and an explanatory variable x is modeled well by the equation $y = 3.6(0.32)^x$. Which of the following plots is most likely to be roughly linear?
(A) A plot of y against x
(B) A plot of y against $\log x$
(C) A plot of $\log y$ against x
(D) A plot of 10^y against x
(E) A plot of $\log y$ against $\log x$

10. Like most animals, small marine crustaceans are not able to
    digest all the food they eat. Moreover, the percentage of
    food eaten that is assimilated (that is, digested) decreases as
    the amount of food eaten increases. A residual plot for the
    regression of Assimilation rate (as a percentage of food
    intake) on Food Intake (μg/day) is shown here.

A scatterplot of ln(Assimilation) versus ln(Food Intake) is strongly linear, suggesting that a linear
regression of these transformed variables may be more appropriate. Below is a computer regression
analysis of the transformed data (note that natural logarithms are used).

```
Predictor              Coef     SE Coef          T          P
Constant             6.3324      0.5218      12.14      0.000
ln Food Intake      -0.6513      0.1047      -6.22      0.000

S = 0.247460        R-Sq = 84.7%      R-Sq(adj) = 82.5%
```

When food intake is 250 g/day, what is the predicted assimilation rate from this model?
(A) 2.7%
(B) 15.4%
(C) 27.4%
(D) 34.3%
(E) 54.4%

Check your answers below. If you got a question wrong, check to see if you made a simple mistake or if
you need to study that concept more. After you check your work, identify the concepts you feel very
confident about and note what you will do to learn the concepts in need of more study.

#	Answer	Concept	Right	Wrong	Simple Mistake?	Need to Study More
1	B	Explanatory vs. Response				
2	C	Association vs. Causation				
3	A	Correlation				
4	D	Predicting with the LSRL				
5	A	Residuals				
6	C	Coefficient of Determination				
7	E	Slope of the LSRL				
8	D	Log y Transformation				
9	C	Exponential Functions/Transformations				
10	B	Prediction from log-log Transformation				

FRAPPY! Free Response AP® Problem, Yay!

The following problem is modeled after actual Advanced Placement Statistics free response questions. Your task is to generate a complete, concise response in 15 minutes. After you generate your response, read over the solution and scoring guide. Score your response and note what, if anything, you would do differently to increase your own score.

A recent study was interested in determining the optimal location for fire stations in a suburban city. Ideally, fire stations should be placed so the distance between the station and residences is minimized. One component of the study examined the relationship between the amount of fire damage y (in thousands of dollars) and the distance between the fire station and the residence x (in miles). The results of the regression analysis are below.

Predictor	Coef	SE Coef	T	P
Constant	10.28	1.42	7.237	0.000
Distance	4.92	0.39	12.525	0.000

$S = 2.232$ R-Sq $= 0.9235$ R-Sq(adj) $= 0.9176$

(a) Write the equation of the least-squares regression line. Define any variables used. Interpret the slope of the equation in context.

(b) A home located 3 miles from the fire station received \$22,300 in damage. Use your equation in part (a) to calculate and interpret the residual for this observation.

(c) Identify and interpret the correlation coefficient.

FRAPPY! Scoring Rubric

Use the following rubric to score your response. Each part receives a score of "Essentially Correct," "Partially Correct," or "Incorrect." When you have scored your response, reflect on your understanding of the concepts addressed in this problem. If necessary, note what you would do differently on future questions like this to increase your score.

Intent of the Question

The goal of this question is to determine your ability to interpret computer regression output and explain key concepts of linear regression.

Solution

(a) $\overline{\text{fire damage}} = 10.28 + 4.92(\text{distance})$ OR $\hat{y} = 10.28 + 4.92x$ where $x = $ distance and $y = $ damage.

   For each additional mile between the fire station and residence, the predicted additional amount in damages increases by about $4,920.

(b) $\overline{\text{fire damage}} = 4.92(3) + 10.28 = 25.04$
   residual $= 22.3 - 25.04 = -2.74$.
   The model overpredicts the damage amount by $2740.

(c) Because $r^2 = 0.9325$, $r = 0.96$. There is a very strong, positive, linear relationship between a residence's damage from a fire and its distance from a fire station.

Scoring

Parts (a), (b), and (c) are scored as essentially correct (E), partially correct (P), or incorrect (I).

Part (a) is essentially correct if the response (1) correctly identifies the least-squares regression equation in context or with variables defined and (2) correctly interprets the slope
Part (a) is partially correct if the response fails to define the variables in context or reverses the coefficients OR if the slope is not correctly defined in context (ex. predicts 4.92 dollars instead of $4920).

Part (b) is essentially correct if (1) the correct residual is calculated and (2) the interpretation is correct.
Part (b) is partially correct if only one of the above elements is correct.

Part (c) is essentially correct if the correlation coefficient is correctly identified and interpreted correctly with all three elements (strong, positive, linear).
Part (c) is partially correct if one of the elements (strong, positive, linear) is missing OR if r^2 is used instead of r.

4   Complete Response

All three parts essentially correct

3   Substantial Response

Two parts essentially correct and one part partially correct

2   Developing Response

Two parts essentially correct and no parts partially correct

One part essentially correct and one or two parts partially correct

Three parts partially correct

2   Minimal Response

One part essentially correct and no parts partially correct

No parts essentially correct and two parts partially correct

My Score:
What I did well:
What I could improve:
What I should remember if I see a problem like this on the AP Exam:

Chapter 3 Formula Sheet

Create a one-page summary of important concepts and formulas found in this chapter. This will serve as a valuable resource as you prepare for the AP Exam.

Chapter 3 Crossword Puzzle
EXPLORING TWO-VARIABLE QUANTITATIVE DATA

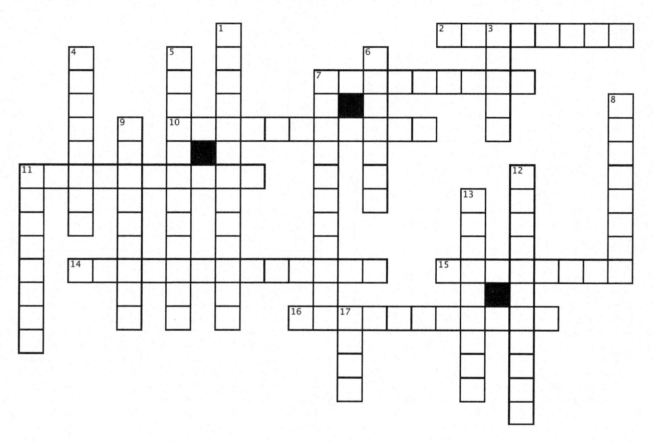

Across

2. the difference between an observed value of the response and the value predicted by a regression line
7. Important note: Association does not imply _____.
10. graphical display of the relationship between two quantitative variables
11. line that describes the relationship between two quantitative variables
14. the coefficient of _____ describes the fraction of variability in y values that is explained by least squares regression on x.
15. A _____ association is defined when above average values of one variable are accompanied by below average values of the other.
16. individual points that substantially change the correlation or slope of the regression line

Down

1. the use of a regression line to make a prediction far outside the observed x values
3. the amount by which y is predicted to change when x increases by one unit
4. The _____ of a relationship in a scatterplot is determined by how closely the point follow a clear form.
5. the ____-_____ regression line is also known as the line of best fit (2 words)
6. an individual value that falls outside the overall pattern of the relationship
7. value that measures the strength of the linear relationship between two quantitative variables
8. A _____ association is defined when above average values of the explanatory are accompanied by above average values of the response
9. y-hat is the _____ value of the y-variable for a given x
11. variable that measures the outcome of a study
12. variable that may help explain or influence changes in another variable
13. The _____ of a scatterplot indicates a positive or negative association between the variables.
17. The ____ of a scatterplot is usually linear or nonlinear.

CHAPTER 4: COLLECTING DATA

*"Not everything that can be counted counts;
and not everything that counts can be counted"* ~George Gallup

CHAPTER OVERVIEW

The first three chapters introduced us to some of the basics of exploratory data analysis. In this chapter, we'll learn about the second major topic in statistics – planning and conducting a study. Because it is difficult to perform a descriptive statistical analysis without data, we need to learn appropriate ways to produce data. We will start by learning the difference between a population and a sample. Then, we will study sampling techniques and learn how to identify potential sources of bias. Our goal is to collect data that is representative of the population we wish to study. Therefore, it is important that our data collection techniques do not systematically over- or under-represent any segment of the population. In the second section, we will learn the difference between observational studies and experiments. We will learn a number of different ways to design experiments so we can establish relationships between variables. Finally, we will conclude this chapter by reviewing some cautions about using studies wisely. This chapter contains a lot of vocabulary and concepts. Be sure to study them, as proper application of terms is important for strong statistical communication!

Sections in this Chapter
Section 4.1: Sampling and Surveys
Section 4.2: Experiments
Section 4.3: Using Studies Wisely

PLAN YOUR LEARNING

Use the following *suggested* guide to help plan your reading and assignments in "The Practice of Statistics, Updated 6th Edition." Put a check mark in the last column when you are done! Note: your teacher may schedule a different pacing or assign different problems. Be sure to follow his or her instructions!

Read	Do	Done!
Section 4.1: p. 249-256	1, 3, 5, 7, 11, 13	
Section 4.1: p. 257-260	15, 17, 19, 21, 22, 23	
Section 4.1: p. 261-264	25, 27, 29, 31, 33, MC 35-40	
Section 4.2: p. 270-275	43, 45, 47, 49, 51, 53	
Section 4.2: p. 275-279	57, 59, 61, 63	
Section 4.2: p. 280-284	55, 65, 67, 69	
Section 4.2: p. 284-289	71, 75, 77, 79, MC 83-90	
Section 4.3: p. 297-302	93, 95, 97, 99	
Section 4.3: p. 303-307	103, 105, 107, MC 117-118	
Chapter Summary	Multiple-Choice FRAPPY!	

Section 4.1: Sampling and Surveys

Before You Read: Section Summary

Often in statistics, our goal is to draw a conclusion about a population based on information gathered from a sample. In order for us to make a valid inference about the population, we must feel confident that the sample obtained will be representative of the group as a whole. There are a number of different ways to select samples from a population—some better than others. In this section, you will explore ways in which you can sample badly, how to sample well, and cautions to consider when sampling. You will be introduced to a number of different sampling methods. Be sure to familiarize yourself with how to select samples using each of the methods and how to explain potential advantages and disadvantages of each.

Learning Targets:

_____ I can identify the population and sample in a statistical study.

_____ I can identify voluntary response sampling and convenience sampling and explain how these sampling methods can lead to bias.

_____ I can describe how to select a simple random sample using slips of paper, technology, or a table of random digits.

_____ I can describe how to select a sample using stratified random sampling, cluster sampling, and systematic random sampling, and explain whether a particular sampling method is appropriate in a given situation.

_____ I can explain how undercoverage, nonresponse, question wording, and other aspects of a sample survey can lead to bias.

While You Read: Key Vocabulary and Concepts

population:
sample:
census:
sample survey:
convenience sampling:
bias:

voluntary response sampling:

random sampling:

simple random sample (SRS):

sampling without replacement:

sampling with replacement:

strata:

stratified random sampling:

cluster:

cluster sampling:

systematic random sampling:

undercoverage:

nonresponse:

response bias:

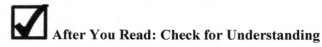**After You Read: Check for Understanding**

Concept 1: Population, Samples, and Inference

The purpose of sampling is to provide us with information about a population without actually gathering the information from every single element of the whole group. A sample is a part of the population from which we collect information. This information is then used to infer something about the population. We can have more faith in our inference if we are confident that the sampling method used is likely to produce a sample that is representative of the population of interest. Some sampling methods may introduce a level of bias into the situation that could cause us to make an incorrect inference about the population. It is important that you can clearly identify the population of interest and describe whether or not the sampling method is unbiased.

Check for Understanding:

_____ *I can identify the population and sample in statistical study.*

A publisher is interested in determining the reading difficulty of mathematics textbooks. Reading difficulty is determined by the length of sentences and the length of words used in the text. Researchers randomly select 10 paragraphs out of the most popular Algebra 1 textbooks and calculate the average sentence length and average word length for that type of mathematic textbook.

Identify the population and sample.

Concept 2: How to Sample Well

The key to sampling is to use a method that helps ensures that the sample is as representative of the population as possible. Because sampling methods like voluntary response and convenience samples can systematically favor certain outcomes in a population, we say they are biased. An unbiased sampling method is one that does not favor any element of the population. We rely on the use of chance to select unbiased samples. The easiest way to do this is to select a simple random sample (SRS) from the population of interest. One way we could select an SRS would be to write the name of each individual in the population on a piece of paper, put the pieces in a hat, mix them well, and draw out the necessary number of slips for our sample. We could also select an SRS by labeling each individual in the population with a number of the same length (ex. one-, two-, three- digit number depending on the size of the population) and then generate random numbers from technology or a random number table until you reach the desired sample size. The labeled individuals that match the generated numbers, ignoring repeats, make up the sample.

Check for Understanding:

_____ *I can describe how to select a simple random sample using slips of paper, technology, or a table of random digits.*

An alphabetized list of names is found below. Use the random digit table provided to choose an SRS of 4 individuals. Clearly indicate how you are using the table to select the SRS.

Abney	Andreasen	Bearden	Bready	Buckley	Brock
Bush	Chauvet	Costello	Derksen	Greenberg	Knott
Lacey	Martin	McDonald	Osters	Preble	Ripp
Rohnkol	Sterken	Tyson	Wilcock	Yankay	

19223 95034 05756 28713 96409 12531 42544 82853

73676 47150 99400 11327 27754 40548 82421 76290

While Simple Random Samples give each group of *n* individuals in the population an equal chance to be selected, they are not always the easiest to obtain. Several other sampling methods are available that can be used instead of an SRS. If the population consists of several groups of individuals that are likely to produce similar responses within groups, but systematically different responses between groups, consider taking a stratified random sample. To do this, select an SRS from each stratum (group) to obtain the sample. Another method, cluster sampling, divides the population into smaller groups (clusters) that mirror the overall population and selects an SRS of those clusters. You should be able to describe how to select a sample using each of these methods as you may be asked to do so on the AP exam!

Concept 3: What Can Go Wrong?

When designing a sample survey, random sampling helps avoid bias. But there are other kinds of mistakes in the sampling process that can lead to inaccurate information about the population. For instance, if the sampling method is designed in a way that leaves out certain segments of the population, the sample survey suffers from undercoverage. When selected individuals cannot be contacted or refuse to participate, the survey suffers from nonresponse. If people give incorrect or misleading responses, a survey suffers from response bias. Finally, if a question is worded in a way that favors certain responses, the survey suffers from question wording bias. Be sure to design sample surveys to avoid these issues and make sure you can identify them in existing studies.

Check for Understanding:

_____ *I can explain how undercoverage, nonresponse, question wording, and other aspects of a sample survey can lead to bias.*

An SRS of 400 recent high school graduates was asked, "Did you ever cheat on an exam during your senior year?" Of the 400 respondents, 64 percent admitted to cheating on at least one test.

What is one practical problem with this survey?

What is the likely direction of the bias?

Section 4.2: Experiments

Before You Read: Section Summary

Sample surveys allow us to gather information about the population without actually doing anything to that population. Such observational studies provide a snapshot of the population, but cannot be used to establish any sort of cause-effect relationship. Observational studies only allow us to describe the population, compare groups, or examine basic relationships between variables. In this section, we will move beyond sampling to study the elements of experimental design. Experiments allow us to produce data in a way that can lead to conclusions about causation. There are a lot of vocabulary terms in this section. It is easy to confuse sampling terms and experimental design terms. Make sure you understand each vocabulary term or concept!

Learning Targets:

_____ I can explain the concept of confounding and how it limits the ability to make cause-and effect conclusions.

_____ I can distinguish between an observational study and an experiment, and identify the explanatory and response variables in each type of study.

_____ I can identify experimental units and treatments in an experiment.

_____ I can describe the placebo effect and the purpose of blinding in an experiment.

_____ I can describe how to randomly assign treatments in an experiment using slips of paper, technology, or a table of random digits.

_____ I can explain the purpose of comparison, random assignment, control, and replication in an experiment.

_____ I can describe a completely randomized design for an experiment.

_____ I can describe a randomized block design and a matched pairs design for an experiment and explain the purpose of blocking in an experiment.

While You Read: Key Vocabulary and Concepts

observational study:
response variable:
explanatory variable:
confounding:
experiment:
placebo:

treatment:

experimental unit:

subjects:

factors:

levels:

control group:

placebo effect:

random assignment:

double-blind/single-blind:

random assignment:

control:

replication:

completely randomized design:

block:

randomized block design:

matched pairs design:

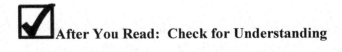

After You Read: Check for Understanding

Concept 1: Observational Studies vs. Experiments

Sample surveys are examples of observational studies. Their goal is to describe the population and examine relationships between variables. Often, however, we wish to determine whether or not a cause-effect relationship exists between an explanatory and a response variable. Observational studies cannot be used to establish this relationship because of confounding between the explanatory variable and one or more other variables.

Check for Understanding:

_____ *I can explain the concept of confounding and how it limits the ability to make cause-and effect conclusions.*

Does shoe size affect spelling ability? A recent study was conducted in a suburban school district to answer this question. 30 students from grades 1 through 8 were randomly selected. Each student was administered a spelling test and had his or her feet measured. Test scores were plotted against shoe size and a strong, positive relationship was observed.

1) Was this an observational study or an experiment?

2) What are the explanatory and response variables?

3) Suggest a possible confounding variable in this setting. Explain carefully how it may confound the results.

Concept 2: How to Experiment Well

If we wish to establish cause and effect, we must conduct an experiment in which treatments are imposed on experimental units and other potential influences on the response variable are controlled as much as possible. The basic idea behind an experiment is that we obtain experimental units, apply treatments, and measure the results. When conducted properly, experiments can provide good evidence of causation. Proper experimental design incorporates three principles. First, we must control for the influences of variables that might affect the response. We want to ensure that any changes are due to the treatment alone. Second, we must randomly assign experimental units to treatments. This helps ensure equivalent groups of units. Random assignment helps ensure that the effects of variables will be felt equally by all groups in the experiment, so that the only systematic difference between groups are the treatments themselves. Finally, replication is necessary to ensure enough experimental units are in each group to convince us the differences in the effects of the treatments can be separated from chance differences between the groups. If a difference between groups is observed that is too large to have occurred by chance alone, we say it is statistically significant. We will learn how to establish statistical significance in a later chapter. For now, focus on how to design a quality experiment!

Check for Understanding:

_____ *I can identify experimental units and treatments in an experiment.*
_____ *I can describe a completely randomized design for an experiment.*

Mr. Tyson teaches statistics to 150 students. He is interested in knowing whether or not listening to classical music while studying results in higher test scores than listening to no music. He wishes to design an experiment to answer this question.

1)   What are the experimental units, explanatory variable, treatments and response variable?

2)   What other potential variables could confound the results in this situation? How could they affect the results? How could we avoid their effects?

3)   Describe a completely randomized design for Mr. Tyson's experiment.

Concept 3: Other Types of Experimental Design

A completely randomized experiment is the simplest design that can give good evidence of cause-effect relationships. In some cases, however, we can add elements to this basic design to control for the effects of other variables. For example, placebos (fake treatments) can be given to control for the placebo effect—the phenomenon that occurs when subjects respond to getting any treatment, whether it is real or not. We can use blinding when there is a concern that knowing who receives what treatment might affect the results. Double-blind experiments ensure that neither the subjects nor the people who interact with the subjects and measure their responses know who receives which treatment.

When groups of subjects share a common characteristic that might systematically affect their responses to the treatments, we can use blocking to control for the effects of this variable. For example, suppose researchers are conducting an experiment to compare the effectiveness of a new medicine for treating high blood pressure with the most commonly prescribed drug. If they believe that older and younger people may respond differently to such medications, the researchers can separate the subjects into blocks of older and younger people and randomly assign treatments within each block. This randomized block design helps isolate the variation in responses due to age, which makes it easier for researchers to find evidence of a treatment effect. If we are only comparing two treatments, we can sometimes conduct a matched pairs design by creating blocks of two similar individuals and then randomly assigning each subject to a treatment. Another type of matched pairs design involves assigning two treatments to each subject in a random order.

In each type of experimental design, our goal is to ensure control, random assignment, and replication. If these principles are addressed in our design, we can establish good evidence of causal relationships. Make sure you can describe how you would conduct an experiment using each of these designs as you may be asked to do so on the AP exam!

Check for Understanding:

_____ *I can describe a randomized block design and a matched pairs design for an experiment and explain the purpose of blocking in an experiment.*

Refer to the previous Check for Understanding. Describe an experimental design involving blocking that will help answer Mr. Tyson's question. Explain why this design is preferable to a completely randomized design.

Section 4.3: Using Studies Wisely

Before You Read: Section Summary

A common mistake on the AP exam is to confuse inference about the population and inference about cause and effect. In this section, we learn about the difference between the two as well as some of the challenges of establishing causation. While it is important to know how to design good surveys and experiments, it is just as important to understand how to properly use their results!

Because some sample surveys and experiments have potential to cause harm to the participants, it is important to consider data ethics when designing a study. Basic data ethics include having an institutional review board that monitors the well-being of the participants. Individuals must give their informed consent before data are collected and all individual results should be kept confidential.

Learning Targets:

_____ I can explain the concept of sampling variability when making an inference about a population and how sample size affects sampling variability.

_____ I can explain the meaning of statistically significant in the context of an experiment and use simulation to determine if the results of an experiment are statistically significant.

_____ I can identify when it is appropriate to make an inference about a population and when it is appropriate to make an inference about cause and effect.

_____ I can evaluate if a statistical study has been carried out in an ethical manner.

While You Read: Key Vocabulary and Concepts

sampling variability:
sampling variability and sample size:
statistically significant:
scope of inference:

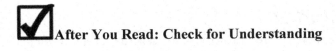**After You Read: Check for Understanding**

Concept 1: Scope of Inference

When the members of a sample are selected at random from a population, we can use the sample results to infer things about the population. That is, well-designed samples allow us to make inferences about the population from which we sampled. Random sampling is what allows us to generalize our results with confidence. Larger random samples tend to provide more precise estimates of the true population value of interest than smaller random samples.

If our goal is to make an inference about cause and effect, we must use a randomized experiment. Unless the experimental units were randomly selected from a larger population of interest, we cannot extend our conclusions beyond individuals like those who took part in the experiment.

Concept 2: The Challenges of Establishing Causation

Well-designed experiments can be used to establish causation. However, lack of realism in some experiments prevents us from seeing similar results outside the laboratory setting. In some cases, it is not practical, safe, or ethical to conduct an experiment. Even with strong evidence from observational studies, it is very difficult to establish a cause and effect conclusion.

Check for Understanding:

_____ *I can explain the concept of sampling variability when making an inference about a population and how sample size affects sampling variability.*

In a random sample of 50 AP Statistics students, the average amount of change carried in their pockets is $0.42.

1) Do you think the true average amount of change carried by all AP Statistics students is $0.42?

2) Which would be more likely to give an estimate close to the true average amount of change carried by all AP Statistics students: a random sample of 50 students, or a random sample of 200 students?

Chapter Summary: Designing Studies

This chapter is an important one in your study of statistics. After all, we cannot describe or analyze data without collecting it first! Because one of the major goals of statistics is to make inferences that go beyond the data, it is critical that we produce data in a way that will allow for such inferences. Biased data production methods can lead to incorrect inferences. Random sampling allows us to make an inference about the population as a whole. Well-designed experiments in which we randomly assign treatments and control for other variables allow us to make inferences about cause and effect. We will learn how to perform these inferences in later chapters. Your goal in this chapter is to be able to describe good sampling and experimental design techniques and recognize when sampling or experimental design has been done poorly. There is always a question about sampling or experimental design on the free-response portion of the AP exam. Study the vocabulary and concepts in this chapter so you can answer that question with confidence!

How well do you understand each of the learning targets?

Learning Target	Got It!	Almost There	Needs Work
I can identify the population and sample in a statistical study.			
I can identify voluntary response sampling and convenience sampling and explain how these sampling methods can lead to bias.			
I can describe how to select a simple random sample using slips of paper, technology, or a table of random digits.			
I can describe how to select a sample using stratified random sampling, cluster sampling, and systematic random sampling, and explain whether a particular sampling method is appropriate in a given situation.			
I can explain how undercoverage, nonresponse, question wording, and other aspects of a sample survey can lead to bias.			
I can explain the concept of confounding and how it limits the ability to make cause-and-effect conclusions.			
I can distinguish between an observational study and an experiment, and identify the explanatory and response variables in each type of study.			
I can identify experimental units and treatments in an experiment.			
I can describe the placebo effect and the purpose of blinding in an experiment.			
I can describe how to randomly assign treatments in an experiment using slips of paper, technology, or a table of random digits.			
I can explain the purpose of comparison, random assignment, control, and replication in an experiment.			
I can describe a completely randomized design for an experiment.			
I can describe a randomized block design and a matched pairs design for an experiment and explain the purpose of blocking in an experiment.			
I can explain the concept of sampling variability when making an inference about a population and how sample size affects sampling variability.			
I can explain statistical significance in the context of an experiment and use simulation to determine if the results of an experiment are statistically significant.			
I can identify when it is appropriate to make an inference about a population and when it is appropriate to make an inference about cause and effect.			

Chapter 4 Multiple Choice Practice

Directions. Identify the choice that best completes the statement or answers the question. Check your answers and note your performance when you are finished.

1. A researcher is testing a company's new stain remover. He has contracted with 40 families who have agreed to test the product. He randomly assigns 20 families to the group that will use the new stain remover and 20 to the group that will use the company's current product. The most important reason for this random assignment is that
   (A) randomization makes the analysis easier since the data can be collected and entered into the computer in any order.
   (B) randomization eliminates the impact of any confounding variables.
   (C) randomization is a good way to create two groups of 20 families that are as similar as possible, except for the treatments they receive.
   (D) randomization ensures that the study is double-blind.
   (E) randomization reduces the impact of outliers.

2. A researcher observes that, on average, the number of traffic violations in cities with Major League Baseball teams is larger than in cities without Major League Baseball teams. The most plausible explanation for this observed association is that the
   (A) presence of a Major League Baseball team causes the number of traffic incidents to rise (perhaps due to the large number of people leaving the ballpark).
   (B) high number of traffic incidents is responsible for the presence of Major League Baseball teams (more traffic incidents means more people have cars, making it easier for them to get to the ballpark).
   (C) association is due to the presence of another variable (Major League teams tend to be in large cities with more people, hence a greater number of traffic incidents).
   (D) association makes no sense, since many people take public transit or walk to baseball games.
   (E) observed association is purely coincidental. It is implausible to believe the observed association could be anything other than accidental.

3. A researcher is testing the effect of a new fertilizer on crop growth. He marks 30 plots in a field, splits the plots in half, and randomly assigns the new fertilizer to one half of the plot and the old fertilizer to the other half. After 4 weeks, he measures the crop yield and compares the effects of the two fertilizers. This design is an example of
   (A) matched pairs experiment
   (B) completely randomized comparative experiment
   (C) cluster experiment
   (D) double-blind experiment
   (E) this is not an experiment

4. A large suburban school wants to assess student attitudes towards their mathematics textbook. The administration randomly selects 15 mathematics classes and gives the survey to every student in the class. This is an example of a
   (A) multistage sample
   (B) stratified sample
   (C) cluster sample
   (D) simple random sample
   (E) convenience sample

5. Eighty volunteers who currently use a certain brand of medication to reduce blood pressure are recruited to try a new medication. The volunteers are randomly assigned to one of two groups. One group continues to take their current medication, the other group switches to the new experimental medication. Blood pressure is measured before, during, and after the study. Which of the following best describes a conclusion that can be drawn from this study?
    (A)   We can determine whether the new drug reduces blood pressure more than the old drug for anyone who suffers from high blood pressure.
    (B)   We can determine whether the new drug reduces blood pressure more than the old drug for individuals like the subjects in the study.
    (C)   We can determine whether the blood pressure improved more with the new drug than with the old drug, but we can't establish cause and effect.
    (D)   We cannot draw any conclusions, since the all the volunteers were already taking the old drug when the experiment started.
    (E)   We cannot draw any conclusions, because there was no control group.

6. To determine employee satisfaction at a large company, the management selects an SRS of 200 workers from the marketing department and a separate SRS of 50 workers from the sales department. This kind of sample is called a
    (A)   simple random sample.
    (B)   simple random sample with blocking.
    (C)   multistage random sample.
    (D)   stratified random sample.
    (E)   random cluster sample.

7. For a certain experiment you have 8 subjects, of which 4 are female and 4 are male. The name of the subjects are listed below:

    Males: Atwater, Bacon, Chu, Diaz.   *Females: Johnson, King, Liu, Moore*

    There are two treatments, A and B. If a randomized block design is used with the subjects blocked by their gender, which of the following is *not* a possible group of subjects who receive treatment A?
    (A)   Atwater, Chu, King, Liu
    (B)   Bacon, Chu, Liu, Moore
    (C)   Atwater, Diaz, Liu, King
    (D)   Atwater, Bacon, Chu, Johnson
    (E)   Atwater, Bacon, Johnson, King

8. An article in the student newspaper of a large university had the headline "A's swapped for evaluations?" Results showed that higher grades directly corresponded to a more positive evaluation. Which of the following would be a valid conclusion to draw from the study?
    (A)   A teacher can improve his or her teaching evaluations by giving good grades.
    (B)   A good teacher, as measured by teaching evaluations, helps students learn better, resulting in higher grades.
    (C)   Teachers of courses in which the mean grade is higher apparently tend to have above-average teaching evaluations.
    (D)   Teaching evaluations should be conducted before grades are awarded.
    (E)   All of the above.

9. A new cough medicine was given to a group of 25 subjects who had a cough due to the common cold. 30 minutes after taking the new medicine, 20 of the subjects reported that their coughs had disappeared. From this information you conclude
    (A) that the remedy is effective for the treatment of coughs.
    (B) nothing, because the sample size is too small.
    (C) nothing, because there is no control group for comparison.
    (D) that the new treatment is better than the old medicine.
    (E) that the remedy is not effective for the treatment of coughs.

10. A study is conducted using 100 volunteers who suffer from anxiety. Half of the volunteers are selected at random and assigned to receive a new drug that is thought to be extremely effective in reducing anxiety. The other 50 are given an existing anti-anxiety drug. A doctor evaluates anxiety levels after two months of treatment to determine if there has been a larger reduction in the anxiety levels of those who take the new drug. This would be double blind if
    (A) both drugs looked the same.
    (B) neither the subjects nor the doctor knew which treatment any subject had received.
    (C) the doctor couldn't see the subjects and the subjects couldn't see the doctor.
    (D) there was a third group that received a placebo.
    (E) all of the above

Check your answers below. If you got a question wrong, check to see if you made a simple mistake or if you need to study that concept more. After you check your work, identify the concepts you feel very confident about and note what you will do to learn the concepts in need of more study.

#	Answer	Concept	Right	Wrong	Simple Mistake?	Need to Study More
1	C	Why we randomize				
2	C	Confounding				
3	A	Matched Pairs				
4	C	Cluster Sampling				
5	B	Inference about the population				
6	D	Stratified random sampling				
7	D	Blocking				
8	C	Surveys vs Experiments				
9	C	Control				
10	B	Definition of Experiments				

FRAPPY! Free Response AP® Problem, Yay!

The following problem is modeled after actual Advanced Placement Statistics free response questions. Your task is to generate a complete, concise response in 15 minutes. After you generate your response, read over the solution and scoring guide. Score your response and note what, if anything, you would do differently to increase your own score.

A large school district is interested in determining student attitudes about their co-curricular offerings such as athletics and fine arts. The district consists of students attending 4 elementary schools (2000 students total), 1 middle school (1000 students total), and 2 high schools (2000 students total).

The administration is considering two sampling plans. The first consists of taking a simple random sample of students in the district and surveying them. The second consists of taking a stratified random sample of students and surveying them.

(a) Describe how you would select a simple random sample of 200 students in the district.

(b) Describe how you would select a stratified random sample consisting of 200 students.

(c) Describe the statistical advantage of using a stratified random sample over the simple random sample in this study.

FRAPPY! Scoring Rubric

Use the following rubric to score your response. Each part receives a score of "Essentially Correct," "Partially Correct," or "Incorrect." When you have scored your response, reflect on your understanding of the concepts addressed in this problem. If necessary, note what you would do differently on future questions like this to increase your score.

Intent of the Question

The goal of this question is to determine your ability to describe sampling methods and explain the advantages of stratifying over simple random sampling

Solution

(a) Write each student's name on a slip of paper. Place the slips of paper in a hat and mix well. Select 200 slips of paper and note the students in the sample. OR Label each student with a number from 0001 to 5000. Use a random number table or technology to produce random 4-digit numbers, ignoring repeats, until 200 are determined. These 200 numbers correspond to the individuals who will be surveyed.

(b) Because student attitudes may differ by level of school (elementary, middle, or high school), we should stratify by level. Label students at each level and randomly select 80 elementary students, 40 middle school students, and 80 high school students. This ensures each level is represented in the same proportion as the overall student enrollments

(c) Stratifying ensures no level is over or under represented in the sample. It is possible to select very few (or even no!) students from one level in a simple random sample. The opinions of students at one level may not reflect the opinions of all students in the district. Stratifying ensures each level is fairly represented.

Scoring:

Parts (a), (b), and (c) are scored as essentially correct (E), partially correct (P), or incorrect (I).

Part (a) is essentially correct if the response describes an appropriate method of selecting a simple random sample. This method should include labeling the individuals and employing a sufficient means of random selection that could be replicated by someone knowledgeable in statistics.
Part (a) is partially correct if random selection is used correctly, but the description does not provide sufficient detail for implementation.

Part (b) is essentially correct if the response describes selecting strata based on a reasonable variable (such as school level) and indicates randomly selecting individuals from each stratum to be a part of the survey. The method can result in an equal number of students from each level OR proportional representation based on the strata.
Part (b) is partially correct if a reasonable variable is identified, but the method is unclear or does not ensure proportional representation.

Part (c) is essentially correct if the response provides a reasonable statistical advantage of stratified random sampling based on the effects of an identified variable on the results context.
Part (c) is partially correct if the response provides a reasonable statistical advantage, but the communication is not clear or lacks context.

4   Complete Response

All three parts essentially correct

3   Substantial Response

Two parts essentially correct and one part partially correct

2   Developing Response

Two parts essentially correct and no parts partially correct

One part essentially correct and one or two parts partially correct

Three parts partially correct

1   Minimal Response

One part essentially correct and no parts partially correct

No parts essentially correct and two parts partially correct

My Score:
What I did well:
What I could improve:
What I should remember if I see a problem like this on the AP Exam:

Chapter 4 Formula Sheet

Create a one-page summary of important concepts and formulas found in this chapter. This will serve as a valuable resource as you prepare for the AP Exam.

Chapter 4 Crossword Puzzle
COLLECTING DATA

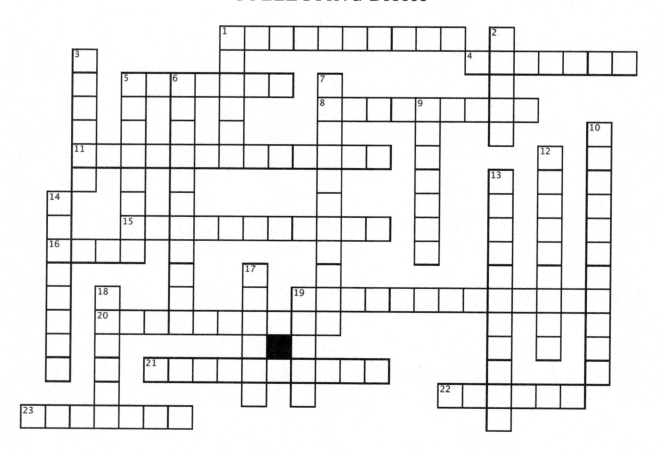

Across

1. a _____ random sample consists of separate simple random samples drawn from groups of similar individuals
4. a "fake" treatment that is sometimes used in experiments
5. the effort to minimize variability in the way experimental units are obtained and treated
8. the process of drawing a conclusion about the population based on a sample
11. this type of student can not be used to establish cause-effect relationships
15. the practice of using enough subjects in an experiment to reduce chance variation
16. a study that systematically favors certain outcomes shows this
19. this occurs when some groups in the population are left out of the process of choosing the sample
20. a study in which a treatment is imposed in order to observe a reasponse
21. the entire group of individuals about which we want information
22. a simple _____ sample consists of individuals from the population, each of which has an equally likely chance of being chosen
23. a _____ sample consists of a simple random sample of small groups from a population

Down

1. groups of similar individuals in a population
2. a group of experimental units that are similar in some way that may affect the response to the treatments
3. the rule used to assign experimental units to treatments is _____ assignment
5. smaller groups of individuals who mirror the population
6. this occurs when an individual chosen for the sample can't be contacted or refuses to participate
7. an observed effect that is too large to have occurred by chance alone
9. a lack of _____ in an experiment can prevent us from generalizing the results
10. a sample in which we choose individuals who are easiest to reach
12. a _____ response sample consists of people who choose themselves by responding to a general appeal
13. neither the subjects nor those measuring the response know which treatment a subject received (two words)
14. when units are humans, they are called
17. the part of the population from which we actually collect information
18. another name for treatments
19. the individuals on which an experiement is done are experimental _____

Chapter 5: Probability

*"The most important questions of life are, for the most part,
really questions of probability." Pierre-Simon LaPlace*

CHAPTER OVERVIEW

Now that we have learned how to collect data and how to analyze it graphically and numerically, we turn
our study to probability, the mathematics of chance. Probability is the basis for the fourth and final theme
in AP Statistics, inference. The next three chapters will provide you with the background in probability
necessary to perform and understand the inferential methods we'll learn later in the course.

In this chapter, you will learn the definition of probability as a long-term relative frequency. You will study
how to use simulation to answer probability questions as well as some basic rules to calculate probabilities
of events. You will also learn two concepts that will reappear later in our studies: conditional probability
and independence. Many of the ideas and methods you will learn in this chapter may be familiar to you.
When it comes to statistics, your goal with probability is to be able to answer the question, "What would
happen if we did this many, many times?" so you can make an informed statistical inference.

Sections in this Chapter
Section 5.1: Randomness, Probability, and Simulation
Section 5.2: Probability Rules
Section 5.3: Conditional Probability and Independence

PLAN YOUR LEARNING

Use the following *suggested* guide to help plan your reading and assignments in "The Practice of Statistics,
Updated 6th Edition." Put a check mark in the last column when you are done. Note: your teacher may
schedule a different pacing or assign different problems. Be sure to follow his or her instructions!

Read	Do	Done!
Section 5.1: p. 326-331	1, 3, 5, 7	
Section 5.1: p. 332-336	9, 11, 15, 21, MC 23-28	
Section 5.2: p. 342-346	31, 33, 35 37, 39	
Section 5.2: p. 347-353	41, 47, 49, 51, 53, MC 55-58	
Section 5.3: p. 358-366	61, 63, 65, 67, 69, 71, 77, 79	
Section 5.3: p. 367-375	81, 83, 87, 89, 91, 93, 99, MC 103-106	
Chapter Summary	Multiple-Choice FRAPPY!	

Section 5.1: Randomness, Probability, and Simulation

Before You Read: Section Summary

This section introduces the basic definition of probability as a long-term relative frequency. That is, probability answers the question, "How often would we expect to see a particular outcome if we repeated a random process many times?" The big idea that emerges when we study random processes is that random behavior is unpredictable in the short run but has a regular and predictable pattern in the long run. This idea seems pretty straightforward, yet there are a lot of common misconceptions about probability. Several are discussed in this section. Be sure to avoid falling for these common myths!

The last topic in this section addresses the use of simulation to estimate probabilities. Simulation is a powerful tool for modeling random behavior that can be used to illustrate many of the inference ideas you'll study later in the course.

Learning Targets:

_____ I can interpret probability as a long-run relative frequency.

_____ I can use simulation to model a random process.

While You Read: Key Vocabulary and Concepts

probability:

law of large numbers:

simulation:

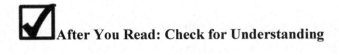

After You Read: Check for Understanding

Concept 1: The Idea of Probability

When we observe random behavior over a long series of repetitions, a useful fact emerges. While random behavior is unpredictable in the short term, a regular and predictable pattern becomes evident in the long run. The law of large numbers tells us that as we observe more and more repetitions of a random behavior, the proportion of times a specific outcome occurs will "settle down" around a single value. This long-term proportion is the probability of the outcome occurring. The probability of an event is always described as a value between 0 and 1 where 0 represents an event that never occurs and 1 means that the event will occur on every repetition.

Check for Understanding:

_____ *I can interpret probability as a long-run relative frequency.*

The probability of drawing a jack, queen, or king from a standard deck of playing cards is approximately 0.23.

1) Explain what this probability means in the context of drawing from a deck of cards.

2) Does this mean if we repeatedly draw a card, replace it, shuffle, and draw again 100 times that we will draw a jack, queen, or king 23 times? Why or why not?

Concept 2: Simulation

In this section, we learn how we can use simulation to estimate the probability of an event occurring. A three-step process can be used to perform a simulation of a question of interest by: 1) describing how to use a random device to imitate a repetition of the random behavior, 2) performing many repetitions of the simulation, and 3) using the results of the simulation to answer the original question. While simulations don't provide exact theoretical probabilities, the use of random numbers and other random devices to imitate random behavior can be a useful tool for estimating the likelihood of events.

Check for Understanding:

_____ *I can use simulation to model a random process.*

A popular airline knows that, in general, 95% of individuals who purchase a ticket for a 10-seat commuter flight actually show up for the flight. In an effort to ensure a full flight, the airline sells 12 tickets for each flight. Design and carry out a simulation to estimate the probability that the flight will be overbooked, that is, more passengers show up than there are seats on the flight.

Section 5.2: Probability Rules

Before You Read: Section Summary

Now that you have the basic idea of probability down, you will learn how to describe probability models and use probability rules to calculate the likelihood of events. You will also learn how to organize information in two-way tables and Venn diagrams to help in determining probabilities. Understanding probability is important for understanding inference. Make sure you are comfortable with the definitions and rules in this section, as it will make your study of probability much easier!

Learning Targets:

_____ I can give a probability model for a random process with equally likely outcomes and use it to find the probability of an event.

_____ I can use basic probability rules, including the complement rule and addition rule for mutually exclusive events.

_____ I can use a two-way table or Venn diagram to model a random process and calculate probabilities involving two events.

_____ I can apply the general addition rule to calculate probabilities.

While You Read: Key Vocabulary and Concepts

sample space:
probability model:
event:
complement:
mutually exclusive (disjoint):
general addition rule:
intersection:
union:
Venn diagram:

☑**After You Read: Check for Understanding**

Concept 1: Probability Models and the Basic Rules of Probability

Random behavior can be described using a probability model. This model provides two pieces of information: a list of possible outcomes (sample space) and the likelihood of each outcome. By describing random behavior with a probability model, we can find the probability of an event—a particular outcome or collection of outcomes. Probability models must obey some basic rules of probability:

- For any event A, $0 \le P(A) \le 1$.
- If S is the sample space in a probability model, $P(S) = 1$.
- In the case of equally likely outcomes, $P(A) = $ (# outcomes in event A) / (# outcomes in S).
- Complement Rule: $P(A^C) = 1 - P(A)$.
- If A and B are mutually exclusive events, $P(A \text{ or } B) = P(A) + P(B)$.

After this section, you should be able to describe a probability model for random behavior and apply the basic probability rules to answer questions about events.

Check for Understanding:

_____ *I can give a probability model for a random process with equally likely outcomes and use it to find the probability of an event.*

_____ *I can use basic probability rules, including the complement rule and addition rule for mutually exclusive events.*

Consider drawing a card from a shuffled fair deck of 52 playing cards.

1) How many possible outcomes are in the sample space for this random process? What's the probability for each outcome?

Define the following events: A: the card drawn is an Ace and B: the card drawn is a heart.

2) Find $P(A)$ and $P(B)$.

3) What is $P(A^C)$?

4) Are events A and B mutually exclusive? Why or why not?

Concept 2: Two-Way Tables and Venn Diagrams

Oftentimes we'll need to find probabilities involving two events. In these cases, it may be helpful to organize and display the sample space using a two-way table or Venn diagram. This can be especially helpful when two events are not mutually exclusive. When dealing with two events A and B, it is important to be able to describe the union (or collection of all outcomes in A, B, or both) and the intersection (the collection of outcomes in both *A* and *B*). The general addition rule expands upon the basic rules presented in this section to help us find the probability of two events that are not mutually exclusive.

$$\text{If A and B are two events, } P(A \cup B) = P(A) + P(B) - P(A \cap B).$$

Check for Understanding:

_____ *I can use a two-way table or Venn diagram to model a random process and calculate probabilities involving two events.*

_____ *I can apply the general addition rule to calculate probabilities.*

Consider drawing a card from a shuffled fair deck of 52 playing cards.
Define the following events: A: the card drawn is an Ace and B: the card drawn is a heart.

1) Use a two-way table to display the sample space.

2) Use a Venn diagram to display the sample space.

3) Find $P(A \cup B)$. Show your work.

Section 5.3: Conditional Probability and Independence

Before You Read: Section Summary

Two important concepts are introduced in this section: conditional probability and independence. These concepts will reappear throughout the remainder of your studies in statistics, so it is important that you understand what they mean! This section will also introduce you to several rules for calculating probabilities: the conditional probability formula, the general multiplication rule, and the multiplication rule for independent events. Not only do you want to know how to use these rules, but also when. As you perform probability calculations, make sure you can justify why you are using a particular rule!

Learning Targets:

_____ I can calculate and interpret conditional probabilities.
_____ I can determine if two events are independent.
_____ I can use the general multiplication rule to calculate probabilities.
_____ I can use a tree diagram to model a random process involving a sequence of outcomes and to calculate probabilities.
_____ I can use the multiplication rule for independent events to calculate probabilities, when appropriate.

While You Read: Key Vocabulary and Concepts

conditional probability:
Independent events:
general multiplication rule:
tree diagram:
multiplication rule for independent events:

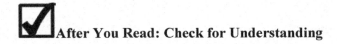

After You Read: Check for Understanding

Concept 1: Conditional Probability and Independence

A conditional probability describes the chance that an event will occur given that another event is already known to have happened. To note that we are dealing with a conditional probability, we use the symbol | to mean "given that." For example, suppose we draw one card from a shuffled deck of 52 playing cards. We could write "the probability that the card is an ace given that it is a red card as $P(\text{ace} \mid \text{red})$. Building on the concept of conditional probabilities, we say that when knowing that one event has occurred has no effect on the probability of another event occurring, the events are independent. That is, events A and B are independent if $P(A \mid B) = P(A)$ and $P(B \mid A) = P(B)$. Note that the events "get an ace" and "get a red card" described earlier are independent – if you know a randomly selected card is red, the probability it is an ace is 2/26. This is equal the same as the probability a randomly selected card (regardless of color) is an ace. That is, 2/26 = 4/52. Likewise, if you know a randomly selected card is an ace, the probability it is red is 1/2. This is the same as the probability a randomly selected card (regardless of value) is red. Therefore, the two events are independent.

Check for Understanding:

_____ *I can calculate and interpret conditional probabilities.*

_____ *I can determine if two events are independent.*

Is there a relationship between gender and candy preference? Suppose 200 high school students were asked to complete a survey about their favorite candies. The table below shows the gender of each student and their favorite candy.

	Male	Female	Total
Skittles	80	60	**140**
M & M's	40	20	**60**
Total	**120**	**80**	**200**

Define A to be the event that a randomly selected student is *male* and B to be the event that a randomly selected student likes *Skittles*. Are the events A and B independent? Justify your answer.

Concept 2: Tree Diagrams and Conditional Probability

When random behavior involves a sequence of events, we can model it using a tree diagram. A tree diagram provides a branch for each outcome of an event along with the associated probabilities of those outcomes. Successive branches represent particular sequences of outcomes. To find the probability of an event, we multiply the probabilities on the branches that make up the event.

This leads us to the general multiplication rule: $P(A \cap B) = P(A) \cdot P(B \mid A)$.

If A and B are independent, the probability that both events occur is $P(A \cap B) = P(A) \cdot P(B)$.

Check for Understanding:

_____ *I can use the general multiplication rule to calculate probabilities.*

_____ *I can use a tree diagram to model a random process involving a sequence of outcomes and to calculate probabilities.*

A study of high school juniors in three districts – Lakeville, Sheboygan, and Omaha – was conducted to determine enrollment trends in AP mathematics courses—Calculus or Statistics. 42% of students in the study came from Lakeville, 37% came from Sheboygan, and the rest came from Omaha. In Lakeville, 64% of juniors took Statistics and the rest took Calculus. 58% of juniors in Sheboygan and 49% of juniors in Omaha took Statistics while the rest took Calculus in each district. No juniors took both Statistics and Calculus. Describe this situation using a tree diagram and find the probability that a randomly selected student in the study took Statistics.

Concept 3: Calculating Conditional Probabilities

By rearranging the terms in the general multiplication rule, we can determine a rule for conditional probabilities. That is, $P(B|A) = \dfrac{P(A \text{ and } B)}{P(A)}$. Most conditional probabilities can be determined by using a two-way table, Venn diagram, or tree diagram. However, the formula can also be used if you know the appropriate probabilities in the situation.

Check for Understanding:

_____ *I can use a tree diagram to model a random process involving a sequence of outcomes and to calculate probabilities.*

A study of high school juniors in three districts – Lakeville, Sheboygan, and Omaha – was conducted to determine enrollment trends in AP mathematics courses—Calculus or Statistics. 42% of students in the study came from Lakeville, 37% came from Sheboygan, and the rest came from Omaha. In Lakeville, 64% of juniors took Statistics and the rest took Calculus. 58% of juniors in Sheboygan and 49% of juniors in Omaha took Statistics while the rest took Calculus in each district. No juniors took both Statistics and Calculus. Describe this situation using a tree diagram and find the probability that a randomly selected student in the study took Statistics.

Find *P*(student is from Lakeville | took Statistics).

Chapter Summary: Probability

Probability describes the long-term behavior of random processes. Because random occurrences display patterns of regularity after many repetitions, we can use the rules of probability to determine the likelihood of observing particular results. At this point, you should be comfortable with the basic definition and rules of probability. In the next two chapters, you will study some further concepts in probability so we can build the foundation necessary for statistical inference.

Note that the AP exam may contain several questions about the probability of particular events. Make sure you understand how and when to apply each formula. More importantly, make sure you show your work when calculating probabilities so anyone reading your response understands exactly how you arrived at your answer!

How well do you understand each of the learning targets?

Target	Got It!	Almost There	Needs Some Work
I can interpret probability as a long-run relative frequency.			
I can use simulation to model a random process.			
I can give a probability model for a random process with equally likely outcomes and use it to find the probability of an event.			
I can use basic probability rules, including the complement rule and addition rule for mutually exclusive events.			
I can use a two-way table or Venn diagram to model a random process and calculate probabilities involving two events.			
I can use the general addition rule to calculate probabilities.			
I can use a tree diagram to describe random behavior.			
I can use the general multiplication rule to solve probability questions.			
I can calculate and interpret conditional probabilities.			
I can determine if two events are independent.			
I can use the general multiplication rule to calculate probabilities.			
I can use a tree diagram to model a random process involving a sequence of outcomes and to calculate probabilities.			
I can use the multiplication rule for independent events to calculate probabilities, when appropriate.			

Chapter 5 Multiple Choice Practice

Directions. Identify the choice that best completes the statement or answers the question. Check your answers and note your performance when you are finished.

1. The probability that you will win a prize in a carnival game is about 1/7. During the last nine attempts, you have failed to win. You decide to give it one last shot. Assuming the outcomes are independent from game to game, the probability that you will win is:
   - (A) 1/7
   - (B) $(1/7) - (1/7)^9$
   - (C) $(1/7) + (1/7)^9$
   - (D) 1/10
   - (E) 7/10

2. A friend has placed a large number of plastic disks in a hat and invited you to select one at random. He informs you that half are red and half are blue. If you draw a disk, record the color, replace it, and repeat 100 times, which of the following is true?

   - (A) It is unlikely you will choose red more than 50 times.
   - (B) If you draw 10 blue disks in a row, it is more likely you will draw a red on the next try.
   - (C) The overall proportion of red disks drawn should be close to 0.50.
   - (D) The chance that the 100th draw will be red depends on the results of the first 99 draws.
   - (E) All of the above are true.

3. The two-way table below gives information on males and females at a high school and their preferred music format.

	CD	mp3	Vinyl	Totals
Males	146	106	48	300
Females	146	64	40	250
Totals	292	170	88	550

   You select one student from this group at random. Which of the following statement is true about the events "prefers vinyl" and "Male"?

   - (A) The events are mutually exclusive and independent.
   - (B) The events are not mutually exclusive but they are independent.
   - (C) The events are mutually exclusive, but they are not independent.
   - (D) The events are not mutually exclusive, nor are they independent.
   - (E) The events are independent, but we do not have enough information to determine if they are mutually exclusive.

4. People with type O-negative blood are universal donors. That is, any patient can receive a transfusion of O-negative blood. Only 7.2% of the American population has O-negative blood. If 10 people appear at random to give blood, what is the probability that at least 1 of them is a universal donor?
   (A) 0
   (B) 0.280
   (C) 0.526
   (D) 0.720
   (E) 1

5. A die is loaded so that the number 6 comes up three times as often as any other number. What is the probability of rolling a 4, 5, or 6?
   (A) 2/3
   (B) 1/2
   (C) 5/8
   (D) 1/3
   (E) 1/4

6. You draw two candies at random from a bag that has 20 red, 10 green, 15 orange, and 5 blue candies without replacement. What is the probability that both candies are red?
   (A) 0.1551
   (B) 0.1600
   (C) 0.2222
   (D) 0.4444
   (E) 0.8000

7. An event A will occur with probability 0.5. An event B will occur with probability 0.6. The probability that both A and B will occur is 0.1.
   (A) Events A and B are independent.
   (B) Events A and B are mutually exclusive.
   (C) Either A or B always occurs.
   (D) Events A and B are complementary.
   (E) None of the above is correct.

8. Event A occurs with probability 0.8. The conditional probability that event B occurs, given that A occurs, is 0.5. The probability that both A and B occur is:
   (A) 0.3
   (B) 0.4
   (C) 0.625
   (D) 0.8
   (E) 1.0

9. At Lakeville South High School, 60% of students have high-speed internet access, 30% have a mobile computing device, and 20% have both. The proportion of students that have neither high-speed internet access nor a mobile computing device is:
    (A) 0%
    (B) 10%
    (C) 30%
    (D) 80%
    (E) 90%

10. Experience has shown that a certain lie detector will show a positive reading (indicates a lie) 10% of the time when a person is telling the truth and 95% of the time when a person is lying. Suppose that a random sample of 5 suspects is subjected to a lie detector test regarding a recent one-person crime. The probability of observing no positive readings if all suspects plead innocent and are telling the truth is:
    (A) 0.409
    (B) 0.735
    (C) 0.00001
    (D) 0.591
    (E) 0.99999

Check your answers below. If you got a question wrong, check to see if you made a simple mistake or if you need to study that concept more. After you check your work, identify the concepts you feel very confident about and note what you will do to learn the concepts in need of more study.

#	Answer	Concept	Right	Wrong	Simple Mistake?	Need to Study More
1	A	Probability Basics				
2	C	Definition of Probability				
3	B	Mutually Exclusive/Independent				
4	C	Probability Calculations				
5	C	Probability Calculations				
6	A	Probability Calculations				
7	C	Probability Basics				
8	B	Conditional Probabilities				
9	C	General Addition Rule				
10	D	Conditional Probabilities				

FRAPPY! Free Response AP® Problem, Yay!

The following problem is modeled after actual Advanced Placement Statistics free response questions. Your task is to generate a complete, concise response in 15 minutes. After you generate your response, read over the solution and scoring guide. Score your response and note what, if anything, you would do differently to increase your own score.

A simple random sample of adults in a metropolitan area was selected and a survey was administered to determine political views. The results are recorded below:

| | | Political Views | | |
Age	Conservative	Moderate	Liberal	Total
18-29	10	15	30	55
30-44	20	30	35	85
45-59	35	15	20	70
Over 60	20	15	10	45
Total	85	75	95	255

(a) What is the probability that a person chosen at random from this sample will have moderate political views?

(b) What is the probability that a person chosen at random from those in the sample who are between the ages of 30 and 44 will have moderate political views? Show your work.

(c) Based on your answers to (a) and (b), are political views and age independent for the population of adults in this metropolitan area? Why or why not?

FRAPPY! Scoring Rubric

Use the following rubric to score your response. Each part receives a score of "Essentially Correct," "Partially Correct," or "Incorrect." When you have scored your response, reflect on your understanding of the concepts addressed in this problem. If necessary, note what you would do differently on future questions like this to increase your score.

Intent of the Question

The goal of this question is to determine your ability to calculate probabilities and determine whether or not two events are independent.

Solution

(a) $P(\text{moderate}) = 75/255 = 0.2941$

(b) $P(\text{moderate} \mid \text{age 30-44}) = 30/85 = 0.3529$

(c) If moderate political views and age were independent, the probabilities in (a) and (b) would be the same. Since they are not equal, age and political views are not independent for the individuals in this sample.

Scoring:

Parts (a), (b), and (c) are scored as essentially correct (E), partially correct (P), or incorrect (I).

Part (a) is essentially correct if the probability is correct. Part (a) is partially correct if the correct formula is shown, but minor arithmetic errors are present. Otherwise it is incorrect.

Part (b) is essentially correct if the conditional probability is calculated correctly. Part (b) is partially correct if the conditioning is reversed and $P(\text{age 30-44} \mid \text{moderate}) = 30/75 = 0.40$ is calculated.

Part (c) is essentially correct if the response indicates the two variables are not independent and justifies the conclusion based on an appropriate probability argument. Part (c) is partially correct if the response indicates the two variables are not independent, but the argument is weak or not based on an appropriate probability argument.

4 Complete Response
All three parts essentially correct

3 Substantial Response
Two parts essentially correct and one part partially correct

2 Developing Response
Two parts essentially correct and no parts partially correct
One part essentially correct and one or two parts partially correct
Three parts partially correct

1 Minimal Response
One part essentially correct and no parts partially correct
No parts essentially correct and two parts partially correct

My Score:
What I did well:
What I could improve:
What I should remember if I see a problem like this on the AP Exam:

Chapter 5 Formula Sheet

Create a one-page summary of important concepts and formulas found in this chapter. This will serve as a valuable resource as you prepare for the AP Exam.

Chapter 5 Crossword Puzzle
PROBABILITY

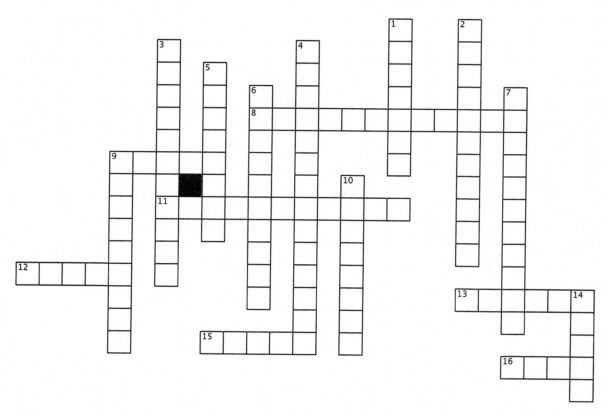

Across

8. The collection of outcomes that occur in both of two events.
9. A collection of outcomes from a chance process.
11. The proportion of times an outcome would occur in a very long series of repetitions.
12. _____ Theorem can be used to find probabilities that require going "backward" in a tree diagram.
13. In statistics, this doesn't mean "haphazard." It means "by chance."
15. The collection of outcomes that occur in either of two events.
16. A ____ diagram can help model chance behavior that involves a sequence of outcomes.

Down

1. The law of large _____ states that the proportion of times an outcome occurs in many repetitions will approach a single value.
2. The probability that one event happens given another event is known to have happened.
3. The set of all possible outcomes for a chance process (two words).
4. The probability that two events both occur can be found using the general _____ rule.
5. P(A or B) can be found using the general _____ rule.
6. The imitation of chance behavior, based on a model that reflects the situation.
7. The occurrence of one event has no effect on the chance that another event will happen.
9. Another term for disjoint: Mutually _____.
10. Two events that have no outcomes in common and can never occur together.
14. A probability ____ describes a chance process and consists of two parts.

Chapter 6: Random Variables and Probability Distributions

"We must become more comfortable with probability and uncertainty." Nate Silver

CHAPTER OVERVIEW

In the last chapter we learned the basic definition and rules of probability. We continue our study of probability by exploring situations that involve the assignment of a numerical value to each possible outcome of a random process. The random variables that result from the foundation for inference procedures in later chapters. In this chapter, you will learn how to calculate probabilities of events involving random variables as well as how to describe their probability distributions. Specifically, you will learn formulas to determine the mean and standard deviation of individual random variables as well as the combination of several independent random variables. Finally, you'll explore two special random variables – binomial and geometric – and learn how to calculate probabilities of events in binomial and geometric settings. This chapter involves a lot of formulas, so you may want to familiarize yourself with the formula sheet provided on the AP exam. Like earlier chapters, you should focus less on memorizing formulas or calculator keystrokes and more on how to apply the formulas and interpret results.

Sections in this Chapter
Section 6.1: Discrete and Continuous Random Variables
Section 6.2: Transforming and Combining Random Variables
Section 6.3: Binomial and Geometric Random Variables

PLAN YOUR LEARNING

Use the following *suggested* guide to help plan your reading and assignments in "The Practice of Statistics, Updated 6th Edition." Put a check mark in the last column when you are done. Note: your teacher may schedule a different pacing or assign different problems. Be sure to follow his or her instructions!

Read	Do	Done!
Section 6.1: p. 389-395	1, 3, 5, 7, 9, 11	
Section 6.1: p. 396-402	13, 19, 21, 23, 27, 29, MC 31-34	
Section 6.2: p. 409-415	37, 39, 41, 43, 47	
Section 6.2: p. 416-425	49, 51, 55, 57, 59, 65, 67, MC 73-74	
Section 6.3: p. 431-440	77, 79, 81, 83, 85, 89	
Section 6.3: p. 441-449	91, 93, 95, 99, 101, 103, 105, 106, 117	
Section 6.3: p. 450-455	107, 109, 111, 113, MC 115-119	
Chapter Summary	Multiple-Choice FRAPPY!	

Section 6.1: Discrete and Continuous Random Variables

Before You Read: Section Summary

A random variable takes numerical values that describe the outcomes of a random process. In the last chapter, we learned that a probability model describes the possible outcomes for a random process and the probability of each outcome. A random variable does the same thing, describing the possible values that the variable takes and the probability of each. Random variables fall into two categories: discrete and continuous. What differentiates the two is the set of values the random variable can take. If the set is limited to fixed values with gaps between, it is discrete. If the variable can take on any value in an interval, it is continuous. Regardless of the type, we are interested in describing the shape of the random variable's probability distribution, its center, and its variability. Knowing these characteristics will give us a sense of what to expect in repeated observations of the random variable as well as what can be considered likely and unlikely results. This idea forms the basis for inferential thinking in later chapters so you want to get used to thinking along these lines in this section!

Learning Targets:

_____ I can use the probability distribution of a discrete random variable to calculate the probability of an event.

_____ I can make a histogram to display the probability distribution of a discrete random variable and describe its shape.

_____ I can calculate and interpret the mean (expected value) of a discrete random variable.

_____ I can calculate and interpret the standard deviation of a discrete random variable.

_____ I can use the probability distribution of a continuous random variable (uniform or Normal) to calculate the probability of an event.

While You Read: Key Vocabulary and Concepts

random variable:
probability distribution:
discrete random variable:
mean (expected value) of a discrete random variable:
standard deviation of a discrete random variable:
continuous random variable:

☑ **After You Read: Check for Understanding**

Concept 1: Discrete and Continuous Random Variables

A random variable can be classified as either discrete or continuous depending on its possible values. If it takes a fixed (finite or infinite) set of possible values with gaps in between, then we call it a discrete random variable. If the random variable takes on *any* value in an interval of numbers, it is continuous. To describe a random variable, we follow the same process as describing a probability model. First, define the random variable, X, as a numerical outcome of a random process. Next, indicate the possible values of the variable. Finally, give the probability that each value occurs using a table, formula, or graph.

Check for Understanding:

_____ *I can use the probability distribution of a discrete random variable to calculate the probability of an event.*

_____ *I can make a histogram to display the probability distribution of a discrete random variable and describe its shape.*

Consider two 4-sided dice, each having sides labeled 1, 2, 3, 4. Let $X =$ the sum of the numbers that appear after a roll of the dice.

1) Is X a discrete or a continuous random variable? Sketch the probability distribution of X below. Describe what you see.

2) If somebody rolled the dice 10 times and got a sum of 3 or less each time, would you be surprised? Why or why not?

Concept 2: Mean and Standard Deviation of Random Variables

In Chapter 1, we learned that when describing distributions of quantitative data, we should always note the shape, center, and variability. The same holds true for random variables. In order to make inferences, we need to know what is considered a "typical" value of the random variable being examined as well as how much variation around that value we can expect to see. As with distributions of quantitative data, the center of a random variable's probability distribution can be described by calculating the mean. However, in the case of random variables, the mean (or expected value) is a *weighted* average, taking into account the probability of each outcome occurring. Likewise, the standard deviation of a random variable takes into account the probability of each outcome occurring, giving more weight to those outcomes that are more likely. Make sure you get comfortable with the formulas for the mean and standard deviation of a discrete random variable so you can calculate and interpret the center and variability of the probability distribution.

Check for Understanding:

_____ *I can calculate and interpret the mean (expected value) of a discrete random variable.*

_____ *I can calculate and interpret the standard deviation of a discrete random variable.*

_____ *I can use the probability distribution of a continuous random variable (uniform or Normal) to calculate the probability of an event.*

1) Suppose the random variable Y = *number of goals in a randomly selected high school hockey game* has the following probability distribution:

Goals:	0	1	2	3	4
Probability:	0.155	0.195	0.243	0.233	0.174

Calculate and interpret the mean and standard deviation of Y.

2) The weights of toddler boys follow an approximately Normal distribution with mean 34 pounds and standard deviation 3.5 pounds. Suppose you randomly choose one toddler boy and record his weight. What is the probability that the randomly selected boy weighs less than 31 pounds?

Section 6.2: Transforming and Combining Random Variables

Before You Read: Section Summary

This section introduces two distinct topics. First, you will explore transforming a single random variable. That is, you will learn how to describe the shape, center, and variability of the probability distribution of a random variable when a linear transformation (such as adding a constant to each value or multiplying each value by a constant) is applied. Second, you will learn how to combine two or more random variables. This topic is critical as many of the statistical inference problems we will explore involve observing the difference between two random variables. You will learn how to describe the mean and standard deviation of the sum and difference of independent random variables as well as how to calculate probabilities of observing particular outcomes in these situations. There are a lot of formulas to keep straight in this section, so you may wish to keep your AP formula sheet handy!

Learning Targets:

_____ I can describe the effect of adding or subtracting a constant or multiplying or dividing by a constant on the probability distribution of a random variable.

_____ I can calculate the mean and standard deviation of the sum or difference of random variables.

_____ I can find probabilities involving the sum or difference of independent Normal random variables.

While You Read: Key Vocabulary and Concepts

effect on a probability distribution of adding/subtracting a constant:
effect on a probability distribution of multiplying/dividing by a constant:
mean (expected value) of a sum of random variables:
mean (expected value) of a difference of random variables:
independent random variables:
standard deviation of the sum of two independent random variables:
standard deviation of the difference of two independent random variables:

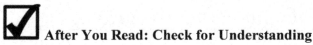 **After You Read: Check for Understanding**

Concept 1: Transforming a Random Variable

We learned how transformations affect the shape, center, and variability of distributions of quantitative data back in Chapter 2. Similar rules apply to random variables. That is, when we multiply (or divide) each value of a random variable by a positive constant b, the shape of the probability distribution does not change. However, measures of center are multiplied (divided) by b and measures of variability are multiplied (divided) by b. When we add (or subtract) a constant a to each value of a random variable, the shape and variability of the probability distribution do not change. However, the measures of center will increase (or decrease) by a.

Check for Understanding:

_____ *I can describe the effect of adding or subtracting a constant or multiplying or dividing by a constant on the probability distribution of a random variable.*

A carnival game involves tossing a ball into numbered baskets with the goal of having your ball land in a high-numbered basket. The probability distribution of X = value of the basket on a randomly selected toss.

Value:	0	1	2	3
Probability:	0.3	0.4	0.2	0.1

The expected value of X is 1.1 and the standard deviation of X is 0.0943.

Suppose it costs $2 to play and you earn $1.50 for each point earned on your toss. That is, if you land in a basket labeled "2," you will earn $3.00.

Define Y to be the amount of profit you make on a randomly selected toss. Describe the shape, center, and spread of the probability distribution of Y in the context of the situation.

Concept 2: Combining Random Variables

Many situations involve two or more random variables. Understanding how to describe the center and variability of the probability distribution for the sum or difference of two random variables is an important skill to have. When given two independent random variables, we can describe the mean and standard deviation of the sum (or difference) of the random variables using the formulas in this section. Basically, when adding or subtracting two or more random variables (whether they are independent or not), the mean of the sum or difference of those random variables will be the sum or difference of their means. However, to describe the spread of the sum or difference of *independent* random variables, we must perform two steps. First, we find the *variance* of the sum or difference of two or more independent random variables by *adding* their variances. Then, we take the square root of the variance to find the standard deviation. A common mistake is to simply add standard deviations. Remember to *always add* variances! Never subtract, and never combine standard deviations!

Check for Understanding:

_____ *I can calculate the mean and standard deviation of the sum or difference of random variables.*

Students in Mr. Costello's class are expected to check their homework in groups of 4 at the beginning of class each day. Students must check it as quickly as possible, one at a time. The means and standard deviations of the time it takes to check homework for the 4 students in one group are noted below. Assume their times are independent.

	Mean	**Standard Deviation**
Alan	1.4 min	0.1 min
Barb	1.2 min	0.4 min
Corey	0.9 min	0.8 min
Doug	1.0 min	0.7 min

1) If each student checks one after the other, what are the mean and standard deviation of the total time necessary for these four students to check their homework on a randomly chosen day?

2) Suppose Alan and Doug like to race to see who can check their homework faster. What are the mean and standard deviation for the difference between their times (Doug – Alan)? Interpret these values in the context of the situation.

Concept 3: Combining Normal Random Variables

If our random variables of interest are Normally distributed, we can calculate the probability of observing particular outcomes using the skills we learned in Chapter 2. To do so, we rely on one important fact. When combining independent Normal random variables, the resulting distribution is also Normal! We can find the mean and standard deviation of the resulting distribution using the formulas we just learned. Then we can apply our knowledge from Chapter 2 to calculate and interpret probabilities about the situation.

Check for Understanding:

_____ *I can find probabilities involving the sum or difference of independent Normal random variables.*

Mr. Molesky and Mr. Liberty are avid video game golfers. Both like to compare times to complete a particular course on their favorite game. Mr. Molesky's times are Normally distributed with a mean of 110 minutes and standard deviation of 10 minutes. Mr. Liberty's times are Normally distributed with mean 100 minutes and standard deviation 8 minutes.

1) Find the mean and standard deviation of the difference of their times (Molesky - Liberty). Assume their times are independent.

2) Find the probability that Mr. Molesky will finish his game before Mr. Liberty on any given day.

Section 6.3: Binomial and Geometric Random Variables

Before You Read: Section Summary

In the first two sections, you learned how to describe the probability distributions of discrete and continuous random variables as well as how to calculate probabilities for situations involving one or more random variables. In this section, you will focus on two special cases of discrete random variables: binomial and geometric. Binomial random variables count the number of successes that occur in a fixed number of independent trials of some random process with a constant probability of success on each trial, while geometric random variables count the number of trials needed to get a success. Binomial random variables appear often on the AP exam, so you will want to pay particular attention to this topic. Again, try not to get bogged down in the formulas in this section. Familiarize yourself with the AP formula sheet and focus your efforts on being able to identify when to use binomial or geometric random variables and how to calculate and interpret probabilities.

Learning Targets:

_____ I can determine whether the conditions for a binomial setting have been met.

_____ I can calculate and interpret probabilities involving binomial random variables.

_____ I can calculate and interpret the mean and standard deviation of a binomial random variable.

_____ I can use the Normal approximation to the binomial distribution to calculate probabilities, when appropriate.

_____ I can calculate and interpret probabilities involving geometric random variables.

_____ I can calculate and interpret the mean and standard deviation of a geometric distribution.

While You Read: Key Vocabulary and Concepts

binomial setting:

binomial random variable:

binomial coefficient:

binomial probability formula:

mean (expected value) of a binomial random variable:

standard deviation of a binomial random variable:

Normal approximation for binomial distributions:

10% condition:

large counts condition:

geometric setting:

geometric random variable:

geometric probability formula:

mean (expected value) of a geometric random variable:

standard deviation of a geometric random variable:

After You Read: Check for Understanding

Concept 1: Binomial Random Variables

When we observe a fixed number of repeated trials of the same random process, we are often interested in how many times a particular outcome occurs. This is the basis for a binomial setting. That is, a binomial setting arises when we perform n independent trials of the same random process and count the number of times a particular outcome occurs.

To be a binomial setting, four conditions must be met. First, we are interested in outcomes that can be classified in one of two ways – success or failure. The particular outcome of interest is considered a success, while anything else is considered a failure. Next, each observed trial of the random process must be independent of the other trials. Third, the number of trials we observe must be fixed in advance. Last, the probability of success on each trial must be the same.

If these conditions are met, we can use the binomial probability formula to determine the likelihood of observing a certain number of successes in a fixed number of trials of the binomial random variable:

$$P(X = k) = \binom{n}{k} p^k (1-p)^{n-k}$$

Note that the formula uses the multiplication rule for independent events from Chapter 5 in multiplying the probabilities of successes and failures across the fixed number of trials. However, the formula also considers the number of ways in which we can arrange those successes across our trials.

Check for Understanding:

_____ *I can determine whether the conditions for a binomial setting have been met.*

_____ *I can calculate and interpret probabilities involving binomial random variables.*

Recall that there are 4 suits—spades, hearts, clubs, and diamonds—in a standard deck of playing cards. Suppose you play a game in which you draw a card, record the suit, replace it, shuffle, and repeat until you have observed 10 cards. Define X = number of hearts observed.

1) Show that X is a binomial random variable.

2) Find the probability of observing fewer than 4 hearts in this game.

Concept 2: Mean and Standard Deviation of a Binomial Distribution and the Normal Approximation

Like other discrete random variables, we can calculate the mean and standard deviation of binomial random variables. This will give us a better sense of what we'd expect to see in the long run as well as how much variability we can expect to observe in the observed number of successes. If a random variable X has a binomial probability distribution based on a random process with n trials each having probability of success p, we can calculate the mean of X by multiplying np. We can find the standard deviation of X by taking the square root of the product $np(1 - p)$. Modified versions of these formulas are useful when trying to make inferences about the proportion of successes in a population. If we take an SRS of size n from a population (where n is less than 10% of the size of the population), then we can use a binomial distribution to model the number of successes in the sample.

Further, if n is so large that both np and $np(1 - p)$ are at least 10, we can use a Normal distribution to approximate binomial probabilities. As always, make sure you not only understand how to use the formulas, but also when to use them and how to interpret their results!

Check for Understanding:

_____ *I can calculate and interpret the mean and standard deviation of a binomial random variable.*

_____ *I can use the Normal approximation to the binomial distribution to calculate probabilities, when appropriate.*

Suppose 72% of students in the U.S. would give their teachers a positive rating if asked to score their effectiveness. A survey is conducted in which 500 students are randomly selected and asked to rate their teachers. Let X = the number of students in the sample who would give their teachers a positive rating.

1) Show that X can be approximated by a Normal distribution.

2) Use a Normal approximation to find the probability that 400 or more students would give their teacher a positive rating in this sample.

Concept 3: Geometric Random Variables

In a binomial setting, we are interested in knowing how many successes will occur in a fixed number of trials. Sometimes we are interested in knowing how long it will take until a success occurs. When we perform independent trials of a random process with the same probability of success on each trial, and record how long it takes to get a success, we have a geometric setting. We can describe the number of trials it takes to get a success using a geometric random variable. As with other random variables, we can describe the probability distribution of a geometric random variable and calculate its mean and standard deviation. Using what we learned in Chapter 5, we can calculate the probability of observing the first success on the kth trial by multiplying the probabilities of $(k-1)$ consecutive failures by the probability of a success:

$$P(Y = k) = (1-p)^{k-1}\,p\,.$$

Check for Understanding:

_____ *I can calculate and interpret probabilities involving geometric random variables.*

_____ *I can calculate and interpret the mean and standard deviation of a geometric distribution.*

Suppose 20% of Super Crunch cereal boxes contain a secret decoder ring. Let $X =$ the number of boxes of Super Crunch that must be opened until a ring is found.

1) Show that X is a geometric random variable.

2) Find the probability that you will have to open 7 boxes to find a ring.

3) Find the probability that it will take fewer than 4 boxes to find a ring.

4) How many boxes would you expect to have to open to find a ring?

5) What is the standard deviation of the number of boxes you would expect to have to open to find a ring? Interpret this value.

Chapter Summary: Random Variables

In the last chapter we learned the basic definition and rules of probability. We continued our study of probability in this chapter by exploring situations that involve assigning a numerical value to each possible outcome of a random process. You learned how to calculate probabilities of events involving random variables as well as how to describe their probability distributions. You learned formulas to determine the mean and standard deviation of individual random variables as well as the combination of several independent random variables. Finally, you explored two special random variables – binomial and geometric – and learned how to calculate probabilities of events in binomial and geometric settings.

Like earlier chapters, you should focus less on memorizing formulas or calculator keystrokes and more on how to apply the formulas and interpret results. Make sure you understand how and when to apply each formula. More importantly, make sure you show your work when calculating probabilities so anyone reading your response understands exactly how you arrived at your answer!

How well do you understand each of the learning targets?

Learning Target	Got It!	Almost There	Needs Some Work
I can use the probability distribution of a discrete random variable to calculate the probability of an event.			
I can make a histogram to display the probability distribution of a discrete random variable and describe its shape.			
I can calculate and interpret the mean (expected value) of a discrete random variable.			
I can calculate and interpret the standard deviation of a discrete random variable.			
I can use the probability distribution of a continuous random variable (uniform or Normal) to calculate the probability of an event.			
I can describe the effect of adding or subtracting a constant or multiplying or dividing by a constant on the probability distribution of a random variable.			
I can calculate the mean and standard deviation of the sum or difference of random variables.			
I can find probabilities involving the sum or difference of independent random variables.			
I can determine whether the conditions for a binomial setting are met.			
I can calculate and interpret probabilities involving binomial random variables.			
I can calculate and interpret the mean and standard deviation of a binomial random variable.			
I can use the Normal approximation to the binomial distribution to calculate probabilities, when appropriate.			
I can calculate and interpret probabilities involving geometric random variables.			
I can calculate and interpret the mean and standard deviation of a geometric distribution.			

Chapter 6 Multiple Choice Practice

Directions. Identify the choice that best completes the statement or answers the question. Check your answers and note your performance when you are finished.

1. A marketing survey compiled data on the number of cars in households. If X = the number of cars in a randomly selected household, and we omit the rare cases of more than 5 cars, then X has the following probability distribution:

X	0	1	2	3	4	5
$P(X)$	0.24	0.37	0.20	0.11	0.05	0.03

What is the probability that a randomly chosen household has at least two cars?
(A)   0.19
(B)   0.20
(C)   0.29
(D)   0.39
(E)   0.61

2. What is the expected value of the number of cars in a randomly selected household?
(A)   2.5
(B)   0.1667
(C)   1.45
(D)   1
(E)   Cannot be determined

3. A dealer in Las Vegas selects 10 cards from a standard deck of 52 cards. Let Y be the number of diamonds in the 10 cards selected. Which of the following best describes this setting?
(A) Y has a binomial distribution with n = 10 observations and probability of success p = 0.25.
(B) Y has a binomial distribution with n = 10 observations and probability of success p = 0.25, provided the deck is shuffled well.
(C) Y has a binomial distribution with n = 10 observations and probability of success p = 0.25, provided that after selecting a card it is replaced in the deck and the deck is shuffled well before the next card is selected.
(D) Y has a geometric distribution with n = 10 observations and probability of success p = 0.25.
(E) Y has a geometric distribution with n = 52 observations and probability of success p = 0.25.

4. What is the variance of the sum of two random variables X and Y?
(A) $\sigma_X + \sigma_Y$
(B) $(\sigma_X)^2 + (\sigma_Y)^2$
(C) $\sigma_X + \sigma_Y$, but only if X and Y are independent.
(D) $(\sigma_X)^2 + (\sigma_Y)^2$, but only if X and Y are independent.
(E)   None of these

5. In the town of Lakeville, the number of cell phones in a household is a random variable W with the following probability distribution:

Value w_i	0	1	2	3	4	5
Probability p_i	0.1	0.1	0.25	0.3	0.2	0.05

What is the standard deviation of the number of cell phones in a randomly selected house?
(A) 1.32
(B) 1.7475
(C) 2.5
(D) 0.09
(E) 2.9575

6. A random variable Y has the following probability distribution:

Y	−1	0	1	2
$P(Y)$	$4C$	$2C$	0.07	0.03

What is the value of the constant C?
(A) 0.10
(B) 0.15
(C) 0.20
(D) 0.25
(E) 0.75

7. It is known that about 90% of the widgets made by Buckley Industries meet specifications. Every hour a sample of 18 widgets is selected at random for testing and the number of widgets that meet specifications is recorded. What is the approximate mean and standard deviation of the number of widgets meeting specifications?
(A) $\mu = 1.62$; $\sigma = 1.414$
(B) $\mu = 1.62$; $\sigma = 1.265$
(C) $\mu = 16.2$; $\sigma = 1.62$
(D) $\mu = 16.2$; $\sigma = 1.273$
(E) $\mu = 16.2$; $\sigma = 4.025$

8. A raffle sells tickets for $10 and offers a prize of $500, $1000, or $2000. Let C be a random variable that represents the prize in the raffle drawing. The probability distribution of C is given below.

Value c_i	$0	$500	$1000	$2000
Probability p_i	0.60	0.05	0.13	0.22

What is the expected profit when playing the raffle?
(A) $145
(B) $585
(C) $865
(D) $635
(E) $485

9. Let the random variable X represent the amount of money Carl makes tutoring statistics students in the summer. Assume that X is Normal with mean \$240 and standard deviation \$60. The probability is approximately 0.6 that, in a randomly selected summer, Carl will make less than about
    (A) \$144
    (B) \$216
    (C) \$255
    (D) \$30
    (E) \$360

10. Which of the following random variables is geometric?
    (A)   The number of phone calls received in a one-hour period.
    (B)   The number of times I have to roll a six-sided die to get two 5s.
    (C)   The number of digits I will read beginning at a randomly selected starting point in a table of random digits until I find a 7.
    (D)   The number of 7s in a row of 40 random digits.
    (E)   All four of the above are geometric random variables.

Check your answers below. If you got a question wrong, check to see if you made a simple mistake or if you need to study that concept more. After you check your work, identify the concepts you feel very confident about and note what you will do to learn the concepts in need of more study.

#	Answer	Concept	Right	Wrong	Simple Mistake?	Need to Study More
1	D	Discrete Random Variable				
2	C	Expected Value of Discrete Random Variables				
3	C	Binomial Settings				
4	D	Combining Random Variables				
5	A	Standard Deviation of Discrete Random Variables				
6	B	Probability Distribution				
7	D	Binomial Approximations				
8	B	Expected Value				
9	C	Normal Approximations				
10	C	Geometric Random Variables				

FRAPPY! Free Response AP® Problem, Yay!

The following problem is modeled after actual Advanced Placement Statistics free response questions. Your task is to generate a complete, concise response in 15 minutes. After you generate your response, read over the solution and scoring guide. Score your response and note what, if anything, you would do differently to increase your own score.

A recent study revealed that a new brand of mp3 player may need to be repaired up to 3 times during its ownership. Let R represent the number of repairs necessary over the lifetime of a randomly selected mp3 player of this brand. The probability distribution of the number of repairs necessary is given below.

r_i	0	1	2	3
p_i	0.4	0.3	0.2	0.1

(a) Compute and interpret the mean and standard deviation of R.

(b) Suppose we also randomly select a phone that may require repairs over its lifetime. The mean and standard deviation of the number of repairs for this brand of phone are 2 and 1.2, respectively. Assuming that the phone and mp3 player break down independently of each other, compute and interpret the mean and standard deviation of the total number of repairs necessary for the two devices.

(c) Each mp3 repair costs $15 and each phone repair costs $25. Compute the mean and standard deviation of the total amount you can expect to pay in repairs over the life of the devices.

FRAPPY! Scoring Rubric

Use the following rubric to score your response. Each part receives a score of "Essentially Correct," "Partially Correct," or "Incorrect." When you have scored your response, reflect on your understanding of the concepts addressed in this problem. If necessary, note what you would do differently on future questions like this to increase your score.

Intent of the Question

The goal of this question is to determine your ability to calculate and interpret the mean and standard deviation of a discrete random variable, combine random variables, and describe linear transformations of random variables.

Solution

(a) Mean: $\mu_R = 0(0.4) + 1(0.3) + 2(0.2) + 3(0.1) = 1$

Standard deviation: $\sigma_R = \sqrt{(0-1)^2(0.4) + (1-1)^2(0.3) + (2-1)^2(0.2) + (3-1)^2(0.1)} = 1$

We can expect to have to repair our mp3 player once over its lifetime, but that can vary on average by about 1 repair.

(b) If T = the total number of repairs across the two devices, the mean of T will be $\mu_T = 1 + 2 = 3$ and the standard deviation will be $\sigma_T = \sqrt{1^2 + 1.2^2} = 1.562$.

We can expect to have to perform 3 repairs, total, on our devices over their lifetime, but that amount can vary on average by about 1.562 repairs.

(c) The total amount we can expect to pay in repairs will be $15(1) + $25(2) = 65.

The standard deviation will be $\sqrt{15^2(1^2) + 25^2(1.2)^2} = \$33.54$.

We can expect to pay $65 in repairs over the lifetime of the devices, but that can vary by an average of $33.52.

Scoring:

Parts (a), (b), and (c) are scored as essentially correct (E), partially correct (P), or incorrect (I).

Part (a) is essentially correct if the mean and standard deviation are calculated correctly AND interpreted correctly.
Part (a) is partially correct if no interpretation or an incorrect interpretation is provided OR if only one calculation/interpretation is correct.

Part (b) is essentially correct if the mean and standard deviation are calculated correctly AND interpreted correctly.
Part (b) is partially correct if no interpretation or an incorrect interpretation is provided OR if only one calculation/interpretation is correct.

Part (c) is essentially correct if the mean and standard deviation are calculated correctly AND interpreted correctly.
Part (c) is partially correct if no interpretation or an incorrect interpretation is provided OR if only one calculation/interpretation is correct.

4   Complete Response

All three parts essentially correct

3   Substantial Response

Two parts essentially correct and one part partially correct

2   Developing Response

Two parts essentially correct and no parts partially correct

One part essentially correct and one or two parts partially correct

Three parts partially correct

1   Minimal Response

One part essentially correct and no parts partially correct

No parts essentially correct and two parts partially correct

My Score:
What I did well:
What I could improve:
What I should remember if I see a problem like this on the AP Exam:

Chapter 6 Formula Sheet

Create a one-page summary of important concepts and formulas found in this chapter. This will serve as a valuable resource as you prepare for the AP Exam.

Chapter 6 Crossword Puzzle
RANDOM VARIABLES AND PROBABILITY DISTRIBUTIONS

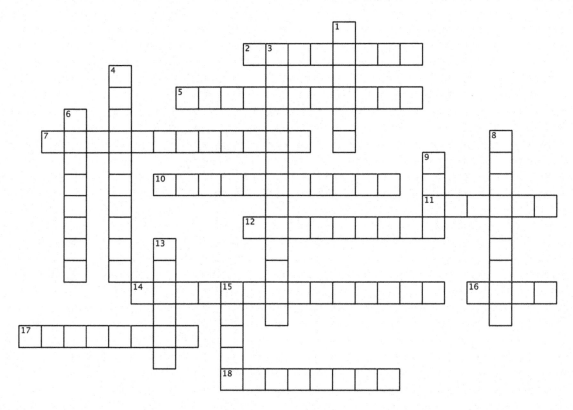

Across

2. The average of the squared deviations of the values of a variable from its mean.
5. Random variables are _____ if knowing whether an event in X has occurred tells us nothing about the occurrence of an event involving Y.
7. The probability _____ of a random variable gives its possible values and their probabilities.
10. The number of ways of arranging k successes among n observations is the binomial ____.
11. The sum or difference of independent Normal random variables follows a _____ distribution.
12. When you combine independent random variable, you always add these.
14. A linear _____ occurs when we add/subtract and multiply/divide by a constant.
16. An easy way to remember the requirements for a geometric setting.
17. This setting arises when we perform several independent trials of a chance process and record the number of times an outcome occurs.
18. The mean of a discrete random variable is also called the _____ value.

Down

1. A ____ variable takes numerical values that describe the outcomes of some chance process.
3. When n is large, we can use a Normal _____ to determine probabilities for binomial settings.
4. A random variable that takes on all values in an interval of numbers.
6. A random variable that takes a fixed set of possible values with gaps between.
8. A ____ setting arises when we perform indeped trials of the same chance process and record the number of trials until a particular outcome occurs.
9. An easy way to remember the requirements for a binmial setting.
13. Adding a constant to each value of a random variable has no effect on the shape or ____ of the distribution.
15. Multiplying each value of a random variable by a constant has no effect on the ____ of the distribution.

Chapter 7: Sampling Distributions

"Statistics may be defined as 'a body of methods
for making wise decisions in the face of uncertainty.'" W.A. Wallis

CHAPTER OVERVIEW

In Chapters 1-3, you learned how to explore a set of data. Chapter 4 introduced you to methods for producing data. Chapters 5 and 6 focused on the basics of probability and random variables. In this chapter, you will study the final piece necessary for statistical inference – sampling distributions. The foundation of statistical inference lies in the concept of the sampling distribution. In order to make a conclusion about a population based on information from a sample, you need to be able to answer the question, "What results would I expect to see if I sampled repeatedly from the population of interest?" Sampling distributions provide an answer to that question, allowing us to draw a conclusion about a population parameter based on an observed statistic from a sample. In this chapter, you will learn how to describe sampling distributions for sample proportions as well as sampling distributions for sample means. You will also learn an important theorem for sample means—the central limit theorem. The final chapters in the textbook will build upon your learning in this chapter to present formal methods for statistical inference. The better you understand sampling distributions, the easier your study of inference will be. Be sure to get a good grasp of these concepts before moving on!

Sections in this Chapter
Section 7.1: What Is a Sampling Distribution?
Section 7.2: Sample Proportions
Section 7.3: Sample Means

PLAN YOUR LEARNING

Use the following *suggested* guide to help plan your reading and assignments in "The Practice of Statistics, Updated 6th Edition." Put a check mark in the last column when you are done. Note: your teacher may schedule a different pacing or assign different problems. Be sure to follow his or her instructions!

Read	Do	Done!
Section 7.1: p. 469-474	1, 3, 5, 7, 9	
Section 7.1: p. 475-481	11, 13, 15, 19, 21, 25, MC 26-30	
Section 7.2: p. 486-492	35, 37, 41, 43	
Section 7.2: p. 493-497	49, 51, MC 53-56	
Section 7.3: p. 502-512	59, 61, 63, 65, 69, 71, 73	
Section 7.3: p. 513-517	75, 77, 83, 85, MC 87-90	
Chapter Summary	Multiple-Choice FRAPPY!	

Section 7.1: What Is a Sampling Distribution?

Before You Read: Section Summary

This section will introduce you to the big ideas behind sampling distributions. First, you will learn how to distinguish between population parameters and statistics derived from samples. Next, you will explore the fact that statistics vary from sample to sample. This simple fact is the reason we study sampling distributions. By describing the shape, center, and variability of the sampling distribution of a statistic, we can determine the critical information necessary to perform statistical inference.

Learning Targets:

_____ I can distinguish between a parameter and a statistic.

_____ I can create a sampling distribution using all possible samples from a small population.

_____ I can use the sampling distribution of a statistic to evaluate a claim about a parameter.

_____ I can distinguish among the distribution of a population, the distribution of a sample and the sampling distribution of a statistic.

_____ I can determine if a statistic is an unbiased estimator of a population parameter.

_____ I can describe the relationship between sample size and the variability of a statistic.

While You Read: Key Vocabulary and Concepts

statistic:
parameter:
sampling variability:
sampling distribution:
population distribution:
distribution of sample data:
unbiased estimator:
variability of a statistic:

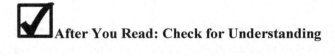**After You Read: Check for Understanding**

Concept 1: Parameters and Statistics

One of the most powerful skills we learn from statistics is the ability to answer a question about a population based on information gathered from a random sample. That is, we can use a statistic calculated from a sample to make a conclusion about the corresponding parameter in the population. However, we must note that the statistics we calculate from a sample may differ somewhat from the population characteristic we are trying to measure. Further, the statistic would likely differ from sample to sample. This sample-to-sample variability poses a problem when we try to generalize our findings to the population. However, based on what we learned in the last chapter we can view a sample statistic as a random variable. That is, while we have no way of predicting exactly what statistic value we will get from a single sample, we know how those values will behave in repeated random sampling. With the probability distribution of this random variable in mind, we can use a sample statistic to estimate the population parameter.

Check for Understanding:

_____ *I can distinguish between a parameter and a statistic.*

For each of the following situations, identify the population of interest, the parameter, and the statistic.

1) A medical researcher is interested in exploring the effects of a new medicine on blood pressure. 500 males with high blood pressure are randomly selected and given the new drug. After two weeks, their blood pressure is measured and the average arterial pressure is calculated.

2) A study is conducted to determine whether or not the dangerous activity of texting while driving is a common practice. 1500 16- to 24-year-olds are randomly selected and asked whether or not they text while driving. Of the 1500 drivers, 12% indicate they text while driving.

Concept 2: Describing Sampling Distributions

To draw a conclusion about a population proportion p, we take a random sample and calculate the sample proportion $\hat{p}$. Likewise, to reach a conclusion about a population mean μ, we take a random sample and calculate the sample mean $\bar{x}$. Because of chance variation in random sampling, the values of our sample statistic will vary from sample to sample. The distribution of statistic values in all possible samples of the same size from a population is called the sampling distribution of the statistic. The sampling distribution describes the sampling variability and provides a foundation for performing inference. The variability of a sampling distribution is an important attribute as all inference calculations depend upon it! When trying to estimate a parameter, we want minimum sampling variability and no bias. Random sampling helps avoid bias and larger samples help minimize sampling variability.

Check for Understanding:

_____ *I can distinguish among the distribution of a population, the distribution of a sample and the sampling distribution of a statistic.*

_____ *I can create a sampling distribution using all possible samples from a small population.*

A breakfast cereal includes marshmallow shapes in the following distribution: 10% stars, 10% crescent moons, 20% rockets, 40% astronauts, 20% planets. We are interested in examining the proportion of rockets in a random sample of 2000 marshmallows from the cereal.

1) Sketch the population distribution of marshmallow shapes.

2) Suppose you were to collect a random sample of 2000 marshmallow shapes. Sketch the distribution of sample data you would expect to see. How many rockets would you expect to see in your sample?

3) Now, suppose you collected many samples of the same size. Sketch the sampling distribution of the proportion of rockets you think you would see in the samples.

Section 7.2: Sample Proportions

Before You Read: Section Summary

The objective of some statistical applications is to reach a conclusion about a population proportion p. For example, we may try to estimate an approval rating through a survey, or test a claim about the proportion of defective light bulbs in a shipment based on a random sample. Since p is unknown to us, we must base our conclusion on a sample proportion, $\hat{p}$. However, as we have noted, we know that the value of $\hat{p}$ will vary from sample to sample. The amount of variability will depend on the size of our sample. In this section, you will learn how to describe the shape, center, and spread of the sampling distribution of $\hat{p}$ and $\hat{p}_1 - \hat{p}_2$ in detail.

Learning Targets:

_____ I can calculate the mean and standard deviation of the sampling distribution of a sample proportion $\hat{p}$ and interpret the standard deviation.

_____ I can determine if the sampling distribution of $\hat{p}$ is approximately Normal.

_____ I can calculate the mean and standard deviation of the sampling distribution of a difference in sample proportions $\hat{p}_1 - \hat{p}_2$ and interpret the standard deviation.

_____ I can determine if the sampling distribution of $\hat{p}_1 - \hat{p}_2$ is approximately Normal.

_____ I can use a Normal distribution to calculate probabilities involving $\hat{p}$ or $\hat{p}_1 - \hat{p}_2$, if appropriate.

While You Read: Key Vocabulary and Concepts

sampling distribution of $\hat{p}$:
mean of the sampling distribution of $\hat{p}$:
standard deviation of the sampling distribution of $\hat{p}$:
Normal approximation for $\hat{p}$:
sampling distribution of $\hat{p}_1 - \hat{p}_2$:
mean of the sampling distribution of $\hat{p}_1 - \hat{p}_2$:
standard deviation of the sampling distribution of $\hat{p}_1 - \hat{p}_2$:

☑ **After You Read: Check for Understanding**

Concept 1: The Sampling Distribution of $\hat{p}$

If we take repeated samples of the same size n from a population with a proportion of interest p, the sampling distribution of $\hat{p}$ will have the following characteristics:

1) The shape of the sampling distribution of $\hat{p}$ will be approximately Normal as long as $np \geq 10$ and $n(1-p) \geq 10$.

2) The mean of the sampling distribution of $\hat{p}$ is $\mu_{\hat{p}} = p$.

3) The standard deviation of the sampling distribution of $\hat{p}$ is $\sigma_{\hat{p}} = \sqrt{\dfrac{p(1-p)}{n}}$.

Note: The formula for the standard deviation is exactly correct only if we are sampling from an infinite population or *with replacement* from a finite population. When we are sampling without replacement from a finite population, the formula is approximately correct as long as the 10% condition is satisfied. That is, the sample size must be less than or equal to 10% of the population size.

Check for Understanding:

_____ *I can calculate the mean and standard deviation of the sampling distribution of a sample proportion $\hat{p}$ and interpret the standard deviation.*

_____ *I can determine if the sampling distribution of $\hat{p}$ is approximately Normal.*

Suppose your job at a potato chip factory is to check each shipment of potatoes for quality assurance. Further, suppose that a truckload of potatoes contains 95% that are acceptable for processing. If more than 10% are found to be unacceptable in a random sample, you must reject the shipment. To check, you randomly select and test 250 potatoes. Let $\hat{p}$ be the sample proportion of unacceptable potatoes.

1) What is the mean of the sampling distribution of $\hat{p}$?

2) Check the 10% condition and calculate the standard deviation of the sampling distribution of $\hat{p}$.

3) Check the Normal condition and sketch the sampling distribution of $\hat{p}$. Based on this sketch, do you think it would be likely to reject the truckload based on a random sample of 250 potatoes? Why or why not?

Concept 2: Using the Normal Approximation for $\hat{p}$

When the sample size n is large enough for np and $n(1-p)$ to both be at least 10, the shape of the sampling distribution of $\hat{p}$ will be approximately Normal. In that case, we can use Normal calculations to determine the probability that an SRS will generate a value of $\hat{p}$ in a particular interval. This calculation is an important component of inference.

Check for Understanding:

_____ *I can use a Normal distribution to calculate probabilities involving $\hat{p}$, if appropriate.*

A phone company is interested in exploring marketing possibilities for a new smartphone for teenagers. They ask an SRS of 1000 high school students whether they own a smartphone. Suppose 65% of all high school students own a smartphone. What is the probability that the random sample selected by the company will result in a value of $\hat{p}$ that is within 3 percentage points of the true population proportion? Show all your work!

Concept 3: The Sampling Distribution of $\hat{p}_1 - \hat{p}_2$

If we take a simple random sample of size n_1 from Population 1 with a proportion of successes p_1 and an independent simple random sample of size n_2 from Population 2 with a proportion of successes p_2 the sampling distribution of $\hat{p}_1 - \hat{p}_2$ will have the following characteristics:

1) The shape of the sampling distribution of $\hat{p}_1 - \hat{p}_2$ will be approximately Normal as long as the Large Counts Condition is met for both samples: $n_1 p_1 \geq 10$, $n_1(1-p_1) \geq 10$, $n_2 p_2 \geq 10$, and $n_2(1-p_2) \geq 10$.

2) The mean of the sampling distribution of $\hat{p}_1 - \hat{p}_2$ is $\mu_{\hat{p}_1 - \hat{p}_2} = p_1 - p_2$.

3) The standard deviation of the sampling distribution of $\hat{p}_1 - \hat{p}_2$ is approximately

$$\sigma_{\hat{p}_1 - \hat{p}_2} = \sqrt{\frac{\hat{p}_1(1-\hat{p}_1)}{n_1} + \frac{\hat{p}_2(1-\hat{p}_2)}{n_2}}$$ as long as the 10% condition is met for both samples:

$n_1 < 0.10N_1$ and $n_2 < 0.10N_2$.

Check for Understanding:

_____ *I can calculate the mean and standard deviation of the sampling distribution of a difference in sample proportions $\hat{p}_1 - \hat{p}_2$ and interpret the standard deviation.*

_____ *I can determine if the sampling distribution of $\hat{p}_1 - \hat{p}_2$ is approximately Normal.*

_____ *I can use a Normal distribution to calculate probabilities involving $\hat{p}_1 - \hat{p}_2$, if appropriate.*

At West High, 45% of the students play sports while at East High 40% of the students play sports. Random samples of 50 students from each large high school are selected. Let $\hat{p}_W - \hat{p}_E$ be the difference in the sample proportion of students that play sports.

1) What is the shape of the sampling distribution of $\hat{p}_W - \hat{p}_E$? Why?

2) What is the mean of the sampling distribution of $\hat{p}_W - \hat{p}_E$?

3) What is the standard deviation of the sampling distribution of $\hat{p}_W - \hat{p}_E$? Why?

4) What is the probability that the proportion of the students that play sports in the sample from East High is greater than the proportion of students that play sports in the sample from West High?

Section 7.3: Sample Means

Before You Read: Section Summary

When the goal of a statistical application is to reach a conclusion about a population mean μ we must rely on a sample mean $\bar{x}$. However, as we have noted, the value of $\bar{x}$ will vary from sample to sample. Like we observed with sample proportions, the amount of variability will depend on the size n of our sample. In this section, you will learn how to describe the shape, center, and variability of the sampling distribution of $\bar{x}$ and $\bar{x}_1 - \bar{x}_2$ in detail.

> **Learning Targets:**
>
> _____ I can calculate the mean and standard deviation of the sampling distribution of a sample mean $\bar{x}$ and interpret the standard deviation.
>
> _____ I can explain how the shape of the sampling distribution of $\bar{x}$ is affected by the shape of the population distribution and the sample size.
>
> _____ I can calculate the mean and standard deviation of the sampling distribution of a sample mean $\bar{x}_1 - \bar{x}_2$ and interpret the standard deviation.
>
> _____ I can determine if the shape of the sampling distribution of $\bar{x}_1 - \bar{x}_2$ is approximately Normal.
>
> _____ I can use a Normal distribution to calculate probabilities involving $\bar{x}$ or $\bar{x}_1 - \bar{x}_2$, if appropriate.

While You Read: Key Vocabulary and Concepts

sampling distribution of $\bar{x}$:
mean of the sampling distribution of $\bar{x}$:
standard deviation of the sampling distribution of $\bar{x}$:
Central Limit Theorem:
sampling distribution of $\bar{x}_1 - \bar{x}_2$:
mean of the sampling distribution of $\bar{x}_1 - \bar{x}_2$:
standard deviation of the sampling distribution of $\bar{x}_1 - \bar{x}_2$:

✓**After You Read: Check for Understanding**

Concept 1: Sampling Distribution of $\bar{x}$

If we take repeated random samples of the same size n from a population with mean μ, the sampling distribution of $\bar{x}$ will have the following characteristics:

1) The shape of the sampling distribution depends upon the shape of the population distribution. If the population is Normally distributed, the sampling distribution of $\bar{x}$ will be Normally distributed. If the population distribution is non-Normal, the sampling distribution of $\bar{x}$ will become more and more Normal as n increases.

2) The mean of the sampling distribution is $\mu_{\bar{x}} = \mu$.

3) The standard deviation of the sampling distribution is $\sigma_{\bar{x}} = \dfrac{\sigma}{\sqrt{n}}$

   Note: The formula for the standard deviation is exactly correct only if we are sampling from an infinite population or *with replacement* from a finite population. When we are sampling without replacement from a finite population, the formula is approximately correct as long as the 10% condition is satisfied. That is, the sample size must be less than 10% of the population size.

Check for Understanding:

____ *I can calculate the mean and standard deviation of the sampling distribution of a sample mean $\bar{x}$ and interpret the standard deviation.*

____ *I can use a Normal distribution to calculate probabilities involving $\bar{x}$, if appropriate.*

The times it takes 5th graders to complete a particular mathematics problem are Normally distributed with mean 2 minutes and standard deviation 0.8 minutes.

1) Find the probability that a randomly chosen 5th grader will take more than 2.5 minutes to complete the problem. Show your work.

2) Suppose you give the problem to an SRS of 20 students. Sketch the sampling distribution of $\bar{x}$. Then use this distribution to determine the probability that the mean time to complete the problem for the SRS of students is greater than 2.5 minutes. Show your work.

Concept 2: The Central Limit Theorem

When the population is Normally distributed, we know that the sampling distribution of $\bar{x}$ will be Normally distributed, so we can use Normal calculations. However, most population distributions are not Normally distributed. If our sampling distribution is skewed or non-Normal in some other way, we cannot use Normal calculations to answer questions. Thankfully, a pretty remarkable fact about sample means helps us out: when the sample size n is large, the shape of the sampling distribution of $\bar{x}$ will be approximately Normal no matter what the shape of the population distribution may be! For our purposes, we'll define "large" to be any sample that is at least 30. So, if $n \geq 30$, we can be safe in assuming that the sampling distribution of $\bar{x}$ will be approximately Normal and we can proceed to perform Normal calculations. If $n < 30$, we must consider the shape of the population distribution.

Check for Understanding:

_____ *I can use a Normal distribution to calculate probabilities involving $\bar{x}$, if appropriate.*

The blood cholesterol level of adult men has mean 188 mg/dl and standard deviation 41 mg/dl. An SRS of 250 men is selected and the mean blood cholesterol level in the sample is calculated.

Sketch the sampling distribution of $\bar{x}$ and calculate the probability that the sample mean will be greater than 193.

Concept 3: Sampling Distribution of $\overline{x}_1 - \overline{x}_2$

If we select a SRS of size n_1 from Population 1 with mean μ_1 and standard deviation σ_1 and an independent SRS of size n_2 from Population 2 with mean μ_2 and standard deviation σ_2, the sampling distribution of $\overline{x}_1 - \overline{x}_2$ will have the following characteristics:

1) The sampling distribution of $\overline{x}_1 - \overline{x}_2$ is Normal if both population distributions are Normal. It is approximately Normal if both sample sizes are large ($n_1 \geq 30$ and $n_2 \geq 30$) or if one population is Normally distributed and the other sample size is large.

2) The mean of the sampling distribution of $\overline{x}_1 - \overline{x}_2$ is $\mu_{\overline{x}_1 - \overline{x}_2} = \mu_1 - \mu_2$.

3) The standard deviation of the sampling distribution of $\overline{x}_1 - \overline{x}_2$ is approximately $\sigma_{\overline{x}_1 - \overline{x}_2} = \sqrt{\dfrac{\sigma_1^2}{n_1} + \dfrac{\sigma_2^2}{n_2}}$

   as long as the 10% condition is met for both samples: $n_1 < 0.10N_1$ and $n_2 < 0.10N_2$.

Check for Understanding:

_____ *I can calculate the mean and standard deviation of the sampling distribution of a difference in sample means $\overline{x}_1 - \overline{x}_2$ and interpret the standard deviation.*

_____ *I can determine if the sampling distribution of $\overline{x}_1 - \overline{x}_2$ is approximately Normal.*

_____ *I can use a Normal distribution to calculate probabilities involving $\overline{x}_1 - \overline{x}_2$, if appropriate.*

At West High, the amount of time that students spend on homework has a mean of 95 minutes and a standard deviation of 25 minutes. At East High, the amount of time that students spend on homework has a mean of 55 minutes and a standard deviation of 35 minutes. Random samples of 50 students from each large high school are selected. Let $\overline{x}_W - \overline{x}_E$ be the difference in the sample mean amount of time the students spend on homework.

1) What is the shape of the sampling distribution of $\overline{x}_W - \overline{x}_E$? Why?

2) What is the mean of the sampling distribution of $\overline{x}_W - \overline{x}_E$?

3) What is the standard deviation of the sampling distribution of $\overline{x}_W - \overline{x}_E$? Why?

4) What is the probability that the sample mean time that the students from East High spend on homework is greater than the sample mean time that students from West High spend on homework?

Chapter Summary: Sampling Distributions

This chapter introduced you to a key concept for inferential thinking – sampling distributions. Because we are interested in drawing conclusions about population proportions and means, it is important to know how statistics will behave in repeated random sampling. Being able to describe the sampling variability for sample statistics allows us to estimate and test claims about population parameters. This chapter provided us with some key facts about sample statistics that will help us as we begin our formal study of inference. First, statistics will vary from sample to sample. Second, if the sample size is large enough, we know that the distribution of sample statistic values will be approximately Normal. Third, the sampling distributions of $\hat{p}$ and $\overline{x}$ will be centered at p and μ, respectively. Finally, the variability of these sampling distributions can be computed (as long as the 10% condition is met). This variability will decrease as the sample size increases, so large random samples are more desirable.

One important fact about sample means was revealed in this chapter. When sampling from a Normal population, the sampling distribution of $\overline{x}$ will be Normal. However, as long as our sample size is at least 30, the shape of the sampling distribution of $\overline{x}$ will be approximately Normal--no matter what the population distribution looks like! The central limit theorem is a powerful fact that will be revisited in the coming chapters. Now that we have a grasp of the basic concept of sampling distributions, we are ready to begin the formal study of statistical inference!

How well do you understand each of the learning targets?

Learning Target	Got It!	Almost There	Needs Work
I can distinguish between a parameter and a statistic.			
I can create a sampling distribution using all possible samples from a small population.			
I can use the sampling distribution of a statistic to evaluate a claim about a parameter.			
I can distinguish among the distribution of a population, the distribution of a sample and the sampling distribution of a statistic.			
I can determine if a statistic is an unbiased estimator of a population parameter.			
I can describe the relationship between sample size and the variability of a statistic.			
I can calculate the mean and standard deviation of the sampling distribution of a sample proportion $\hat{p}$ and interpret the standard deviation.			
I can determine if the sampling distribution of $\hat{p}$ is approximately Normal.			
I can calculate the mean and standard deviation of the sampling distribution of a difference in sample proportions $\hat{p}_1 - \hat{p}_2$ and interpret the standard deviation.			
I can determine if the sampling distribution of $\hat{p}_1 - \hat{p}_2$ is approximately Normal.			
I can use a Normal distribution to calculate probabilities involving $\hat{p}$ or $\hat{p}_1 - \hat{p}_2$, if appropriate.			
I can calculate the mean and standard deviation of the sampling distribution of a sample mean $\bar{x}$ and interpret the standard deviation.			
I can explain how the shape of the sampling distribution of $\bar{x}$ is affected by the shape of the population distribution and the sample size.			
I can calculate the mean and standard deviation of the sampling distribution of a difference in sample proportions $\bar{x}_1 - \bar{x}_2$ and interpret the standard deviation.			
I can determine if the sampling distribution of $\bar{x}_1 - \bar{x}_2$ is approximately Normal.			
I can use a Normal distribution to calculate probabilities involving $\bar{x}$, if appropriate.			

Chapter 7 Multiple Choice Practice

Directions. Identify the choice that best completes the statement or answers the question. Check your answers and note your performance when you are finished.

1. The variability of a statistic is described by
    (A) the spread of its sampling distribution.
    (B) the amount of bias present.
    (C) the vagueness in the wording of the question used to collect the sample data.
    (D) probability calculations.
    (E) the stability of the population it describes.

2. Here are dot plots of the values taken by three different statistics in 30 samples from the same population. The true value of the population parameter is marked with an arrow.

    Which statistic has the largest *bias* among these three?

    (A) Statistic A
    (B) Statistic B
    (C) Statistic C
    (D) A and B have similar bias, and it is larger than the bias of C.
    (E) B and C have similar bias, and it is larger than the bias of A.

3. According to a recent poll, 27% of Americans prefer to read their news in a physical newspaper instead of online. Let's assume this is the parameter value for the population. If you take a simple random sample of 25 Americans and let $\hat{p}$ = the proportion in the sample who prefer a newspaper, is the shape of the sampling distribution of $\hat{p}$ approximately Normal?
    (A) No, because $p < 0.50$
    (B) No, because $np = 6.75$
    (C) Yes, because we can reasonably assume there are more than 250 individuals in the population.
    (D) Yes, because we took a simple random sample.
    (E) Yes, because $n(1 - p) = 18.25$

4. The time it takes students to complete a statistics quiz has a mean of 20.5 minutes and a standard deviation of 15.4 minutes. What is the probability that a random sample of 40 students will have a mean completion time greater than 25 minutes?
    (A) 0.9678
    (B) 0.0322
    (C) 0.0344
    (D) 0.3851
    (E) 0.6149

5. A fair coin (one for which both the probability of heads and the probability of tails are 0.5) is tossed 60 times. What is the probability that more than 1/3 of the tosses are heads?

   (A) 0.9951
   (B) 0.33
   (C) 0.109
   (D) 0.09
   (E) 0.0049

6. The histogram below was obtained from data on 750 high school basketball games in a regional athletic conference. It represents the number of three-point baskets made in each game.

   What is the range of sample sizes a researcher could take from this population without violating conditions required for performing Normal calculations with the sampling distribution of $\bar{x}$?

   (A) $0 \leq n \leq 30$
   (B) $30 \leq n \leq 50$
   (C) $30 \leq n \leq 75$
   (D) $30 \leq n \leq 750$
   (E) $75 \leq n \leq 750$

7. The incomes in a certain large population of college teachers have a normal distribution with mean $60,000 and standard deviation $5000. Four teachers are selected at random from this population to serve on a salary review committee. What is the probability that their average salary exceeds $65,000?

   (A) 0.0228
   (B) 0.1587
   (C) 0.8413
   (D) 0.9772
   (E) essentially 0

8. A random sample of size 25 is to be taken from a population that is Normally distributed with mean 60 and standard deviation 10. The mean $\bar{x}$ of the observations in our sample is to be computed. The sampling distribution of $\bar{x}$

   (A) is Normal with mean 60 and standard deviation 10.
   (B) is Normal with mean 60 and standard deviation 2.
   (C) is approximately Normal with mean 60 and standard deviation 2.
   (D) has an unknown shape with mean 60 and standard deviation 10.
   (E) has an unknown shape with mean 60 and standard deviation 2.

9. The scores of individual students on a college entrance examination have a left-skewed distribution with mean 18.6 and standard deviation 6.0. At Millard North High School, 36 seniors take the test. The sampling distribution of mean scores for random samples of 36 students is

    (A)   approximately Normal.

    (B)   symmetric and mound-shaped, but non-Normal.

    (C)   skewed right.

    (D)   neither Normal nor non-normal. It depends on the particular 36 students selected.

    (E)   exactly Normal.

10. The distribution of prices for home sales in Minnesota is skewed to the right with a mean of $290,000 and a standard deviation of $145,000. Suppose you take a simple random sample of 100 home sales from this (very large) population. What is the probability that the mean of the sample is above $325,000?

    (A)   0.0015

    (B)   0.0027

    (C)   0.0079

    (D)   0.4046

    (E)   0.4921

Check your answers below. If you got a question wrong, check to see if you made a simple mistake or if you need to study that concept more. After you check your work, identify the concepts you feel very confident about and note what you will do to learn the concepts in need of more study.

#	Answer	Concept	Right	Wrong	Simple Mistake?	Need to Study More
1	A	Sampling Variability				
2	C	Bias and Variability				
3	B	Normality Condition				
4	B	Normal Probability Calculation				
5	A	Normal Probability Calculation				
6	C	10% Condition and CLT				
7	A	Normal Probability Calculation				
8	B	Sampling Distribution for Means				
9	A	Sampling Distribution for Means				
10	C	Normal Probability Calculation				

FRAPPY! Free Response AP® Problem, Yay!

A television producer must schedule a selection of paid advertisements during each hour of programming. The lengths of the advertisements are Normally distributed with a mean of 28 seconds and standard deviation of 5 seconds. During each hour of programming, 45 minutes are devoted to the program and 15 minutes are set aside for advertisements. To fill in the 15 minutes, the producer randomly selects 30 advertisements.

(a) Describe the sampling distribution of the sample mean length for random samples of 30 advertisements.

(b) If 30 advertisements are randomly selected, what is the probability that the total time needed to air them will exceed the 15 minutes available? Show your work.

FRAPPY! Scoring Rubric

Use the following rubric to score your response. Each part receives a score of "Essentially Correct," "Partially Correct," or "Incorrect." When you have scored your response, reflect on your understanding of the concepts addressed in this problem. If necessary, note what you would do differently on future questions like this to increase your score.

Intent of the Question

The goal of this question is to determine your ability to describe the sampling distribution of a sample mean and use it to perform a probability calculation.

Solution

(a) The sampling distribution of the sample mean length for random samples of 30 advertisements has mean 28 seconds and standard deviation $\sigma_{\bar{x}} = \dfrac{5}{\sqrt{30}} = 0.913$ seconds. Because we are told that the population of advertisement lengths is Normally distributed, the shape of the sampling distribution will be Normal.

(b) The probability that a random sample of 30 advertisements will exceed the allotted time is equivalent to the probability that the sample mean length of the 30 advertisements is greater than 900/30 = 30 seconds. In part (a), we determined that the sampling distribution is Normal with mean = 28 and standard deviation = 0.913.

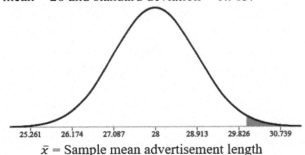

25.261   26.174   27.087   28   28.913   29.826   30.739

$\bar{x}$ = Sample mean advertisement length

$$P(\bar{x} > 30) = P\left(Z > \frac{30-28}{0.913}\right) = P(Z > 2.19) = 1 - 0.9857 = 0.0143$$

There is a 1.43% chance the randomly selected advertisements will exceed the allotted time.

Scoring:

Parts (a), (b), and (c) are scored as essentially correct (E), partially correct (P), or incorrect (I).

Part (a) is essentially correct if the response correctly identifies the shape (Normal), center (mean = 28 seconds) and variability (standard deviation = 0.913 seconds) of the sampling distribution. The calculation of the standard deviation should be shown to earn an essentially correct score. Part (a) is partially correct if the solution only identifies 2 of the 3 components correctly or correctly identifies the standard deviation, but fails to show the calculation.

Part (b) is essentially correct if the response sets up and performs a correct probability calculation. Part (b) is partially correct if the response includes a correctly set up calculation, but fails to calculate the correct value OR if it sets up an incorrect, but plausible, calculation but carries it through correctly.

4   Complete Response

All three parts essentially correct

3   Substantial Response

Two parts essentially correct and one part partially correct

2   Developing Response

Two parts essentially correct and no parts partially correct

One part essentially correct and one or two parts partially correct

Three parts partially correct

1   Minimal Response

One part essentially correct and no parts partially correct

No parts essentially correct and two parts partially correct

My Score:
What I did well:
What I could improve:
What I should remember if I see a problem like this on the AP Exam:

Chapter 7 Formula Sheet

Create a one-page summary of important concepts and formulas found in this chapter. This will serve as a valuable resource as you prepare for the AP Exam.

Chapter 7 Crossword Puzzle
SAMPLING DISTRIBUTIONS

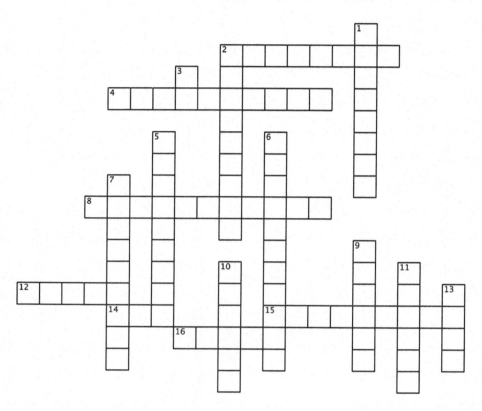

Across

2. _____ distribution: the distribution of values taken by the statistic in all possible samples of the same size from the population
4. _____ distribution: the distribution of all values of a variable in the population
8. _____ of a statistic is described by the spread of the sampling distribution
12. Greek letter used for the population standard deviation
14. the Normal approximation for the sampling distribution of a sample proportion can be used when both the number of successes and failures are greater than _____
15. sampling distributions and sampling variability provide the foundation for performing _____
16. central _____ theorem tells us if the sample size is large, the sampling distribution of the sample mean is approximately Normal, regardless of the shape of the population

Down

1. a statistic is an _____ estimator if the mean of the sampling distribution is equal to the true value of the parameter being estimated.
2. a number, computed from sample data, that estimates a parameter
3. Greek letter used for the population mean
5. standard _____ : measure of spread of a sampling distribution
6. sampling _____ notes the value of a statistic may be different from sample to sample
7. a number that describes a population
9. the rule of thumb for using the central limit theorem - the sample size should be greater than _____
10. when the sample size is large, the sampling distribution of a sample proportion is approximately _____
11. to draw a conclusion about a population parameter, we can look at information from a _____ sample
13. center of a sampling distribution

Chapter 8: Estimating Proportions with Confidence

"Do not put your faith in what statistics say until
you have carefully considered what they do not say." William W. Watt

CHAPTER OVERVIEW

Now that you have learned the basics of probability and sampling distributions, you are ready to begin your formal study of inference. In this chapter, you will use what you have learned about sampling distributions to construct confidence intervals for population proportions and population means. In later chapters, you'll learn how to determine confidence intervals for paired data, differences in means and proportions, and slopes of regression lines. Each of those procedures uses the same approach as the intervals you'll construct in this chapter, so you'll want to get a solid foundation in the basics here!

Sections in this Chapter
Section 8.1: Confidence Intervals: The Basics
Section 8.2: Estimating a Population Proportion
Section 8.3: Estimating a Difference in Proportions

PLAN YOUR LEARNING

Use the following *suggested* guide to help plan your reading and assignments in "The Practice of Statistics, Updated 6th Edition." Put a check mark in the last column when you are done. Note: your teacher may schedule a different pacing or assign different problems. Be sure to follow his or her instructions!

Read	Do	Done!
Section 8.1: p. 536-541	1, 3, 5, 7, 9	
Section 8.1: p. 542-548	11, 15, 17, 19, 21, MC 23-26	
Section 8.2: p. 552-558	29, 31, 35, 37, 39	
Section 8.2: p. 559-562	41, 45, 49, MC 55-58	
Section 8.3: p. 567-573	61, 65, 67, 71, MC 73-75	
Chapter Summary	Multiple-Choice FRAPPY!	

Section 8.1: Confidence Intervals: The Basics

Before You Read: Section Summary

In this section you will be introduced to the basic ideas behind constructing and interpreting a confidence interval for a population parameter. You will learn how we can take a point estimate for a population parameter and use what we know about sampling variability to construct an interval of plausible values for the parameter. You will focus on the big ideas in this section. Make sure you understand the different components of a confidence interval as well as the correct interpretation of both the interval and the confidence level. The next two sections will build upon the concepts presented here and focus on the details for estimating proportions and means.

Learning Targets:

_____ I can identify an appropriate point estimator and calculate the value of a point estimate.

_____ I can interpret a confidence interval in context.

_____ I can determine the point estimate and margin of error from a confidence interval.

_____ I can use a confidence interval to make a decision about the value of a parameter.

_____ I can interpret a confidence level in context.

_____ I can describe how the sample size and confidence level affect the margin of error.

_____ I can explain how practical issues like nonresponse, undercoverage, and response bias can affect the interpretation of a confidence interval.

While You Read: Key Vocabulary and Concepts

point estimator:
point estimate:
confidence interval:
confidence level C:
margin of error:
critical value:

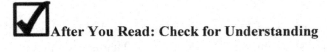**After You Read: Check for Understanding**

Concept 1: The Idea of a Confidence Interval
When our goal is to estimate a population parameter, we often must rely on a sample statistic to provide a "point estimate." However, as we learned in the last chapter, that estimate will vary from sample to sample. A confidence interval takes that variation in to account to provide an interval of plausible values, based on the statistic, for the true parameter. All confidence intervals have two main components: an interval based on the estimate that includes a margin of error and a confidence level C that reports the success rate of the method used to construct the interval in capturing the parameter in repeated constructions. For example, "$C\%$ confident" means $C\%$ of all samples of the same size from the population of interest would yield an interval that captures the true parameter. We can then interpret the interval itself to say "We are $C\%$ confident that the interval from a to b captures the true value of the population parameter."

Check for Understanding:
_____ *I can interpret a confidence interval in context.*
_____ *I can interpret a confidence level in context.*

How much do the volumes of bottles of water vary? A random sample of 50 "20 oz." water bottles is collected and the contents are measured. A 90% confidence interval for the population mean μ is 19.10 to 20.74.

1) Interpret the confidence interval in context.

2) Interpret the confidence level in context.

3) Based on this interval, what can you say about the contents of the bottles in the sample? What can you say about the contents of bottles in the population?

Concept 2: Constructing a Confidence Interval

We will learn in the next section that to construct a confidence interval, we must work through several steps. First, you MUST check that the conditions for constructing the interval are met. That is, we must be assured that the data come from a random sample or randomized experiment. Next, the sampling distribution of the statistic must be approximately Normal. And, finally, the individual observations must be independent (which means checking the 10% condition if we're sampling without replacement from a finite population).

We construct the interval using the formula

statistic ± (critical value) · (standard deviation of the statistic)

where the critical value is determined based on the confidence level C and the standard deviation is based on the sampling distribution of the statistic. We interpret the interval using the language we learned earlier in this section.

Our goal with confidence intervals is to provide as precise an estimate as possible. That is, we wish to construct a narrow interval that we are confident captures the parameter of interest. We can achieve this in two ways: by decreasing our confidence or by increasing our sample size.

Check for Understanding:

_____ *I can describe how the sample size and confidence level affect the margin of error.*

_____ *I can explain how practical issues like nonresponse, undercoverage, and response bias can affect the interpretation of a confidence interval.*

A large company is interested in developing a new bake ware product for consumers. In an effort to determine baking habits of adults, a researcher selects a random sample of 50 addresses in a large, midwestern, metropolitan area. She calls each selected home in the late morning to collect information on their baking habits. The proportion of adults who bake at least twice a week is calculated and a 95% confidence interval is constructed.

1) Explain what would happen to the width of the interval if the confidence level were decreased to 90%.

2) How would a 95% confidence interval, based on a sample of size 100, compare to the original 95% confidence interval?

3) Describe one potential source of bias in this study that is not accounted for by the margin of error.

Section 8.2: Estimating a Population Proportion

Before You Read: Section Summary

In the last section, you learned the basic ideas behind confidence intervals. In the next two sections, you will learn how to construct and interpret confidence intervals for a population proportion and a difference in population proportions. You will start by constructing them for a single proportion, focusing on the application of the four-step process.

Learning Targets:

_____ I can state and check the Random, 10%, and Large Counts conditions for constructing a confidence interval for a population proportion.

_____ I can determine the critical value for calculating a C% confidence interval for a population proportion using a table or technology.

_____ I can construct and interpret a confidence interval for a population proportion.

_____ I can determine the sample size required to obtain a C% confidence interval for a population proportion with a specified margin of error.

While You Read: Key Vocabulary and Concepts

one-sample z interval for a population proportion:
standard error:
conditions for constructing a confidence interval about a proportion:
sample size for a desired margin of error when estimating p:

✓**After You Read: Check for Understanding**

Concept 1: Conditions for Estimating p

When constructing a confidence interval for p, it is critical that you begin by checking that the conditions are met. First, check to make sure that the sample was randomly selected. If sampling was done without replacement be sure to check the 10% condition, which states that the size of the sample must be less than 10% of the size of the population. Because the construction of the interval is based on the sampling distribution of $\hat{p}$, next you must ensure that the Large Counts Condition is met. That is, check to see that $n\hat{p}$ and $n(1-\hat{p})$ are both at least 10. If all three of these conditions are met, you can safely proceed to construct and interpret a confidence interval for a population proportion p.

Concept 2: Constructing a Confidence Interval for p

To construct a confidence interval for a population proportion p, you should follow a four-step process.

- **State** the parameter you want to estimate and at what confidence level.
- **Plan** which confidence interval you will construct and verify that the conditions have been met.
- **Do** the actual construction of the interval using $\hat{p}\pm z^*\sqrt{\dfrac{\hat{p}(1-\hat{p})}{n}}$ where z^* is the critical value for the standard Normal curve with area C between $-z^*$ and z^*.
- **Conclude** by interpreting the interval in the context of the problem.

Check for Understanding:

_____ *I can state and check the Random, 10%, and Large Counts conditions for constructing a confidence interval for a population proportion.*

_____ *I can construct and interpret a confidence interval for a population proportion.*

According to a recent study, not everyone can roll their tongue. A researcher observed a random sample of 300 adults and found 68 who could roll their tongue. Use the four-step process to construct and interpret a 90% confidence interval for the true proportion of adults who can roll their tongue.

Concept 3: Choosing the Sample Size

As noted in Section 8.1, our goal is to estimate the parameter as precisely as possible. We want high confidence and a low margin of error. To achieve that, we can determine how large a sample size is necessary before proceeding with the data collection. To calculate the sample size necessary to achieve a set margin of error at a confidence level C, we simply solve the following inequality for n:

$$z^* \sqrt{\frac{\hat{p}(1-\hat{p})}{n}} \leq ME$$

where the sample proportion is estimated based on a previous study or set to 0.5 to account for the maximum possible margin of error.

Check for Understanding:

_____ *I can determine the sample size required to obtain a C% confidence interval for a population proportion with a specified margin of error.*

A researcher would like to estimate the proportion of adults who can roll their tongues. However, unlike the previous example, she'd like the margin of error to be at most 2% at a 95% confidence level. How large a sample is needed?

Section 8.3: Estimating a Difference in Proportions

Before You Read: Section Summary

In this section, you will learn how to construct and interpret a confidence interval for a difference in two proportions. Like you did with a single proportion, you will learn the conditions necessary for performing inference and then how to construct the confidence interval. By the end of this section, you should be able to provide an estimate of the difference between two proportions.

Learning Targets:

_____ I can determine whether the conditions are met for doing inference about a difference between two proportions.

_____ I can construct and interpret a confidence interval for a difference between two proportions.

While You Read: Key Vocabulary and Concepts

conditions for a confidence interval about a difference in proportions:

two-sample z interval for a difference between two proportions:

After You Read: Check for Understanding

Concept 1: Conference Intervals for $p_1 - p_2$

To construct a confidence interval for the difference between two proportions $p_1 - p_2$, you should follow the four-step process. The logic behind its construction is the same as the logic behind the construction of a confidence interval for a single proportion. That is, we will estimate the difference by comparing the sample proportions from two random samples and build an interval around that point estimate by using the standard error of the statistic and a critical z value. To construct a two-sample z interval for a difference between two proportions:

- **State** the parameters of interest and the confidence level you will be using to estimate the difference.
- **Plan:** Indicate the type of confidence interval you are constructing and verify that the Random, 10%, and Large Counts conditions are satisfied for both samples.
- **Do** the actual construction of the interval using the following formula:

$$(\hat{p}_1 - \hat{p}_2) \pm z^* \sqrt{\frac{\hat{p}_1(1-\hat{p}_1)}{n_1} + \frac{\hat{p}_2(1-\hat{p}_2)}{n_2}}$$

where z^* is the critical value for the standard Normal curve with area C between $-z^*$ and z^*.
- **Conclude** by interpreting the interval in the context of the problem.

Check for Understanding:

_____ *I can determine whether the conditions are met for doing inference about a difference between two proportions.*

_____ *I can construct and interpret a confidence interval for a difference between two proportions.*

In 1990, 551 of 1500 randomly sampled adults indicated they smoked. In 2010, 652 of 2000 randomly sampled adults indicated they smoked. Use this information to construct and interpret a 95% confidence interval for the difference in the proportion of adults who smoke in 1990 and 2010.

Chapter Summary: Estimating Proportions with Confidence

Statistical inference is the practice of drawing a conclusion about a population based on information gathered from a sample. This chapter introduced us to the practice of estimating a parameter based on a statistic. By using what we learned about sampling distributions, we can construct an interval around a point estimate that we are confident captures the parameter of interest. The confidence level itself tells what would happen if we used the construction method for the interval many times for samples of the same size. It is basically the capture rate for all of the constructed intervals. So, when we build a level C interval, we can interpret it by saying "We are $C\%$ confident the interval from a to b captures the true parameter of interest."

In the next chapter, we will learn how to test a claim about a parameter. Make sure you continue to practice confidence intervals, though, as they are just as important as the significance tests you are about to learn!

How well do you understand each of the learning targets?

Learning Target	Got It!	Almost There	Needs Some Work
I can identify an appropriate point estimator and calculate the value of a point estimate.			
I can interpret a confidence interval in context.			
I can determine the point estimate and margin of error from a confidence interval.			
I can use a confidence interval to make a decision about the value of a parameter.			
I can interpret a confidence level in context.			
I can describe how the sample size and confidence level affect the margin of error.			
I can explain how practical issues like nonresponse, undercoverage, and response bias can affect the interpretation of a confidence interval.			
I can state and check the Random, 10%, and Large Counts conditions for constructing a confidence interval for a population proportion.			
I can determine the critical value for calculating a $C\%$ confidence interval for a population proportion using a table or technology.			
I can construct and interpret a confidence interval for a population proportion.			
I can determine the sample size required to obtain a $C\%$ confidence interval for a population proportion with a specified margin of error.			
I can determine whether the conditions are met for constructing a confidence interval about a difference between two proportions.			
I can construct and interpret a confidence interval for a difference between two proportions.			

Chapter 8 Multiple Choice Practice

Directions. Identify the choice that best completes the statement or answers the question. Check your answers and note your performance when you are finished.

1. Gallup Poll interviews 1600 people. Of these, 18% say that they jog regularly. A news report adds: "The poll had a margin of error of plus or minus three percentage points." You can safely conclude
   (A) 95% of all Gallup Poll samples like this one give answers within ±3% of the true population value.
   (B) the percent of the population who jog is certain to be between 15% and 21%.
   (C) 95% of the population jog between 15% and 21% of the time.
   (D) we can be 3% confident that the sample result is true.
   (E) if Gallup took many samples, 95% of them would find that 18% of the people in the sample jog.

2. An agricultural researcher plants 25 plots with a new variety of corn. A 90% confidence interval for the average yield for these plots is found to be 162.72 ± 4.47 bushels per acre. Which of the following is the correct interpretation of the interval?
   (A) There is a 90% chance the interval from 158.28 to 167.19 captures the true average yield.
   (B) 90% of sample average yields will be between 158.28 and 167.19 bushels per acre.
   (C) We are 90% confident the interval from 158.28 to 167.19 captures the true average yield.
   (D) 90% of the time, the true average yield will fall between 158.28 and 167.19.
   (E) We are 90% confident the true average yield is 162.72.

3. I collect a random sample of size n from a population and from the data collected compute a 95% confidence interval for the mean of the population. Which of the following would produce a wider confidence interval, based on these same data?
   (A) Use a larger confidence level.
   (B) Use a smaller confidence level.
   (C) Increase the population size.
   (D) Increase the sample size.
   (E) Nothing can ensure that you will get a larger interval. One can only say the chance of obtaining a larger interval is 0.05.

4. A marketing company discovered the following problems with a recent poll:
   I. Some people refused to answer questions
   II. People without telephones could not be in the sample
   III. Some people never answered the phone in several calls
   Which of these sources is included in the ±2% margin of error announced for the poll?
   (A) Only source I.
   (B) Only source II.
   (C) Only source III.
   (D) All three sources of error.
   (E) None of these sources of error.

5. You are told that the proportion of those who answered "yes" to a poll about internet use is 0.70, and that the standard error is 0.0459. What is the sample size?

(A) 50

(B) 99

(C) 100

(D) 200

(E) cannot be determined from the information given.

6. A newspaper conducted a statewide survey concerning the 2008 race for state senator. The newspaper took a random sample (assume it is an SRS) of 1200 registered voters and found that 620 would vote for the Republican candidate. Let p represent the proportion of registered voters in the state that would vote for the Republican candidate. What is a 90% confidence interval for p?

(A) 0.517 ± 0.014

(B) 0.517 ± 0.022

(C) 0.517 ± 0.024

(D) 0.517 ± 0.028

(E) 0.517 ± 0.249

7. After a college's football team once again lost a football game to the college's arch rival, the alumni association decided to conduct a survey to see if alumni were in favor of firing the coach. Let p represent the proportion of all living alumni who favor firing the coach. Which of the following is the smallest sample size needed to guarantee an estimate that's within 0.05 of p at a 95% confidence level?

(A) 269

(B) 385

(C) 538

(D) 768

(E) 1436

8. A teacher would like to know which of two homework incentive plans is more effective. To do so, she randomly assigns the 60 students in her class to one of two incentive plans by having each student flip a coin. Of the 34 students that were assigned to Plan A, 23 successfully completed all homework assignments. The remaining students were assigned to Plan B, of which 20 successfully completed all homework assignments. The teacher would like to construct a 90% confidence interval for $p_A - p_B =$ the difference in the proportion of all students like these that would successfully complete all homework assignments under these two plans. Which of the following conditions for inference, if any, are not met?

(A) The random condition is the only condition that is not met.

(B) The 10% condition is the only condition that is not met.

(C) The large counts condition is the only condition that is not met.

(D) All conditions for inference are met.

(E) Both the 10% condition and the large counts condition are not met.

9.   An SRS of 100 teachers showed that 64 owned smartphones. An SRS of 100 students showed that 80 owned smartphones. Let p_T be the proportion of all teachers who own smartphones and p_S be the proportion of all students who own smartphones. A 95% confidence interval for $p_T - p_S$ is
   (A)   (0.264, 0.056)
   (B)   (0.098, 0.222)
   (C)   (−0.222, −0.098)
   (D)   (−0.264, −0.056)
   (E)   (−0.283, −0.038)

10. A school receives textbooks independently from two suppliers. An SRS of 400 textbooks from supplier 1 finds 20 that are defective. An SRS of 100 textbooks from supplier 2 finds 10 that are defective. Let p_1 and p_2 be the proportions of all textbooks from suppliers 1 and 2, respectively that are defective. Which of the following represents a 95% confidence interval for $p_1 - p_2$?

   (A) $-0.05 \pm 1.96\sqrt{\dfrac{(0.05)(0.95)}{400} - \dfrac{(0.1)(0.9)}{100}}$

   (B) $-0.05 \pm 1.96\sqrt{\dfrac{(0.05)(0.95)}{400} + \dfrac{(0.1)(0.9)}{100}}$

   (C) $-0.05 \pm 1.64\sqrt{\dfrac{(0.05)(0.95)}{400} - \dfrac{(0.1)(0.9)}{100}}$

   (D) $-0.05 \pm 1.64\sqrt{\dfrac{(0.05)(0.95)}{400} + \dfrac{(0.1)(0.9)}{100}}$

   (E) $-0.05 \pm 1.64\sqrt{\dfrac{(0.06)(0.94)}{500}}$

Check your answers below. If you got a question wrong, check to see if you made a simple mistake or if you need to study that concept more. After you check your work, identify the concepts you feel very confident about and note what you will do to learn the concepts in need of more study.

#	Answer	Concept	Right	Wrong	Simple Mistake?	Need to Study More
1	A	Interpreting Confidence				
2	C	Interpret a Confidence Interval				
3	A	Width of a Confidence Interval				
4	E	Biased Samples				
5	C	Standard Error of $\hat{p}$				
6	C	Confidence Interval for p				
7	B	Choosing Sample Size				
8	C	Conditions for Inference				
9	E	Confidence Interval for Difference in Proportions				
10	B	Confidence Interval for Difference in Proportions				

FRAPPY! Free Response AP® Problem, Yay!

The following problem is modeled after actual Advanced Placement Statistics free response questions. Your task is to generate a complete, concise response in 15 minutes. After you generate your response, read over the solution and scoring guide. Score your response and note what, if anything, you would do differently to increase your own score.

A pollster conducts a survey in the Eastern U.S. to determine the percentage of American Adults from this area that approve of our current president. The results of the survey show that 629 of the 1000 participants approve.

(a) Construct a 95% confidence interval for the proportion of American adults in the Eastern U.S. that approve of our current president.

(b) Shortly thereafter, a similar study is conducted in the western U.S. with the intention of constructing a 95% confidence interval for the proportion of adults from the Western U.S. that approve of our current president. What is the smallest sample size that can be used to guarantee that the margin of error will be less than or equal to 0.01?

FRAPPY! Scoring Rubric

Use the following rubric to score your response. Each part receives a score of "Essentially Correct," "Partially Correct," or "Incorrect." When you have scored your response, reflect on your understanding of the concepts addressed in this problem. If necessary, note what you would do differently on future questions like this to increase your score.

Intent of the Question

The goal of this question is to determine your ability to construct and interpret a confidence interval and correctly determine the necessary sample size.

Solution

(a) Name: One-sample interval for p

Conditions:

- Random: A random sample of 1000 American adults was selected.
- 10%: 1000 < 10% of the population of American adults.
- Large Counts:
  - $n\hat{p} \geq 10$: $829 \geq 10$
  - $n(1-\hat{p}) \geq 10$: $171 \geq 10$

Correct Mechanics: $0.829 \pm 1.96\sqrt{\dfrac{0.829(1-0.829)}{1000}} = (0.806, 0.852)$

Interpretation: Based on the sample, we are 95% confident that the interval from 0.806 to 0.852 captures the true proportion of American adults that would say they are doing ok.

(b) Because we need to find the sample size required to guarantee that the margin of error will be no larger than 0.01, we will use the value $\hat{p} = 0.5$ in this calculation.

$0.01 = 1.96\sqrt{\dfrac{0.5(1-0.5)}{n}}$ → $n = 9604$

The margin of error will equal 0.01 when n is 9604.

Scoring

Parts (a) is split into two parts of which each part, along with part (b) are scored as essentially correct (E), partially correct (P), or incorrect (I).

Part (a) – Name and Conditions: This is essentially correct if the response correctly checks the conditions AND correctly names the confidence interval (one-sample z confidence interval for a proportion). Part (a) is partially correct if the conditions are not properly checked but the interval is correctly named.

Part (a) – Calculations and Conclusion: This is essentially correct if the response correctly calculates the interval AND writes a correct conclusion in context that references the parameter ("true proportion of all adults from the Easter U.S. who would say". Part (a) is partially correct if one of these requirements is not met.

Part (b) is essentially correct if the response correctly calculates the necessary sample size AND shows their work (formula with correct values) Part (b) is partially correct if a value other than 0.5 is used.

4   Complete Response

All three parts essentially correct

3   Substantial Response

Two parts essentially correct and one part partially correct

2   Developing Response

Two parts essentially correct and no parts partially correct

One part essentially correct and one or two parts partially correct

Three parts partially correct

1   Minimal Response

One part essentially correct and no parts partially correct

No parts essentially correct and two parts partially correct

My Score:
What I did well:
What I could improve:
What I should remember if I see a problem like this on the AP Exam:

Chapter 8 Formula Sheet

Create a one-page summary of important concepts and formulas found in this chapter. This will serve as a valuable resource as you prepare for the AP Exam.

Chapter 8 Crossword Puzzle
ESTIMATING PROPORTIONS WITH CONFIDENCE

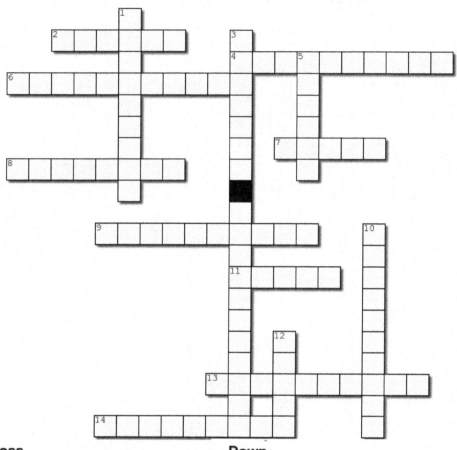

Across

2. The large _____ condition says that the number of successes and failures must be at least 10.

4. We can decrease the width of a confidence interval by _____ the sample size.

6. When selecting two random samples for the purpose of statistical inference, the two samples must be _____.

7. A single value used to estimate a parameter is called a _____ estimator.

8. The margin of error consists of a _____ value and the standard error of the sampling distribution.

9. A _____ interval provides an estimate for a population parameter.

11. The confidence _____ is the success rate of the method in repeated random sampling.

13. We can construct an interval that is less wide by _____ the confidence level.

14. The conclusion should always be written in terms of the population _____.

Down

1. When you draw a conclusion about a population based upon a sample you are performing statistical _____.

3. The 10% condition applies when sampling _____.

5. To estimate with confidence, the estimate should be based upon a _____ sample.

10. The 10% condition says that the size of the sample must be less than 10% of the size of the _____.

12. A confidence interval consists of an estimate, plus or minus the margin of _____.

Chapter 9: Testing Claims About Proportions

"A statistical analysis, properly conducted, is a delicate dissection of uncertainties, a surgery of suppositions." M.J. Moroney

CHAPTER OVERVIEW

In the last chapter, you learned how to estimate a parameter based on a sample statistic. In this chapter, you will learn how to use data from a random sample to test a claim about a population proportion and a difference in population proportions. Significance tests are the second type of inference you will be introduced to in this course. By the end of this chapter, you should understand the logic behind a significance test, as well as how to use a four-step procedure to carry out a significance test. In the next few chapters, you'll learn how to estimate and test claims about a mean a difference in means, as well as how to perform significance tests for slopes of regression lines and distributions of categorical variables. In each case, you will use the same logic and the same four-step procedure. Be sure to take the time in this chapter to get a solid understanding of both concepts!

Sections in this Chapter
Section 9.1: Significance Tests: The Basics
Section 9.2: Tests About a Population Proportion
Section 9.3: Tests About a Difference in Proportions

PLAN YOUR LEARNING

Use the following *suggested* guide to help plan your reading and assignments in "The Practice of Statistics, Updated 6th Edition." Put a check mark in the last column when you are done. Note: your teacher may schedule a different pacing or assign different problems. Be sure to follow his or her instructions!

Read	Do	Done!
Section 9.1: p. 584-591	1, 3, 5, 7, 9, 13, 14, 15, 19	
Section 9.1: p. 592-595	21, 23, 25, 27, MC 29-32	
Section 9.2: p. 600-604	35, 37, 39, 41	
Section 9.2: p. 605-611	43, 45, 47, 51, 53, 55	
Section 9.2: p. 612-618	59, 61, 63, 65, 67, MC 70-73	
Section 9.3: p. 624-631	77, 79, 83, 85	
Section 9.3: p. 632-635	87, 89, 93, MC 95-98	
Chapter Summary	Multiple-Choice FRAPPY!	

Section 9.1: Significance Tests: The Basics

Before You Read: Section Summary

In this section, you will learn the basic ideas and logic behind a significance test. You will be introduced to stating hypotheses, checking conditions, calculating a standardized test statistic, and drawing a conclusion. *P*-values will be introduced as a means of weighing the strength of evidence against a claim. Because we are basing our conclusion on a sample statistic that would vary from sample to sample, we must be aware of the fact that our conclusion could be wrong. This section ends with a discussion of the types of errors that could occur when performing a significance test and how to deal with them. Be sure to get a good understanding of the logic and format for a significance test. You will be using them throughout the rest of the course!

Learning Targets:

_____ I can state appropriate hypotheses for a significance test about a population parameter.
_____ I can interpret a *P*-value in context.
_____ I can make an appropriate conclusion for a significance test.
_____ I can interpret a Type I error and a Type II error in context, and give a consequence of each error in a given setting.

While You Read: Key Vocabulary and Concepts

null hypothesis:
alternative hypothesis:
one-sided and two-sided alternative hypotheses:
P-value:
How to make a conclusion:
significance level:
Type I error:
Type II error:

☑️ **After You Read: Check for Understanding**

Concept 1: The Reasoning Behind Significance Tests

A significance test is a procedure that allows us to test a claim about a population parameter by studying a statistic from a random sample. If an observed statistic is "far" away from a hypothesized claim about a parameter, we have some evidence that the claim is wrong. Whether or not the statistic is "far enough" away depends on the sampling distribution of the statistics. That is, statistics will vary from sample to sample. What a significance test does is answers the question, "What are the chances we would observe a sample statistic at least this extreme, assuming the claim about the parameter was true?" If the chances are low, there is evidence that the claim may be wrong. If the chances are pretty good, then there is little evidence to suggest the claim is wrong. Of course, to even begin making that argument, you must start by setting up a null hypothesis (or claim about the parameter you are trying to find evidence against) and an alternative hypothesis (the claim about the parameter you are trying to find evidence for). Note: the null hypothesis will always be a statement of equality. That is, it says, "Let's assume the parameter is equal to _____." The alternative hypothesis is set up to test whether or not the actual value of the parameter is greater than, less than, or simply not equal to the value in the null hypothesis.

Check for Understanding:

_____ I can state appropriate hypotheses for a significance test about a population parameter.

Suppose you suspect a "chute" of playing cards is not fair. The chute supposedly contains 10 standard decks shuffled together. You are interested in knowing whether there are more hearts than usual. To test this, you select 12 cards at random and calculate the proportion of hearts in your hand.

1) Describe the parameter of interest in this setting.

2) Write the appropriate null and alternative hypotheses for this situation.

3) Suppose your deal contains 7 hearts. What is the sample proportion of hearts? Is it possible to deal 7 hearts out of 12 cards if the chute really does contain standard decks? Is it likely? Why or why not?

Concept 2: Statistical Significance

To conclude that we have convincing evidence against a null hypothesis, our sample statistic must have a low likelihood of occurring under the assumption that the null hypothesis is true. To determine this, we must consider the sampling distribution of the statistic under the assumption that the null hypothesis is true and calculate the probability of observing a statistic at least as extreme as the one observed. If the conditions for inference are met, we can describe the sampling distribution and calculate a standardized test statistic. This test statistic can then be used to determine a *P*-value. If this *P*-value is low enough, we can say the data are statistically significant and we have evidence to reject the null hypothesis. The general rule of thumb is to use a significance level of 5%, although some situations may specify levels of 1% or even 10%. If the *P*-value is smaller than the chosen significance level, we have convincing evidence to reject the null hypothesis and conclude that the alternative is true. The reasoning behind this is that if we observe an outcome that has an extremely low chance of occurring under a given assumption, then there is evidence that the assumption may be false. If we observe an outcome under that has a fairly likely chance of occurring under a given assumption, then we have little reason to doubt the assumption!

Check for Understanding:

_____ *I can interpret a P-value in context.*
_____ *I can make an appropriate conclusion for a significance test.*

Refer to the hypotheses you set in the previous check for understanding. Suppose you conduct a significance test for the proportion of hearts in the chute and find the *P*-value for obtaining 7 hearts in 12 randomly selected cards is 0.004.

1) Explain what it means for the null hypothesis to be true in this setting.

2) Interpret the *P*-value in context.

3) Do these data provide convincing evidence against the null hypothesis at a 5% significance level? Explain.

Concept 3: Type I and Type II Errors

Because our conclusion is based on what we would expect to see in a sampling distribution, there is a chance our sample statistic does not accurately reflect the true value of the parameter. That is, due to sampling variability, it is possible that the random sample that is collected will lead to an incorrect conclusion about the parameter. If we obtain a very small *P*-value and reject the null when, in fact, the null hypothesis is true, we commit a Type I error. The probability of committing a Type I error is equal to the significance level, α. If we obtain a relatively large *P*-value and fail to reject the null when, in fact, the null hypothesis is false, we commit a Type II error. You will not be expected to calculate the probability of Type II errors. However, you should be able to interpret both Type I and Type II errors in the context of the situation and explain the consequences of each.

Check for Understanding:

_____ *I can interpret a Type I error and a Type II error in context, and give a consequence of each error in a given setting.*

Refer to the previous checks for understanding.

1) Describe a Type I error in this setting.

2) Describe a Type II error in this setting.

Section 9.2: Tests About a Population Proportion

Before You Read: Section Summary

In this section, you will apply the logic of significance tests and the four-step process to test a claim about a population proportion. You will learn how to check the conditions for a significance test as well as how to calculate a standardized test statistic and *P*-value. Finally, you will learn how to write an appropriate conclusion in context. Your study will also include an introduction to two-sided tests to find evidence that a population proportion is different than a hypothesized value. You will then wrap up the section by studying the connection between confidence intervals and two-sided tests. Again, this section introduces you to concepts that will be used throughout the rest of the course. Make sure to get additional help if you struggle at all with the ideas behind significance testing!

Learning Targets:

_____ I can state and check the Random, 10%, and Large Counts conditions for performing a significance test about a population proportion.

_____ I can calculate the standardized test statistic and *P*-value for a test about a population proportion.

_____ I can perform a significance test about a population proportion.

_____ I can interpret the power of a significance test and describe what factors affect the power of a test.

While You Read: Key Vocabulary and Concepts

conditions for performing a significance test about a proportion:
standardized test statistic:
significance tests – a four-step process:
one-sample z test for a proportion:
power:

After You Read: Check for Understanding

Concept 1: One-Sample z Test for a Proportion

Significance tests and confidence intervals are both based on the same concept—sampling distributions. Therefore, when performing inference with either of these methods, it is important to follow a process that ensures the calculations are justified. To test a claim about a population parameter, the following four-step process should be used:

1) **STATE the parameter of interest and the hypotheses you would like to test.**

   When testing a claim about a population proportion, we start by defining hypotheses about the parameter. The null hypothesis assumes that the population proportion is equal to a particular value while the alternative hypothesis is that the population proportion is greater than, less than, or not equal to that value:

   $$H_0: p = p_0$$
   $$H_a: p > p_0 \quad \text{OR} \quad p < p_0 \quad \text{OR} \quad p \neq p_0$$

   State a significance level.

2) **PLAN: Choose the appropriate inference method and check the conditions.**

   We must check the Random, 10%, and Normal/Large Sample conditions before proceeding with inference. To ensure that the sampling distribution of $\hat{p}$ is approximately Normal, check to make sure np_0 and $n(1 - p_0)$ are both at least 10. If sampling is done without replacement, verify that the sample size is less than 10% of the size of the population.

3) **DO: If conditions are met, calculate a test statistic and *P*-value.**

   Compute the z test statistic

   $$z = \frac{\hat{p} - p_0}{\sqrt{\dfrac{p_0(1 - p_0)}{n}}}$$

   and find the *P*-value by calculating the probability of observing a z statistic at least this extreme in the direction of the alternative hypothesis.

4) **CONCLUDE by interpreting the results of your calculations in the context of the problem.**

   If the *P*-value is smaller than the stated significance level, you have significant evidence to reject the null hypothesis. If it is greater than the significance level, then you fail to reject the null hypothesis.

This four-step procedure can be used with *any* significance test! The details change slightly depending on the inference procedure, but the overall process is the same for all significance tests. Be sure to get a good grasp of this process here as you will be using it a lot in the coming chapters!

Check for Understanding:

_____ *I can state and check the Random, 10%, and Large Counts conditions for performing a significance test about a population proportion.*

_____ *I can calculate the standardized test statistic and P-value for a test about a population proportion.*

_____ *I can perform a significance test about a population proportion.*

A study of classic authors uncovered a distinguishable speech pattern that differed from author to author. Plato utilized this pattern in 21.4% of the passages in his works. The owner of a rare bookstore claims to have an original Plato work, but you suspect the speech pattern occurs too frequently to be an original Plato work. A random sample of passages from the work in question was taken and it was found that 136 of the 439 selected passages followed the speech pattern. Do these data provide convincing evidence that the work was not written by Plato?

Concept 2: Confidence Intervals Give More Information

Significance tests provide evidence that supports or rejects a claim about a population parameter. If an observed sample statistic is far enough away from a parameter's assumed value, a significance test will suggest there is evidence to question that claimed value. However, the test does not say anything about what the actual parameter value may be. A confidence interval provides more information by suggesting a range of plausible values for the parameter. There is also a link between confidence intervals and *two-sided* tests. While not a perfect connection, a two-sided test at a significance level α and a $100(1 - \alpha)\%$ confidence interval give similar information about the population parameter.

Check for Understanding:

_____ *I can use a confidence interval to make a conclusion for a two-sided test about a population parameter.*

A recent study suggested that 77% of teenagers have texted while driving. A random sample of 27 teenage drivers was selected and 15 admitted to texting while driving. Use a 99% confidence interval to determine whether there is convincing evidence that the population proportion of teens who text while driving is different than 77%.

Concept 3: The Power of a Test

The power of a test is the probability it will find convincing evidence for H_a when a specific alternative value of the parameter is true. You can think of this as the probability of avoiding a Type II error. Therefore, for a specific alternative value, Power $= 1 - P$(Type II error).

There are a few ways we can increase the power of a significance test. We can increase the sample size, increase the significance level, or increase the difference that is important to detect between the null and alternative parameter values. The design of our study can also increase power. Specifically, controlling for other variables and blocking in experiments or stratified random sampling can increase power.

Check for Understanding:

_____ _I can interpret the power of a significance test and describe what factors affect the power of a test._

A computer manufacturer requires each batch of processors it uses meets high quality standards. If the manufacturer finds convincing evidence that greater than 3% of the processors use more than 70W of power, the batch will be sent for expensive additional testing. A quality control engineer inspects a random sample of processors from each shipment and performs a test of H_0: $p = 0.03$ versus H_a: $p > 0.03$, where $p =$ the true proportion of processors that use more than 70 watts of power in a given batch.

1) The power of the test to detect that $p = 0.04$, based on a random sample of 30 processors and a significance level $\alpha = 0.05$, is 0.12. Interpret this value.

Determine if each of the following changes would increase or decrease the power of the test. Explain your answers.

2) Change the significance level to $\alpha = 0.01$.

3) Take a random sample of 50 processors, instead of 30.

4) The true proportion is $p = 0.05$ instead of $p = 0.04$.

Section 9.3: Tests About a Difference in Proportions

Before You Read: Section Summary

In this section, you will learn how to carry out a significance test about a difference in two population proportions. The logic behind this process is rooted in an understanding of the sampling distribution of a difference between two proportions. Like you did with a single proportion, you will learn the conditions necessary for performing inference and then will learn how to perform a significance test. By the end of this section, you should be able to draw a conclusion about a claim that is made about the difference between two proportions.

Learning Targets:

_____ I can state appropriate hypotheses for a significance test about a difference between two proportions.

_____ I can determine whether the conditions are met for performing a test about a difference between two proportions.

_____ I can calculate the standardized test statistic and *P*-value for a test about a difference between two proportions.

_____ I can perform a significance test about a difference between two proportions.

While You Read: Key Vocabulary and Concepts

conditions for inference about a difference in proportions:

two-sample z test for the difference between two proportions:

✓**After You Read: Check for Understanding**

Concept 1: Significance tests for $p_1 - p_2$

To test a claim about the difference between two proportions, we will follow the same four-step process learned in the previous section. The key difference when performing a test about $p_1 - p_2$ is that when we assume these two parameters are equal (in the null hypotheses), we need to estimate just what value they are equal to. To calculate this "pooled" proportion, simply divide the sum of the successes in the two samples by the sum of the sample sizes. This pooled proportion can then be used in the formula for the standard deviation of the sampling distribution. To conduct a two-sample z test for the difference between two proportions:

1) **STATE the parameter of interest and the hypotheses you would like to test.**
   The null hypothesis assumes that the parameters are equal while the alternative hypothesis is that one proportion is greater than, less than, or not equal to the other:
   $$H_0: p_1 = p_2$$
   $$H_a: p_1 > p_2 \quad \text{OR} \quad p_1 < p_2 \quad \text{OR} \quad p_1 \neq p_2$$
   State a significance level.

2) **PLAN: Choose the appropriate inference method and check the conditions.**
   We must check the Random, 10%, and Large Counts conditions for both samples or groups. First, verify that the data come from two independent random samples or two groups in a randomized experiment. Next, if sampling without replacement took place, check that each sample size is less than 10% of its respective population size. Finally, to ensure that the sampling distribution of $\hat{p}_1 - \hat{p}_2$ is approximately Normal, check that $n_1\hat{p}_C$, $n_1(1-\hat{p}_C)$, $n_2\hat{p}_C$, and $n_2(1-\hat{p}_C)$ are all at

   least 10. The value of the pooled proportion is $\hat{p}_C = \dfrac{X_1 + X_2}{n_1 + n_2}$.

3) **DO: If conditions are met, calculate a test statistic and *P*-value.**
   Compute the pooled proportion $\hat{p}_C = \dfrac{X_1 + X_2}{n_1 + n_2}$ and z test statistic

   $$z = \frac{(\hat{p}_1 - \hat{p}_2) - 0}{\sqrt{\dfrac{\hat{p}_C(1-\hat{p}_C)}{n_1} + \dfrac{\hat{p}_C(1-\hat{p}_C)}{n_2}}}$$

   and find the *P*-value by calculating the probability of observing a z statistic at least this extreme in the direction of the alternative hypothesis.

4) **CONCLUDE by interpreting the results of your calculations in the context of the problem.**
   If the *P*-value is smaller than the stated significance level, you can conclude that you have significant evidence to reject the null hypothesis. If it is larger than or equal to the significance level, then you fail to reject the null hypothesis.

Check for Understanding:

_____ *I can perform a significance test about a difference between two proportions.*

A school official suspects the difference in the proportion of students who own digital tools between Lakeville North and Lakeville South high schools may be a result of a difference in the socioeconomic status of the students in the two schools. The results of a random sampling of student registration records indicated 28 out of 120 students at Lakeville North came from low-income families while 30 out of 150 students at Lakeville South came from low-income families. Both schools are very large. Do these data provide convincing evidence that the proportion of low-income students at Lakeville North is greater than the proportion at Lakeville South? Use a 5% significance level.

Chapter Summary: Testing Claims About Proportions

A significance test tells us whether or not a sample provides convincing evidence against a claim about a population parameter. The test answers the question, "How likely would it have been to observe this particular sample statistic (or one more extreme) if the claim about the parameter was true?" This probability, the *P*-value, gives us an idea just how surprising an observed statistic is under the assumption that the null hypothesis is true. If the *P*-value is small (less than 5% or some other chosen significance level), we have enough evidence to reject the null hypothesis, suggesting the actual parameter value may be greater than, less than, or different from the claim. If the *P*-value is greater than or equal to a specified significance level, we do not have convincing evidence against the claim about the parameter. Keep in mind, however, that because we are basing our decision on a likelihood calculated from a sampling distribution, it is possible that we may be wrong. Type I and Type II errors occur when we mistakenly reject a null hypothesis that is true or fail to reject a null hypothesis that is false, respectively. You should be able to define each of these errors in the context of the situation as well as explain the consequences of each.

This chapter not only introduced you to the logic behind significance tests, but also a four-step procedure for carrying them out. This procedure will be used throughout the rest of the course, so hopefully you are comfortable with it at this point! If not, be sure to practice a few more tests and focus on stating the parameter and hypotheses, checking the appropriate conditions, calculating a test statistic and *P*-value, and concluding in the context of the problem. If you follow those steps, you should have very few problems performing significance tests in the upcoming chapters!

How well do you understand each of the learning targets?

Learning Target	Got It!	Almost There	Needs Some Work
I can state correct hypotheses for a significance test about a population parameter.			
I can interpret a *P*-value in context.			
I can make an appropriate conclusion for a significance test.			
I can interpret a Type I error and a Type II error in context, and give a consequence of each error in a given setting.			
I can state and check the Random, 10%, and Large Counts conditions for performing a significance test about a population proportion.			
I can calculate the standardized test statistic and *P*-value for a test about a population proportion.			
I can perform a significance test about a population proportion.			
I can interpret the power of a significance test and describe what factors affect the power of a test.			
I can state appropriate hypotheses for a significance test about a difference between two proportions.			
I can determine whether the conditions are met for performing a test about a difference between two proportions.			
I can calculate the standardized test statistic and *P*-value for a test about a difference between two proportions.			
I can perform a significance test about a difference between two proportions.			

Chapter 9 Multiple Choice Practice

Directions. Identify the choice that best completes the statement or answers the question. Check your answers and note your performance when you are finished.

1. An opinion poll asks a random sample of 200 adults how they feel about voting for an amendment in an upcoming election. In all, 150 say they are in favor of the amendment. Does the poll provide evidence that the proportion p of adults who are in favor of the amendment is greater than 60%? What are the null and alternative hypotheses?
    (A) $H_0: p = 0.6$ against $H_a: p > 0.6$
    (B) $H_0: p = 0.6$ against $H_a: p \neq 0.6$
    (C) $H_0: p = 0.6$ against $H_a: p < 0.6$
    (D) $H_0: p = 0.6$ against $H_a: p = 0.75$
    (E) $H_0: p = 0.75$ against $H_a: p < 0.6$

2. A test of significance produces a P-value of 0.035. Which conclusion is appropriate?
    (A) Accept H_a at the $\alpha = 0.05$ level
    (B) Reject H_a at the $\alpha = 0.01$ level
    (C) Fail to reject H_0 at the $\alpha = 0.05$ level
    (D) Reject H_0 at the $\alpha = 0.05$ level
    (E) Accept H_0 at the $\alpha = 0.01$ level

3. A Type II error is
    (A) rejecting the null hypothesis when it is true.
    (B) failing to reject the null hypothesis when it is false.
    (C) rejecting the null hypothesis when it is false.
    (D) failing to reject the null hypothesis when it is true.
    (E) more serious than a Type I error.

4. A researcher plans to conduct a significance test at the $\alpha = 0.05$ significance level. She designs her study to have a power of 0.85 for a particular alternative value of the parameter. What is the probability the researcher will commit a Type II error?
    (A) 0.05
    (B) 0.15
    (C) 0.80
    (D) 0.95
    (E) equal to "$1 - P$-value" and cannot be determined until the data have been collected.

5. In hypothesis testing β is the probability of committing a Type II error in a test with significance level α. The probability of committing a Type I error is
    (A) $1 - \beta$
    (B) $1 - \alpha$
    (C) $\beta - \alpha$
    (D) α
    (E) Cannot be determined

6. A claimed psychic was presented with 200 cards face down and asked to determine if the card was one of five symbols: a star, cross, circle, square, or three wavy lines. The "psychic" was correct in 50 cases. To determine if he has ESP, we test the hypotheses $H_0: p = 0.20$, $H_a: p > 0.20$, where p = the true proportion of cards for which the psychic would correctly identify the symbol in the long run. The conditions for inference are met. What is the P-value of this test?
    (A) between 0.10 and 0.05
    (B) between 0.05 and 0.025
    (C) between 0.025 and 0.01
    (D) between 0.01 and 0.001
    (E) below 0.001

7. A student decides to carry out a statistical study as a graduation project. The student would like to study the effect of music on perception. Specifically, he recruited 50 students for study. He randomly assigned the 50 students to two groups of 25. The members of the first group watched a short video of someone being dishonest while happy music played in the background. The members of the second group watched the same short video while sad music played in the background. Of the 25 members of the first group, 12 of the students acknowledged that the person in the video was dishonest, while 22 members of the second group made the same acknowledgement. The student would like to conduct a z test for a difference in two proportions. Which of the following statements is true?
    (A) The random condition is not met because the students were not randomly selected.
    (B) The 10% condition is not needed in this case because random sampling did not occur.
    (C) The Large Counts condition is met because the expected number of successes and failures in each group is at least 10.
    (D) The expected number of successes in each group are 12 and 22.
    (E) All conditions for inference are met.

8. Is the proportion of marshmallows in Mr. Miller's favorite breakfast cereal lower than it used to be? To determine this, you test the hypotheses $H_0: p_{old} = p_{new}$, $H_a: p_{old} > p_{new}$ at the $\alpha = 0.05$ level. You calculate a test statistic of 1.980. Which of the following is the appropriate P-value and conclusion for your test?
    (A) P-value = 0.047; fail to reject H_0; we do not have convincing evidence that the proportion of marshmallows has been reduced.
    (B) P-value = 0.047; accept H_a; there is convincing evidence that the proportion of marshmallows has been reduced.
    (C) P-value = 0.024; fail to reject H_0; we do not have convincing evidence that the proportion of marshmallows has been reduced.
    (D) P-value = 0.024; reject H_0; we have convincing evidence that the proportion of marshmallows has been reduced.
    (E) P-value = 0.024; fail to reject H_0; we have convincing evidence that the proportion of marshmallows has not changed.

9. In a random sample of 80 male students at a college, 28 said they frequently send at least one text message before getting out of bed in the morning. In a random sample of 105 female students at the same college, 50 said they frequently texted before getting out of bed. Let p_1 = the proportion of all male students at this college who frequently text before getting up, and let p_2 = the corresponding proportion for female students. For a test of the hypothesis $H_0 : p_1 - p_2 = 0$ versus $H_0 : p_1 - p_2 \neq 0$, which of the following is a correct expression for the test statistic?

(A) $z = \dfrac{0.35 - 0.48}{\sqrt{\dfrac{0.35(0.65)}{80}} + \sqrt{\dfrac{0.48(0.52)}{105}}}$

(B) $z = \dfrac{0.35 - 0.48}{\sqrt{\dfrac{0.35(0.65)}{80} + \dfrac{0.48(0.52)}{105}}}$

(C) $z = \dfrac{0.35 - 0.48}{\sqrt{\dfrac{(0.42)(0.58)}{185}}}$

(D) $z = \dfrac{0.35 - 0.48}{\sqrt{\dfrac{0.42(0.58)}{80} + \dfrac{0.42(0.58)}{105}}}$

(E) $z = \dfrac{0.35 - 0.48}{\sqrt{\dfrac{0.42(0.58)}{80^2} + \dfrac{0.42(0.58)}{105^2}}}$

10. Return to the previous scenario. What is the P-value of this test?
    (A) 0.01
    (B) 0.043
    (C) 0.05
    (D) 0.085
    (E) 0.10

Check your answers below. If you got a question wrong, check to see if you made a simple mistake or if you need to study that concept more. After you check your work, identify the concepts you feel very confident about and note what you will do to learn the concepts in need of more study.

#	Answer	Concept	Right	Wrong	Simple Mistake?	Need to Study More
1	A	Writing Hypotheses				
2	D	Significance Level and P-value				
3	B	Type I and Type II Errors				
4	B	Power				
5	D	Type I and Type II Errors				
6	B	Calculating P-value for proportions				
7	B	Conditions for inference				
8	D	Significance Test, P-value, Conclusion				
9	D	Test Statistic				
10	D	P-value				

FRAPPY! *Free Response AP® Problem, Yay!*

The following problem is modeled after actual Advanced Placement Statistics free response questions. Your task is to generate a complete, concise response in 15 minutes. After you generate your response, read over the solution and scoring guide. Score your response and note what, if anything, you would do differently to increase your own score.

During a recent movie promotion, Fruity O's cereal placed mini action figures in some of its boxes. The advertisement on the box states 1 out of every 4 boxes contains an action figure. A group of promotional-toy collectors suspects the proportion of boxes containing the action figure may be lower than 0.25. The group purchased 70 boxes of cereal and found 12 action figures. Assuming the 70 boxes represent a random sample of all of the cereal boxes, is there evidence to support the toy collector's belief that the proportion of boxes containing the figure is less than 0.25? Provide statistical evidence to support your answer.

FRAPPY! Scoring Rubric

Use the following rubric to score your response. Each part receives a score of "Essentially Correct," "Partially Correct," or "Incorrect." When you have scored your response, reflect on your understanding of the concepts addressed in this problem. If necessary, note what you would do differently on future questions like this to increase your score.

Intent of the Question

The goal of this question is to determine your ability to conduct a significance test for a single proportion.

Solution

The solution should contain:

- **Hypotheses** must be stated appropriately. H_0: $p = 0.25$ and H_a: $p < 0.25$ where p = true proportion of boxes containing the action figure.
- **Name of test and conditions**: The test must be identified by name or formula as a one-sample z test for a population proportion. Random sample is given. 10%: $70 < 10\%$ of the population of all cereal boxes. Large Counts: $70(0.25) = 17.5$ and $70(0.75) = 52.5$ Both are at least 10.
- **Mechanics**: $z = -1.52$ and P-value $= 0.064$
- **Conclusion**: Because the P-value is greater than the typical significance level of 0.05, we fail to reject the null hypothesis. There is not sufficient evidence to suggest that the actual proportion of boxes with the action figure is less than 0.25.

Scoring

Each element scored as essentially correct (E), partially correct (P), or incorrect (I).

Hypotheses and Name is essentially correct if the hypotheses are written correctly and the response correctly identifies the test by name or formula. This part is partially correct if the test isn't identified or if the hypotheses are written incorrectly. Incorrect otherwise.

Conditions and Mechanics is essentially correct if the response correctly does 4 of the 5 following things: (1) checks the Normal condition, (2) checks the 10% condition, (3) checks the large counts condition, (4) correct test statistic, (5) correct P-value. This part is partially correct if 3 or more of those 3 things are done correctly. Incorrect otherwise.

Conclusion is essentially correct if the response correctly fails to reject the null hypothesis because the P-value is greater than a significance level of 5% OR if the response is to reject the null hypothesis because the P-value is less than a significance level of 10% and provides an interpretation in context. This part is partially correct if the response fails to justify the decision by comparing the P-value to a significance level OR if the conclusion lacks an interpretation in context. Incorrect otherwise.

Scoring

4   Complete Response

All three parts essentially correct

3   Substantial Response

Two parts essentially correct and one part partially correct

2   Developing Response

Two parts essentially correct and no parts partially correct

One part essentially correct and one or two parts partially correct

Three parts partially correct

1   Minimal Response

One part essentially correct and no parts partially correct

No parts essentially correct and two parts partially correct

My Score:
What I did well:
What I could improve:
What I should remember if I see a problem like this on the AP Exam:

Chapter 9 Formula Sheet

Create a one-page summary of important concepts and formulas found in this chapter. This will serve as a valuable resource as you prepare for the AP Exam.

Chapter 9 Crossword Puzzle
TESTING CLAIMS ABOUT PROPORTIONS

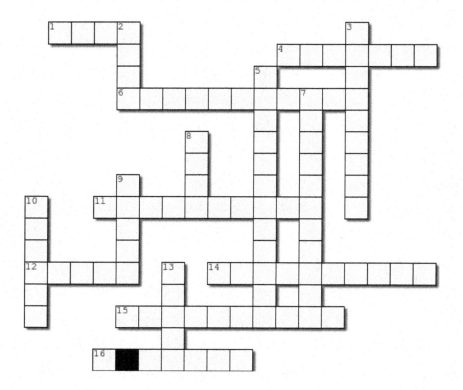

Across

1. If the P-value is greater than the significance level, we _____ to reject the null hypothesis.

4. Conclusions should always be written in _____.

6. If an observed difference is too small to have occurred due to chance alone, the difference is statistically _____.

11. Hypotheses always refer to the _____.

12. If we reject the null hypothesis when it is actually true, we commit a Type I error.

14. Always check the _____ before carrying out an inference procedure.

15. The statements a statistical test is designed to compare.

16. The probability that we would observe a statistic as least as extreme as the one observed assuming the null is true.

Down

2. Reject the null hypothesis if the P-value is _____ than the significance level.

3. The test _____ is a standardized value that assesses how far the estimate is from the hypothesized parameter.

5. We can use a _____ test to compare the observed data with a hypothesis about a population.

7. The _____ hypothesis is the claim about the population we are finding evidence for.

8. The _____ hypothesis is the claim for which we are seeking evidence against.

9. The probability that a significance test will reject the null when a particular alternative value of the parameter is true.

10. If we calculate a very small P-value, we have evidence to _____ the null hypothesis.

13. The Greek letter used to designate the significance level.

Chapter 10: Estimating Means with Confidence

*"We must be careful not to confuse data with the abstractions
we use to analyze them." William James*

CHAPTER OVERVIEW

Up to this point, our studies have focused on inference about proportions. However, many statistical studies involve estimating or carrying out a test about a single mean or a difference in means. In this chapter, we will expand our collection of inference procedures to include confidence intervals about a mean and a difference in means as well as a mean difference (paired data). The procedures for means follow the same structure as those we learned for proportions. The only difference is that now you will need to rely on the sampling distribution of the sample mean or difference in sample means to perform your calculations. As in the previous chapters, you will follow a four-step process for carrying out the inference procedures. However, now your job will increasingly include the decision about *which* inference procedure you should use!

Sections in this Chapter
Section 10.1: Estimating a Population Mean
Section 10.2: Estimating a Difference in Means

PLAN YOUR LEARNING

Use the following *suggested* guide to help plan your reading and assignments in "The Practice of Statistics, Updated 6th Edition." Put a check mark in the last column when you are done. Note: your teacher may schedule a different pacing or assign different problems. Be sure to follow his or her instructions!

Read	Do	Done!
Section 10.1: p. 648-658	1, 3, 5, 7	
Section 10.1: p. 659-663	9, 13, 15, MC 21-24	
Section 10.2: p. 668-675	27, 31, 33, 35	
Section 10.2: p. 676-682	37, 41, 45, MC 49-52	
Chapter Summary	Multiple-Choice FRAPPY!	

Section 10.1: Estimating a Population Mean

Before You Read: Section Summary

In this section, you will continue your study of confidence intervals by learning how to construct and interpret a confidence interval for a mean. While the overall procedure is identical to that for a proportion, there is one major difference. When dealing with means and unknown population standard deviations, we must use a new distribution to determine critical values. You will be introduced to the t distributions and learn how to use them to construct a confidence interval for a population mean.

Learning Targets:

_____ I can determine the critical value for calculating a $C\%$ confidence interval for a population mean using a table or technology.

_____ I can state and check the Random, 10%, and Normal/Large Sample conditions for constructing a confidence interval for a population mean.

_____ I can construct and interpret a confidence interval for a population mean.

While You Read: Key Vocabulary and Concepts

t-distribution:
degrees of freedom:
standard error of the sample mean:
one-sample t-interval for a population mean:
conditions for constructing a confidence interval about a mean:

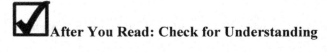**After You Read: Check for Understanding**

Concept 1: Conditions for Estimating μ

Like proportions, when constructing a confidence interval for μ, it is critical that you begin by checking that the conditions are met. First, determine if the sample was randomly selected. If the sample was selected without replacement, then be sure to check the 10% condition. Because the construction of the interval is based on the sampling distribution of $\overline{x}$, ensure that the condition for Normality is met. That is, check to see that the population distribution is Normal, the sample size is at least 30, or the shape of the distribution of the sample has no strong skewness and no outliers. If all three of these conditions are met, you can safely proceed to construct and interpret a confidence interval about a population mean μ.

Concept 2: t Distributions

When the population standard deviation is unknown, we can no longer model distribution of the test statistic with the Normal distribution. Therefore, we can't use z^* critical values to determine the margin of error in the confidence interval. Fortunately, it turns out that when the Normal condition is met, the test statistic calculated using the sample standard deviation s_x has a distribution similar in appearance to the Normal distribution, but with more area in the tails. That is, the statistic has the t distribution with $(n-1)$ degrees of freedom. As the sample size and, subsequently, the degrees of freedom increase, the t distribution approaches the standard Normal distribution. We calculate standardized t values the same way we calculate z values. However, we must refer to a t table and consider the degrees of freedom when determining critical values. For now, we will focus on calculating the critical t^* for different sample sizes and confidence levels.

Check for Understanding:

_____ *I can determine the critical value for calculating a C% confidence interval for a population mean using a table or technology.*

1) An 80% confidence interval from a sample with size $n = 19$

2) A 95% confidence interval from 248 degrees of freedom

3) A 99% confidence interval for a sample with size $n = 30$

Concept 3: Constructing a Confidence Interval for μ

To construct a confidence interval for a population mean μ when the population standard deviation is unknown, you should follow the four-step process.

- **State** the parameter you want to estimate and at what confidence level.
- **Plan** which confidence interval you will construct and verify that the conditions are met.
- **Do** the actual construction of the interval.

$$\bar{x} \pm t^* \cdot \frac{s_x}{\sqrt{n}}$$

where t^* is the critical value for the t_{n-1} distribution with area C between $-t^*$ and t^*.

- **Conclude**, by interpreting the interval in the context of the problem.

Check for Understanding:

_____ *I can construct and interpret a confidence interval for a population mean.*

The amount of sugar in soft drinks is increasingly becoming a concern. To test sugar content, a researcher randomly sampled 8 soft drinks from a particular manufacturer and measured the sugar content in grams/serving. The following data were produced:

26   31   23   22   11   22   14   31

Use these data to construct and interpret a 95% confidence interval for the mean amount of sugar in this manufacturer's soft drinks.

Section 10.2: Estimating a Difference in Means

Before You Read: Section Summary

In this section, you will learn to estimate the difference in two population means. You will start by learning the conditions necessary to perform inference. Then you will learn how to estimate a difference between two means. Like you did with a single mean, you will rely on t distributions when performing calculations. Because some of the calculations are complex, you may want to rely on your calculator to do most of the work. As always, though, make sure you can interpret the results your calculator gives you!

Learning Targets:

_____ I can determine whether the conditions are met for constructing a confidence interval for a difference between two means.

_____ I can construct and interpret a confidence interval for a difference between two means.

_____ I can analyze the distribution of differences in a paired data set using graphs and summary statistics.

_____ I can construct and interpret confidence intervals for a mean difference.

While You Read: Key Vocabulary and Concepts

conditions for inference about a difference in means:
two-sample t interval for $\mu_1 - \mu_2$:
paired data:
analyzing paired data:
conditions for inference about a mean difference:
One-sample t interval for μ_{diff}

✓ **After You Read: Check for Understanding**

Concept 1: Conference Intervals for $\mu_1 - \mu_2$

To construct a confidence interval for the difference between two population or treatment means $\mu_1 - \mu_2$, you should follow the familiar four-step process. We will estimate the difference by comparing the sample means and build an interval around that point estimate by using the standard error of the statistic and a critical t value. To construct a two-sample t interval for a difference between two means:

- **State** the parameters of interest and the confidence level.
- **Plan:** Identify the appropriate inference method and verify that the conditions are met: Two independent random samples or two groups in a randomized experiment, 10% condition for both samples or groups, and the Normal / Large Sample condition for both samples or groups.

- **Do** the actual construction of the interval using the formula: $(\bar{x}_1 - \bar{x}_2) \pm t^* \sqrt{\dfrac{s_1^2}{n_1} + \dfrac{s_2^2}{n_2}}$

  where t^* is the critical value for the t distribution curve having df = smaller of $n_1 - 1$ and $n_2 - 1$ OR given by technology with area C between $-t^*$ and t^*.
- **Conclude,** by interpreting the interval in the context of the problem.

Check for Understanding:

_____ *I can construct and interpret a confidence interval for a difference between two means.*

Researchers are interested in determining the effectiveness of a new diet for individuals with heart disease. 200 heart disease patients are selected and randomly assigned to the new diet or the current diet used in the treatment of heart disease. The 100 patients on the new diet lost an average of 9.3 pounds with standard deviation 4.7 pounds. The 100 patients continuing with their current prescribed diet lost an average of 7.4 pounds with standard deviation 4 pounds. Construct and interpret a 95% confidence interval for the difference in mean weight loss for the two diets.

Concept 2: Confidence Interval for Paired Data

Studies that involve making two observations on the same individual or making an observation on each of two very similar individuals result in paired data. In these types of studies, we are often interested in analyzing the differences in responses within each pair. If the conditions for inference are met, we can use one-sample t procedures to estimate or test a claim about the mean difference, μ_{diff}.

Check for Understanding:

_____ *I can construct and interpret confidence intervals for a mean difference.*

A study measured how fast subjects could repeatedly push a button when under the effects of caffeine. Subjects were asked to push a button as many times as possible in two minutes after consuming a typical amount of caffeine. During another test session, they were asked to push the button after taking a placebo. The subjects did not know which treatment they were administered each day and the order of the treatments was randomly assigned. The data, given in presses per two minutes for each treatment follows. Use a paired t procedure to estimate, with 95% confidence, the mean difference in the number of beats for subjects like these.

Subject	# of Presses Caffeine	# of Presses Placebo
1	251	201
2	284	262
3	300	283
4	321	290
5	240	259
6	294	291
7	377	354
8	345	346
9	303	283
10	340	361
11	408	411

Chapter Summary: Estimating Means with Confidence

In this chapter, you learned the inference procedures that help us estimate a population mean or a difference in population means. Whether you are estimating one mean or a difference in two means, the processes for constructing a confidence interval are the same. Both procedures use a t critical value, which is based upon the degrees of freedom of the distribution. Like we learned when we estimated proportions, it is important to identify which procedure you are using, verify that the appropriate conditions are met, perform the necessary calculations, and interpret your results in the context of the problem.

How well do you understand each of the learning targets?

Learning Target	Got It!	Almost There	Needs Some Work
I can determine the critical value for calculating a $C\%$ confidence interval for a population mean using a table or technology.			
I can state and check the Random, 10%, and Normal/Large Sample conditions for constructing a confidence interval for a population mean.			
I can construct and interpret a confidence interval for a population mean.			
I can determine whether the conditions are met for constructing a confidence interval for a difference between two means.			
I can construct and interpret a confidence interval for a difference between two means.			
I can analyze the distribution of differences in a paired data set using graphs and summary statistics.			
I can construct and interpret a confidence interval for a mean difference.			

Chapter 10 Multiple Choice Practice

Directions. Identify the choice that best completes the statement or answers the question. Check your answers and note your performance when you are finished.

1. What critical value t^* should be used when constructing a 99% confidence interval based on a random sample of 25 observations?
    (A)   2.576
    (B)   2.678
    (C)   2.779
    (D)   2.787
    (E)   2.797

2. A student would like to estimate the mean amount of time that students in his statistics class studied for the most recent test. To do so, he randomly selected 10 of the 30 students in his class and found that the mean amount of time they spent studying was 2.5 hours with a standard deviation of 0.75 hours. A dotplot of the distribution of study times showed no strong skewness and no outliers. Which of the conditions for inference has been violated, if any?
    (A)   The random condition is the only condition that has been violated.
    (B)   The 10% condition is the only condition that has been violated.
    (C)   The Normal/Large Sample condition is the only condition that has been violated.
    (D)   None of the conditions for inference have been violated.
    (E)   More than one of the conditions for inference have been violated.

3. The standardized test scores of 16 students have mean $\bar{x} = 85$ and standard deviation $s_x = 20$. What is the standard error of $\bar{x}$?
    (A)   20
    (B)   10
    (C)   5
    (D)   1.25
    (E)   0.80

4. An SRS of 100 postal employees found that the average time these employees had worked for the postal service was $\bar{x} = 7$ years with standard deviation $s_x = 2$ years. Assume the distribution of the time the population of employees has worked for the postal service is approximately Normal. What is a 95% confidence interval for the mean time μ the population of postal service employees has spent with the postal service?
    (A) 7 ± 2
    (B) 7 ± 1.984
    (C) 7 ± 0.525
    (D) 7 ± 0.4
    (E) 7 ± 0.2

5. Refer to Problem 4. If the sample size were increased to 400, what effect would this have on the width of the confidence interval?
    (A)   The width of the interval would double.
    (B)   The width of the interval would be cut in half.
    (C)   The width of the interval would remain the same.
    (D)   The width of the interval would be 4 times as large.
    (E)   The width of the interval would be divided by 4.

6. A researcher wished to test the effect of the addition of extra calcium on the "tastiness" of yogurt. Sixty-two adult volunteers were randomly divided into two groups of 31 subjects each. Group 1 tasted yogurt containing the extra calcium. Group 2 tasted yogurt from the same batch as group 1 but without the added calcium. Both groups rated the flavor on a scale of 1 to 10, with 1 being "very unpleasant" and 10 being "very pleasant." The mean rating for group 1 was 6.5 with a standard deviation of 1.5. The mean rating for group 2 was 7.0 with a standard deviation of 2.0. Let μ_1 and μ_2 represent the true mean ratings we would observe for the entire population represented by the volunteers if all of them tasted, respectively, the yogurt with and without the added calcium. Which of the following would lead us to believe that the t procedures were not safe to use in this situation?
   (A) The sample medians and means for the two groups were slightly different.
   (B) The distributions of the data for the two groups were both slightly skewed right.
   (C) The data are integers between 1 and 10 and so cannot be normal.
   (D) The standard deviations from both samples were very different from each other.
   (E) None of the above.

7. A researcher wishes to compare the effect of two stepping heights (low and high) on heart rate in a step-aerobics workout. The researcher constructs a 98% confidence interval for the difference in mean heart rate between those who did the high and those who did the low stepping heights. Which of the following is a correct interpretation of this interval?
   (A) 98% of the time, the true difference in the mean heart rate of subjects in the high-step vs. low-step groups will be in this interval.
   (B) We are 98% confident that this interval captures the true difference in mean heart rate of subjects like these who receive the high-step and low-step treatments.
   (C) There is a 0.98 probability that the true difference in mean heart rate of subjects in the high-step vs. low-step groups in this interval.
   (D) 98% of the intervals constructed in this way will contain the value 0.
   (E) There is a 98% probability that we have <u>not</u> made a Type I error.

8. The researcher in question 7 randomly assigned 50 adult volunteers to two groups of 25 subjects each. Group 1 did a standard step-aerobics workout at the low height. The mean heart rate at the end of the workout for the subjects in group 1 was 90 beats per minute with a standard deviation of 9 beats per minute. Group 2 did the same workout but at the high step height. The mean heart rate at the end of the workout for the subjects in group 2 was 95.2 beats per minute with a standard deviation of 12.3 beats per minute. Assuming the conditions are met, which of the following could be the standard error for a 98% confidence interval for the difference in mean heart rates based on these results?

   (A) $\sqrt{\dfrac{9^2}{25}+\dfrac{12.3^2}{25}}$

   (B) $\sqrt{\dfrac{9^2}{25}-\dfrac{12.3^2}{25}}$

   (C) $\sqrt{\dfrac{9^2}{24}+\dfrac{12.3^2}{24}}$

   (D) $\sqrt{\dfrac{9(1-9)}{24}-\dfrac{12.3(1-12.3)}{24}}$

   (E) $\sqrt{\dfrac{9(1-9)}{25}+\dfrac{12.3(1-12.3)}{25}}$

9. Refer to problem 8. Assuming the conditions are met, which of the following could be the 98% confidence interval for the difference in mean heart rates based on these results?
    (A) (2.15, 8.25)
    (B) (−0.77, 11.17)
    (C) (−2.13, 12.54)
    (D) (−2.16, 12.56)
    (E) (−4.09, 14.49)

10. Do students tend to improve their SAT Mathematics (SAT-M) score the second time they take the test? A random sample of four students who took the test twice earned the following scores.

Student	1	2	3	4
First Score	450	520	720	600
Second Score	440	600	720	630

Assume that the change in SAT-M score (second score − first score) for the population of all students taking the test twice is approximately Normally distributed with mean μ. What is a 90% confidence interval for μ?
    (A) 25.0 ± 118.03
    (B) 25.0 ± 64.29
    (C) 25.0 ± 47.56
    (D) 25.0 ± 43.08
    (E) 25.0 ± 33.24

Check your answers below. If you got a question wrong, check to see if you made a simple mistake or if you need to study that concept more. After you check your work, identify the concepts you feel very confident about and note what you will do to learn the concepts in need of more study.

#	Answer	Concept	Right	Wrong	Simple Mistake?	Study More
1	E	Finding the critical value				
2	B	Conditions for inference				
3	C	Standard Error of $\overline{x}$				
4	D	Confidence Interval for μ				
5	B	Effect of sample size on the width of the interval				
6	E	Conditions for Inference				
7	B	Interpret Confidence Interval				
8	A	Standard Error				
9	D	Confidence Interval for Difference in Means				
10	C	Confidence Interval for μ (paired)				

FRAPPY! Free Response AP® Problem, Yay!

The following problem is modeled after actual Advanced Placement Statistics free response questions. Your task is to generate a complete, concise response in 15 minutes. After you generate your response, read over the solution and scoring guide. Score your response and note what, if anything, you would do differently to increase your own score.

An athletic trainer wanted to study the effect of being cheered for on athletic performance. To do so, he used 10 student volunteers. Half of the volunteers were randomly assigned to show up at the track to run one mile in front of a group of their peers who cheered for their classmates as they ran. The other half of the volunteers were assigned to show up at the track at a different time when no one was there other than the trainer, who did not cheer for them. They also each ran one mile. On a different day, the treatments were reversed for each student. Their one-mile times were recorded again. Here are the one-mile times, in minutes, for each student:

Student	1	2	3	4	5	6	7	8	9	10	Mean	SD
Not Cheered	10.45	7.23	8.85	7.15	8.23	8.78	7.80	8.43	10.00	6.98	8.39	1.176
Cheered	10.35	6.65	8.40	6.15	7.95	8.38	6.92	8.20	9.38	7.03	7.94	1.295
Difference	0.10	0.58	0.45	1	0.28	0.40	0.88	0.23	0.62	−0.05	0.45	0.331

The trainer would like to estimate, with 95% confidence, the true mean difference in one-times for students like these using the order "No Cheering – Cheering".

(a) What is the appropriate inference procedure? Explain.

(b) Compute the 95% confidence interval identified in part (a).

(c) Does the confidence interval give reason to believe that students like these run faster when they are being cheered for than when they are not being cheered for?

FRAPPY! Scoring Rubric

Use the following rubric to score your response. Each part receives a score of "Essentially Correct," "Partially Correct," or "Incorrect." When you have scored your response, reflect on your understanding of the concepts addressed in this problem. If necessary, note what you would do differently on future questions like this to increase your score.

Intent of the Question

The goal of this question is to determine your ability to conduct a significance test for a single proportion the difference between two means.

Solution

(a) Paired t confidence interval. We have two data values recorded for each student.

(b) State: 95% confidence interval for μ_{diff} = the true mean difference in one-mile times (no cheering – cheering).

Plan: Random: The volunteers were randomly assigned a treatment order. 10%: not needed.
Normal/Large Sample: The distribution of differences shows no strong skewness or outliers.

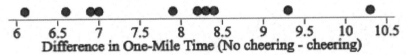

Difference in One-Mile Time (No cheering – cheering)

Do: df = 9, $0.45 \pm 2.262\left(\dfrac{0.331}{\sqrt{10}}\right) = (0.212, 0.686)$.

Conclude: I am 95% confident that the interval from –0.71 to 1.61 contains the true difference in one-mile run times (not cheered – cheered).

(c) Because the confidence interval is entirely positive, we do have reason to believe that students like these will run faster when being cheered for than when not being cheered for.

Scoring

Each element scored as essentially correct (E), partially correct (P), or incorrect (I).

Name and conditions are essentially correct if the response correctly does all of the following 4 things: (1) identifies the interval by name or formula (2) checks the Normal condition, (3) checks the 10% condition, (4) checks the Normal/Large Sample condition. This part is partially correct if the response correctly does 3 of the 4 items and is incorrect if fewer than 3 of the 4 items are correct.

Mechanics is essentially correct if the response correctly calculates the confidence interval and correctly states the degrees of freedom. This part is partially correct if only 1 of those 2 things are done correctly. Incorrect otherwise.

Conclusion is essentially correct if the response correctly interprets the interval in context. This part is partially correct if the response fails to include context and is incorrect if the interval is interpreted incorrectly (refers to the sample or uses past tense).

Scoring

4   Complete Response

All three parts essentially correct

3   Substantial Response

Two parts essentially correct and one part partially correct

2   Developing Response

Two parts essentially correct and no parts partially correct

One part essentially correct and one or two parts partially correct

Three parts partially correct

1   Minimal Response

One part essentially correct and no parts partially correct

No parts essentially correct and two parts partially correct

My Score:
What I did well:
What I could improve:
What I should remember if I see a problem like this on the AP Exam:

Chapter 10 Formula Sheet

Create a one-page summary of important concepts and formulas found in this chapter. This will serve as a valuable resource as you prepare for the AP Exam.

Chapter 10 Crossword Puzzle
ESTIMATING MEANS WITH CONFIDENCE

Across

5. For two sample problems, the data may arise from two _____ in a randomized experiment.

7. In a one-sample problem, df = the _____ _____ minus 1.

10. The 10% condition should be checked when the sample(s) are selected _____

_____.

11. This type of data result from recording two values of the same quantitative variable for each individual.

12. The Normal/Large Sample condition is met for inference about the difference of means if both sample sizes are at least

___.

Down

1. The margin of error in a confidence interval consists of a critical value and standard _____ of the statistic.

2. A particular t distribution is specified by its _____ of freedom.

3. A confidence interval is used to _____ an unknown population parameter.

4. The margin of error decreases as the sample size _____.

6. If all else remains the same and the sample size is quadrupled, the margin of error will be cut in _____.

8. To perform two-sample inference procedures, the random samples must be

_____.

9. The margin of error is larger for higher _____ levels.

Chapter 11: Testing Claims About Means

"A judicious man looks on statistics not to get knowledge,
but to save himself from having ignorance foisted on him." Thomas Carlyle

CHAPTER OVERVIEW

So far, you have learned how to estimate proportions, test a claim about proportions, and estimate means. In this chapter, you will learn how to test a claim about means. This chapter will conclude your study about inference for means and proportions. We will continue to follow the four-step process. We will state the null and alternative hypotheses, define the parameter of interest, and state the significance level that will be used. Then we will name the inference procedure and check the conditions for that procedure. After that we will calculate the standardized test statistic and the P-value. Finally, we will compare the P-value to the significance level and write a conclusion in context. Significance tests about means will continue to rely on the t distribution, just like you learned in the previous chapter. You will also learn about the connection between two-sided tests and confidence intervals. The goal, by the end of this chapter, is for you to have a solid understanding of statistical inference which is a substantial portion of the AP Exam. Do your best!

Sections in this Chapter
Section 11.1: Tests About a Population Mean
Section 11.2: Tests About a Difference in Means

PLAN YOUR LEARNING

Use the following *suggested* guide to help plan your reading and assignments in "The Practice of Statistics, Updated 6th Edition." Put a check mark in the last column when you are done. Note: your teacher may schedule a different pacing or assign different problems. Be sure to follow his or her instructions!

Read	Do	Done!
Section 11.1: p. 698-708	1, 3, 5, 9, 11	
Section 11.1: p. 709-713	13, 15, 17, 19, 21, 23, MC 27-32	
Section 11.2: p. 718-722	35, 37, 39	
Section 11.2: p. 723-727	41, 43, 45, 47, 51	
Section 11.2: p. 728-734	53, 55, 57, 59, MC 65-69	
Chapter Summary	Review Exercises FRAPPY!	

Section 11.1: Tests About a Population Mean

Before You Read: Section Summary

In this section, you'll learn how to perform a significance test about a population mean μ. Just like you did for proportions, you'll learn how to set up hypotheses, check the appropriate conditions, calculate a standardized test statistic and P-value, and draw a conclusion in context. You will also learn how tests involving "paired data" can be performed using one-sample t procedures.

Learning Targets:

_____ I can state and check the Random, 10%, and Normal/Large Sample conditions for performing a significance test about a population mean.

_____ I can calculate the standardized test statistic and P-value for a test about a population mean.

_____ I can perform a significance test about a population mean.

_____ I can use a confidence interval to make a conclusion for a two-sided test about a population mean.

While You Read: Key Vocabulary and Concepts

conditions for performing a significance test about a mean:

t-distribution:

one-sample t test for a mean:

two-sided tests and confidence intervals:

✔️**After You Read: Check for Understanding**

Concept 1: One Sample t Test for μ

The process for testing a claim about a population mean follows the same format as the process used for a population proportion. However, like confidence intervals for means, you usually need to base your calculations on the t distributions (unless σ is somehow known).

1) **STATE the parameter of interest and the hypotheses you would like to test.**

   The null hypothesis assumes that the population mean is equal to a particular value while the alternative hypothesis is that the population mean is greater than, less than, or not equal to that value:

   H_0: $\mu = \mu_0$

   H_a: $\mu > \mu_0$ OR $\mu < \mu_0$ OR $\mu \neq \mu_0$

   State a significance level.

2) **PLAN: Choose the appropriate inference method and check the conditions.**

   We must check the Random, 10%, and Normal/Large Sample conditions before proceeding with inference. To ensure that the sampling distribution of $\bar{x}$ is approximately Normal, check that the population distribution is Normal OR $n \geq 30$. If $n < 30$, it is sufficient if the sample data show no signs of strong skewness or outliers. If sampling is done without replacement, verify that the sample size is less than 10% of the size of the population.

3) **DO: If conditions are met, calculate a standardized test statistic and *P*-value.**

   Compute the t test statistic

   $$t = \frac{\bar{x} - \mu_0}{\frac{s_x}{\sqrt{n}}}$$

   and find the *P*-value by calculating the probability of observing a t statistic at least this extreme in the direction of the alternative hypothesis in a t distribution with $n - 1$ degrees of freedom.

4) **CONCLUDE by interpreting the results of your calculations in the context of the problem.**

   If the *P*-value is smaller than the stated significance level, you have significant evidence to reject the null hypothesis. If it is larger than the significance level, then you fail to reject the null hypothesis.

As with proportions, a confidence interval for a population mean can be used to test a two-sided claim. Further, constructing a confidence interval gives a range of plausible values for μ, while a significance test only allows you to conclude that μ may be different from a particular value.

Check for Understanding:

_____ *I can state and check the Random, 10%, and Normal/Large Sample conditions for performing a significance test about a population mean*

_____ *I can perform a significance test about a population mean.*

Humerus bones from the same species of animal tend to have approximately the same length-to-width ratios. When fossils of humerus bones are discovered, archeologists can often determine the species of animal by examining these ratios. It is known that the species Molekius Primatium exhibits a mean ratio of $\mu = 8.9$. Suppose 41 fossils of humerus bones are unearthed at a site on Minnesota's Iron Range, where this species was known to have lived. Researchers are willing to view these as a random sample of all such humerus bones. The length-to-width ratios were calculated and are listed below. Test whether the population mean for the species that left these bones differs from 8.9 at $\alpha = 0.05$.

9.73	10.89	9.07	9.20	9.33	9.98	9.84	9.59	9.48	8.71	9.57	10.02	11.67	8.07	8.37
6.85	8.52	8.87	6.23	9.41	6.66	9.35	8.86	9.93	8.91	11.77	10.48	10.39	9.39	9.17
9.89	8.17	8.39	8.80	8.38	8.30	9.17	9.38	9.29	9.94	12.00				

Concept 2: Connection Between Two-Sided Tests and Confidence Intervals

In Chapter 9, you learned that confidence intervals give more information than significance tests. Confidence intervals provide a range of plausible values for the population parameter, while significance tests only draw a conclusion about the plausibility of a specific value. However, when you were studying proportions, you learned that the standard error used in confidence intervals is not the same as the denominator of the standardized test statistic used in significance tests.

Confidence interval:

$$\hat{p} \pm z^* \sqrt{\frac{\hat{p}(1-\hat{p})}{n}}$$

Standardized test statistic:

$$z = \frac{\hat{p} - p_0}{\sqrt{\frac{p_0(1-p_0)}{n}}}$$

In this case, we said that the confidence interval gives *similar* information to that of a two-sided significance test. Meaning, the confidence interval for p gives an *approximate set* of plausible values for p_0.

When dealing with means, the standard error of $\bar{x}$ is used in both calculations.

Confidence interval:

$$\bar{x} \pm t^* \left(\frac{s_x}{\sqrt{n}} \right)$$

Standardized test statistic:

$$t = \frac{\bar{x} - \mu}{\frac{s_x}{\sqrt{n}}}$$

In this case, the confidence interval gives the exact same information as that of a two-sided significance test. Meaning, the confidence interval for μ gives an exact set of plausible values for μ_0. Here's how it works:

- If a 95% confidence interval for μ does not capture the null value μ_0, then we reject the null hypothesis of the two-sided test at the $\alpha = 0.05$ significance level.
- If a 95% confidence interval for μ does capture the null value μ_0, then we fail to reject the null hypothesis of the two-sided test at the $\alpha = 0.05$ significance level.

Check for Understanding:

_____ *I can use a confidence interval to make a conclusion for a two-sided test about a population mean.*

A manufacturer of cleaning products sells a 20-ounce bottle of glass cleaner. The manufacturer suspects the filling machine may be improperly filling the bottles. To test this belief, a random sample of 50 bottles are selected and the contents are measured. The manufacturer wants to test the hypotheses: H_0: $\mu = 20$ versus H_a: $\mu \neq 20$ using the significance level $\alpha = 0.01$. Based upon the sample, a 99% confidence interval for the true mean content for all 20-ounce bottles of glass cleaner is (19.25, 19.85). Based on this interval, what conclusion would you make for the test of the given hypotheses?

Section 11.2: Tests About a Difference in Means

Before You Read: Section Summary

In this section, you will learn how to carry out a significance test about a difference in two means as well as a significance test about a mean difference (for paired data). Like you did with a single mean, you will rely on t distributions when performing calculations. Because some of the calculations are complex, you may wish to rely on your calculator to do most of the work. As always, though, you will want to make sure you can interpret the results that your calculator gives you!

Learning Targets:

_____ I can state appropriate hypotheses for a significance test about a difference between two means.

_____ I can determine whether the conditions are met for performing a test about a difference between two means.

_____ I can calculate the standardized test statistic and P-value for a test about a difference between two means.

_____ I can perform a significance test about a difference between two means.

_____ I can perform a significance test about a mean difference.

_____ I can determine when it is appropriate to used paired t procedures versus two-sample t procedures.

While You Read: Key Vocabulary and Concepts

conditions for inference about a difference between two means:

two-sample t test for a difference between two means:

conditions for inference about a mean difference:

paired t test for a mean difference:

☑️ **After You Read: Check for Understanding**

Concept 1: Significance test for $\mu_1 - \mu_2$

To test a claim about the difference between two population means or the means of two groups in a randomized experiment, we will follow the same four-step process learned previously.

To conduct a two-sample *t* test for the difference between two means:

1) **STATE the parameter of interest and the hypotheses you would like to test.**

   The null hypothesis usually states that the parameters are equal while the alternative hypothesis is that one mean is greater than, less than, or not equal to the other:
   H_0: $\mu_1 = \mu_2$
   H_a: $\mu_1 > \mu_2$ OR $\mu_1 < \mu_2$ OR $\mu_1 \neq \mu_2$
   State the significance level.

2) **PLAN: Choose the appropriate inference method and check the conditions.**

   Name the test: *t* test for a difference in means, or *t* test for $\mu_1 - \mu_2$.
   Next, check the conditions. Verify that the data come from two independent random samples or two groups in a randomized experiment. If the sampling took place, without replacement, check that each sample size is less than 10% of its respective population size. To ensure that the sampling distribution of $\bar{x}_1 - \bar{x}_2$ is at least approximately Normal, check that the population distributions are Normal OR n_1 and n_2 are both at least 30. If one (or both) of the sample sizes are less than 30 and the population distribution(s) is(are) unknown, then look at a distribution of the sample(s). If there is no strong skewness or outliers then it is safe to proceed.

3) **DO: If conditions are met, calculate a test statistic and *P*-value.**
   $$t = \frac{(\bar{x}_1 - \bar{x}_2) - (\mu_1 - \mu_2)}{\sqrt{\dfrac{s_1^2}{n_1} + \dfrac{s_2^2}{n_2}}}$$
   Find the *P*-value by calculating the probability of observing a *t* statistic at least this extreme in the direction of the alternative hypothesis.
   Use the *t* distribution with df = smaller of $n_1 - 1$ and $n_2 - 1$ OR use the df that is given by technology.

4) **Conclude by interpreting the results of your calculations in the context of the problem.**

   If the *P*-value is smaller than the stated significance level, you have significant evidence to reject the null hypothesis. If it is larger than or equal to the significance level, then you fail to reject the null hypothesis.

Check for Understanding:

_____ *I can calculate the standardized test statistic and P-value for a test about a difference between two means.*

_____ *I can perform a significance test about a difference between two means.*

Do boys have better short-term memory than girls? A random sample of 200 boys and 150 girls was administered a short-term memory test. The average score for boys was 48.9 with standard deviation 12.96. The girls had an average score of 48.4 with standard deviation 11.85. Is there significant evidence at the 5% level to suggest boys have better short-term memory than girls? Note: higher test scores indicate better short-term memory.

Concept 2: Inference for Paired Data

Studies that involve making two observations on the same individual or making an observation on each of two very similar individuals result in paired data. In these types of studies, we are often interested in analyzing the differences in responses within each pair. If the conditions for inference are met, we can use one-sample t procedures to estimate or test a claim about the mean difference μ_{diff}. In this case, we refer to the inference method as a paired t procedure.

Check for Understanding:

_____ *I can perform a significance test about a mean difference.*

A study measured how fast subjects could repeatedly push a button when under the effects of caffeine. Subjects were asked to push a button as many times as possible in two minutes after consuming a typical amount of caffeine. During another test session, they were asked to push the button after taking a placebo. The subjects did not know which treatment they were administered each day and the order of the treatments was randomly assigned. The data, given in presses per two minutes for each treatment follows. Use a paired t procedure to determine whether or not caffeine results in a higher rate of presses, on average, per two-minute period. Use $\alpha = 0.05$.

Subject		1	2	3	4	5	6	7	8	9	10	11
# of Presses	Caffeine	251	284	300	321	240	294	377	345	303	340	408
	Placebo	201	262	283	290	259	291	354	346	283	361	411
Difference	Caffeine – Placebo	50	22	17	31	–19	3	23	–1	20	–21	–3

Chapter Summary: Testing Claims About Means

In this chapter, you learned the inference procedures for carrying out a significance test for a mean as well as a difference in means and paired data. The process for carrying out a significance test for paired data is the same as a significance test for a single mean, except that the single mean comes from a list of differences. When trying to decide between a significance test for two means versus a paired test, determine if the data arose from two independent random samples or two groups in a randomized experiment. If so, then the correct procedure is a t test for the difference in two means. If the data are paired (two measurements on each individual) or if physical pairing occurs then the correct procedure is a paired t test.

How well do you understand each of the learning targets?

Learning Target	Got It!	Almost There	Needs Some Work
I can state and check the random, 10%, and Normal/Large Sample conditions for performing a significance test about a population mean.			
I can calculate the standardized test statistic and P-value for a test about a population mean.			
I can perform a significance test about a population mean.			
I can use a confidence interval to make a conclusion for a two-sided test about a population mean.			
I can state appropriate hypotheses for a significance test about a difference between two means.			
I can determine whether the conditions are met for performing a test about a difference between two means.			
I can calculate the standardized test statistic and P-value for a test about a difference between two means.			
I can perform a significance test about a difference between two means.			
I can perform a significance test about a mean difference.			
I can determine when it is appropriate to use paired t procedures versus two-sample t procedures.			

Chapter 11 Multiple Choice Practice

Directions. Identify the choice that best completes the statement or answers the question. Check your answers and note your performance when you are finished.

1. The average yield of a certain crop is 10.1 bushels per plant. A biologist claims that a new fertilizer will result in a greater yield when applied to the crop. A random sample of 25 of plants given the fertilizer has an average yield of 10.8 bushels and a standard deviation of 2.1 bushels. What are the appropriate null and alternative hypotheses to test the biologist's claim?
    (A) H_0: μ = 10.8 against H_a: μ > 10.8
    (B) H_0: μ = 10.8 against H_a: μ ≠ 10.8
    (C) H_0: μ = 10.1 against H_a: μ > 10.1
    (D) H_0: μ = 10.1 against H_a: μ < 10.1
    (E) H_0: μ = 10.1 against H_a: μ ≠ 10.1

2. The manager of an assembly line manufacturing plant wants to determine if there is convincing evidence the mean number of units that are assembled per worker in a given work day is greater than 50 units. To do so, a random sample of 20 employees from this large company is selected. The distribution of the number of units assembled is skewed right, because some employees are far more productive than others. The manager wants to carry out a t test for one mean. Are the conditions for inference met?
    (A)   No, the random condition is the only condition not met.
    (B)   No, the 10% condition is the only condition not met.
    (C)   No, the Normal/Large Sample condition is the only condition not met.
    (D)   No, more than one condition for inference is not met.
    (E)   Yes, the conditions for inference are met.

3. At a toy store, a package containing a rubber lizard that is 12 inches long claims that when left to soak in water the lizard will grow 600%. This means, when full grown, the lizard will be 6 feet long! To investigate this claim, a random sample of 30 such lizards are selected. The mean length of the fully-grown lizards, however, is only 40 inches with a standard deviation of 6 inches. We want to know if these data provide convincing evidence that the true mean length for all fully-grown lizards is less than 72 inches (6 feet). What is the test statistic of this significance test?
    (A) $t = \dfrac{40 - 72}{\dfrac{6}{\sqrt{30}}}$ (B) $t = \dfrac{72 - 40}{\dfrac{6}{\sqrt{30}}}$ (C) $t = \dfrac{40 - 6}{\dfrac{6(1 - 6)}{\sqrt{30}}}$

    (D) $t = \dfrac{40 - 6}{\dfrac{6(6 - 1)}{\sqrt{30}}}$ (E) $t = \dfrac{72 - 40}{\dfrac{6(1 - 6)}{\sqrt{30}}}$

4. Based upon a random sample of 50 adults, a researcher estimates that the true mean amount of time that an individual can focus on a single task is 20 minutes with a standard deviation of 8 minutes. A 95% confidence interval for the mean amount of time that adults can focus on a single task is 17.73 minutes to 22.27 minutes. Which of the following hypotheses would be rejected at the significance level α = 0.05?
    (A) H_0: μ = 19 versus H_a: μ ≠ 19
    (B) H_0: μ = 20 versus H_a: μ ≠ 20
    (C) H_0: μ = 21 versus H_a: μ ≠ 21
    (D) H_0: μ = 22 versus H_a: μ ≠ 22
    (E) H_0: μ = 23 versus H_a: μ ≠ 23

5. The mean weight of a random sample of 35 athletes is found to be 165 pounds with a standard deviation of 20 pounds. It is believed that a mean weight of 160 pounds would be normal for this group. To see if there is evidence that the mean weight of the population of all athletes of this type is significantly higher than 160 pounds, the hypotheses H_0: $\mu = 160$ vs. H_a: $\mu > 160$ are tested. You obtain a P-value of 0.0742. Which of the following is true?
    (A) At the 5% significance level, you have proved that H_0 is true.
    (B) You have failed to obtain sufficient evidence against H_0.
    (C) At the 5% significance level, you have failed to prove that H_0 is true, and a larger sample size is needed to do so.
    (D) Only 7.42% of the athletes weigh less than 160 pounds.
    (E) None of the above. A significance test is inappropriate in this setting.

6. Some researchers have conjectured that stem-pitting disease in peach tree seedlings might be controlled with weed and soil treatment. An experiment was conducted to compare peach tree seedling growth with soil and weeds treated with one of two herbicides. In a field containing 20 seedlings, 10 were randomly selected from throughout the field and assigned to receive Herbicide A. The remaining 10 seedlings were to receive Herbicide B. Soil and weeds for each seedling were treated with the appropriate herbicide, and at the end of the study period, the height (in centimeters) was recorded for each seedling. A box plot of each data set showed no indication of non-Normality. The following results were obtained:

	$\bar{x}$ (cm)	s_x (cm)
Herbicide A	94.5	10
Herbicide B	109.1	9

Suppose we wished to determine if there is a significant difference in mean height for the seedlings treated with the different herbicides. Based on our data, which of the following is the value of test statistic?
    (A) 14.60
    (B) 7.80
    (C) 3.43
    (D) 2.54
    (E) 1.14

7. A researcher wishes to compare the effect of two stepping heights (low and high) on heart rate in a step-aerobics workout. The researcher constructs a 98% confidence interval for the difference in mean heart rate between those who did the high and those who did the low stepping heights. The researcher decides to test the hypotheses H_0: $\mu_1 - \mu_2 = 0$ vs. H_a: $\mu_1 - \mu_2 < 0$ at the $\alpha = 0.05$ level and produces a P-value of 0.0475. Which of the following is a correct interpretation of this result?
    (A) The probability that there is a difference is 0.0475.
    (B) The probability that this test resulted in a Type II error is 0.0475.
    (C) If this test were repeated many times, we would make a Type I error 4.75% of the time.
    (D) If the null hypothesis is true, the probability of getting a difference in sample means as far or farther from 0 as the difference in our samples is 0.0475.
    (E) If the null hypothesis is false, the probability of getting a difference in sample means as far or farther from 0 as the difference in our samples is 0.0475.

8. A medical researcher wishes to investigate the effectiveness of exercise versus diet in losing weight. Two groups of 25 overweight adult subjects are used, with a subject in each group matched to a similar subject in the other group on the basis of a number of physiological variables. One member of each pair is placed on a regular program of vigorous exercise but with no restriction on diet, and the other is placed on a strict diet but with no requirement to exercise. The weight losses after 20 weeks are determined for each subject, and the difference between each pairs of subjects (weight loss of subject in exercise group – weight loss of matched subject in diet group) is computed. The mean of these differences in weight loss is found to be 2 lb with standard deviation $s_x = 4$ lb. Is this convincing evidence of a difference in mean weight loss for the two methods? To answer this question, you should use

   (A) one-proportion z test.
   (B) one-sample z interval for μ_{diff} .
   (C) one-proportion z interval.
   (D) one-sample t test for μ_{diff} .
   (E) none of the above.

9. Refer to the scenario of problem 8. What are the appropriate hypotheses?
   (A) $H_0: \mu_{diff} = 0, H_a: \mu_{diff} > 0$
   (B) $H_0: \mu_{diff} = 0, H_a: \mu_{diff} \neq 0$
   (C) $H_0: \mu_{diff} = 0, H_a: \mu_{diff} < 0$
   (D) $H_0: \mu_1 - \mu_2 = 0, H_a: \mu_1 - \mu_2 > 0$
   (E) $H_0: \mu_1 - \mu_2 = 0, H_a: \mu_1 - \mu_2 \neq 0$

10. Refer to the scenario of problem 8. What are the values of the test statistic and P-value of this test?
   (A) $t = 2.50$, P-value $= 0.0098$
   (B) $t = 2.50$, P-value $= 0.0197$
   (C) $t = 2.50$, P-value $= 0.0394$
   (D) $z = 2.50$, P-value $= 0.0062$
   (E) $z = 2.50$, P-value $= 0.0124$

Check your answers below. If you got a question wrong, check to see if you made a simple mistake or if you need to study that concept more. After you check your work, identify the concepts you feel very confident about and note what you will do to learn the concepts in need of more study.

#	Answer	Concept	Right	Wrong	Simple Mistake?	Need to Study More
1	C	Writing Hypotheses				
2	C	Checking Conditions				
3	A	Determine the Correct Test Statistic				
4	E	Two-sided Test and Confidence Intervals				
5	B	Making a Conclusion				
6	C	Significance Test for Difference in Means				
7	D	Interpret P-value				
8	D	Choosing the Appropriate Test				
9	B	Writing Hypotheses				
10	B	Determine the Correct Test Statistic				

FRAPPY! Free Response AP® Problem, Yay!

The following problem is modeled after actual Advanced Placement Statistics free response questions. Your task is to generate a complete, concise response in 15 minutes. After you generate your response, read over the solution and scoring guide. Score your response and note what, if anything, you would do differently to increase your own score.

Researchers are interested in whether or not women who are part of a prenatal care program give birth to babies with a higher average birth weight than those who do not take part in the program. A random sample of hospital records indicates that the average birth weight for 75 babies born to mothers enrolled in a prenatal care program was 3100 g with standard deviation 420 g. A separate random sample of hospital records indicates that the average birth weight for 75 babies born to women who did not take part in a prenatal care program was 2750 g with standard deviation 425 g. Do these data provide convincing evidence that mothers who participate in a prenatal care program have babies with a higher average birth weight than those who don't? Use $\alpha = 0.05$.

FRAPPY! Scoring Rubric

Use the following rubric to score your response. Each part receives a score of "Essentially Correct," "Partially Correct," or "Incorrect." When you have scored your response, reflect on your understanding of the concepts addressed in this problem. If necessary, note what you would do differently on future questions like this to increase your score.

Intent of the Question

The goal of this question is to determine your ability to conduct a significance test for a single proportion the difference between two means.

Solution

The solution should contain 4 parts:

- **Hypotheses**: Must be stated correctly: H_0: $\mu_Y - \mu_N = 0$ and H_a: $\mu_Y - \mu_N > 0$ where μ_Y = true mean birth weight of babies born to mothers enrolled in a prenatal care program and μ_N = true mean birth weight of babies born to mothers who were not enrolled in a prenatal care program.

- **Name of Test and Conditions**: The test must be identified by name or formula as a two-sample t test for a difference in population means. Two random samples were obtained. Both sample sizes are greater than 30. Both samples are less than 10% of their respective population sizes because this is a large hospital.

- **Mechanics**: $t = 5.07$ and P-value ≈ 0 with 147.97 degrees of freedom.

- **Conclusion**: Because the P-value is smaller than any reasonable significance level we reject the null in favor of the alternative hypothesis. There is significant evidence to suggest the mean birth weight of babies born to mothers who participate in a prenatal care program is higher than the weight of those born to mothers who do not participate.

Scoring

Each element scored as essentially correct (E), partially correct (P), or incorrect (I).

Hypotheses and Name is essentially correct if the hypotheses are written correctly and the response correctly identifies the test by name or formula. This part is partially correct if the test isn't identified or if the hypotheses are written incorrectly. Incorrect otherwise.

Conditions and Mechanics is essentially correct if the response correctly does 4 of the 5 following things: (1) checks the Normal condition, (2) checks the 10% condition, (3) checks the large counts condition, (4) correct test statistic, (5) correct P-value. This part is partially correct if 3 or more of those 3 things are done correctly. Incorrect otherwise.

Conclusion is essentially correct if the response correctly rejects the null hypothesis because the P-value is less than the significance level of 0.05 and provides an interpretation in context. This part is partially correct if the response fails to justify the decision by comparing the P-value to a significance level OR if the conclusion lacks an interpretation in context. Incorrect otherwise.

Scoring

4   Complete Response

All three parts essentially correct

3   Substantial Response

Two parts essentially correct and one part partially correct

2   Developing Response

Two parts essentially correct and no parts partially correct

One part essentially correct and one or two parts partially correct

Three parts partially correct

1   Minimal Response

One part essentially correct and no parts partially correct

No parts essentially correct and two parts partially correct

My Score:
What I did well:
What I could improve:
What I should remember if I see a problem like this on the AP Exam:

Chapter 11 Formula Sheet

Create a one-page summary of important concepts and formulas found in this chapter. This will serve as a valuable resource as you prepare for the AP Exam.

Chapter 11 Crossword Puzzle
TESTING CLAIMS ABOUT MEANS

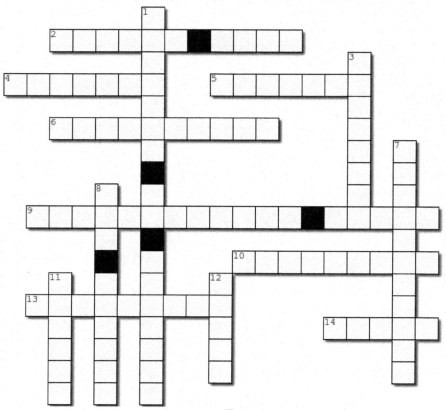

Across

2. _____ result from recording two values of the same quantitative variable for each individual or pair of similar individuals.

4. If the P-value is _____ than the significance level, we fail to reject the null hypothesis.

5. To draw a conclusion about a test compare the _____ to the significance level.

6. In a significance test for a _____ in means, the data may come from two groups in a randomized experiment.

9. If the P-value is less than the _____ _____ then reject the null hypothesis.

10. A 95% confidence interval about a mean will give consistent results as a _____ test.

13. When stating the hypotheses, always define the _____ of interest.

14. We can increase the _____ of a test by increasing the sample size.

Down

1. In a one-sample t test, the _____ _____ _____ = n - 1.

3. We can ___ the probability of type II error by increasing the sample size.

7. When performing inference for a difference in means, if two samples are selected they must be _____.

8. For paired data, use _____ _____ t procedures.

11. When performing inference about one or two samples, the sample(s) must be selected at _____.

12. If the sample size(s) are small, look at a _____ of the sample data. There should be no strong skewness or outliers.

Chapter 12: Inference for Distributions and Relationships

"By a small sample, we may judge the whole piece." Miguel de Cervantes (Don Quixote)

CHAPTER OVERVIEW

So far, our study of inference has focused on how to estimate and test claims about single means and proportions as well as about differences between means and proportions for quantitative variables.

In the first two sections of this chapter, we will shift our focus to inference about distributions of and relationships between categorical variables. You will learn how to perform three different significance tests for distributions of categorical data, allowing you to determine (1) whether or not a sample distribution differs significantly from a hypothesized distribution, (2) whether or not the distribution of a categorical variable differs between multiple populations, or (3) whether or not an association exists between two categorical variables. It is easy to confuse the three tests, so be sure to study the differences between them so you know when to use each one!

In the third section, you will learn how to determine whether or not there is convincing evidence of a relationship between two quantitative variables. You will learn how to construct and interpret a confidence interval for the slope as well as how to perform a significance test for the slope. This chapter will refresh your memory on some of the key concepts of regression while introducing you to some new inference techniques. As you wrap up your studies and begin your preparations for the AP exam, look back at the learning targets to determine what topics are in need of a little extra review!

Sections in this Chapter
Section 12.1: Chi-Square Tests for Goodness-of-Fit
Section 12.2: Inference for Two-Way Tables
Section 12.3: Inference for Slope

PLAN YOUR LEARNING

Use the following *suggested* guide to help plan your reading and assignments in "The Practice of Statistics, Updated 6th Edition." Put a check mark in the last column when you are done. Your teacher may schedule a different pacing or assign different problems. Be sure to follow his or her instructions!

Read	Do	Done!
Section 12.1: p. 760-769	1, 3, 5, 7	
Section 12.1: p. 770-773	9, 13, MC 19-22	
Section 12.2: p. 778-792	27, 29, 31, 33, 35	
Section 12.2: p. 793-804	41, 43, 47, 49, 51, MC 55-60	
Section 12.3: p. 812-820	65, 67, 69	
Section 12.3: p. 821-826	71, 73, 75	
Section 12.3: p. 827-830	79, 83, MC 87-92	
Chapter Summary	Review Exercises FRAPPY!	

Section 12.1: Chi-Square Tests for Goodness-of-Fit

Before You Read: Section Summary

In this section, you will be introduced to the chi-square distributions and the chi-square test statistic. The chi-square statistic provides us with a way to measure the difference between an observed and a hypothesized distribution of categorical data. When certain conditions are satisfied, we can model the sampling distribution of this statistic with a chi-square distribution and calculate P-values. We can use the chi-square goodness-of-fit test to determine whether or not a significant difference between an observed and hypothesized distribution of a categorical variable exists. Finally, we can use a follow-up analysis to determine which categories contributed the most to the difference.

Learning Targets:

_____ I can state appropriate hypotheses and compute the expected counts and chi-square test statistic for a chi-square test for goodness of fit.

_____ I can state and check the Random, 10%, and Large Counts conditions for performing a chi-square test for goodness of fit.

_____ I can calculate the degrees of freedom and P-value for a chi-square test for goodness of fit.

_____ I can perform a chi-square test for goodness of fit.

_____ I can conduct a follow-up analysis when the results of a chi-square test are statistically significant.

While You Read: Key Vocabulary and Concepts

expected count:
chi-square statistic:
chi-square distribution:
conditions for performing a chi-square test for goodness of fit:
chi-square test for goodness-of-fit:

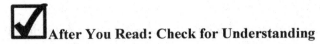
After You Read: Check for Understanding

Concept 1: The Chi-Square Test Statistic and Distributions

When testing a claim about a distribution of categorical data, we are interested in knowing how the observed counts from the sample compare to the counts that would be expected if the null hypothesis were true. Like we did with means and proportions, we will standardize the difference between observed and expected values using a test statistic. To determine the chi-square test statistic for a table of observed counts, use the following formula:

$$\chi^2 = \sum \frac{(\text{observed count} - \text{expected count})^2}{\text{expected count}}$$

This test statistic can then be used with the appropriate chi-square distribution to determine a *P*-value. If the observed values are far from the expected values, our test statistic will be large, giving evidence against the null hypothesis. The chi-square distributions are a family of right-skewed distributions that are defined by degrees of freedom based on the number of categories the variable takes on. We can use a table or technology to find a *P*-value for a particular χ^2 value.

Check for Understanding:

_____ *I can state appropriate hypotheses and compute the expected counts and chi-square test statistic for a chi-square test for goodness of fit.*

After playing a dice game with a friend, you suspect the 6-sided die may not be fair. That is, you suspect some numbers may be rolled more often than you would expect. To test your suspicion, you roll the die 300 times and record the results.

Value:	1	2	3	4	5	6
Frequency:	42	55	38	57	64	44

Use these observed counts to determine the chi-square test statistic for this example.

Concept 2: Chi-Square Test for Goodness-of-Fit

To perform a chi-square test for goodness-of-fit for a claim about a population distribution of categorical data, we will follow the same basic process as we did for means and proportions. That is, to test a claim about the population distribution of a categorical variable:

1) **STATE the hypotheses you would like to test.**

When testing a claim about a distribution of a categorical variable, we start by defining hypotheses. The null hypothesis assumes that the hypothesized distribution is correct as stated while the alternative hypothesis is that the specified distribution is different:

H_0: The specified distribution of the categorical variable is correct.
H_a: The specified distribution of the categorical variable is not correct.

State a significance level.

2) **PLAN: Choose the appropriate inference method and check the conditions.**

Name: Chi-Square Test for Goodness of Fit
Conditions: The data must come from a random sample from the population. When sampling without replacement, check that the sample size is less than 10% of the size of the population. All expected counts must be at least 5.

3) **DO: If conditions are met, calculate a test statistic and *P*-value.**

Compute the chi-square test statistic $\chi^2 = \sum \dfrac{(\text{observed count-expected count})^2}{\text{expected count}}$

Find the *P*-value by using a chi-square distribution with $k - 1$ degrees of freedom (where k is the number of categories).

4) **CONCLUDE by interpreting the results of your calculations in the context of the problem.**

If the *P*-value is smaller than the stated significance level, you can conclude that you have significant evidence to reject the null hypothesis. If the *P*-value is larger than or equal to the significance level, then you fail to reject the null hypothesis.

If you find evidence to reject the null hypothesis, you should perform a follow up analysis to determine the components that contributed the most to the chi-square statistic. That is, determine which observed categories differed the most from the expected values.

Check for Understanding:

_____ *I can state and check the Random, 10%, and Large Counts conditions for performing a chi-square test for goodness of fit.*

_____ *I can calculate the degrees of freedom and P-value for a chi-square test for goodness of fit.*

_____ *I can perform a chi-square test for goodness of fit.*

_____ *I can conduct a follow-up analysis when the results of a chi-square test are statistically significant.*

Use the observed counts from the previous Check for Understanding to determine whether or not you have convincing evidence that the die is not fair. If you have significant evidence, perform a follow-up analysis. Recall, to test your suspicion, you rolled the die 300 times. Use $\alpha = 0.05$.

Value:	1	2	3	4	5	6
Frequency:	42	55	38	57	64	44

Section 11.2: Inference for Two-Way Tables

Before You Read: Section Summary

Chi-square goodness-of-fit tests allow us to compare the distribution of one categorical variable to a hypothesized distribution. However, sometimes we are interested in comparing the distribution of a categorical variable across several populations or treatments. Chi-square tests for homogeneity allow us to do this. In this section you will learn how to conduct the chi-square test for homogeneity and how to perform a follow-up analysis, just like you did for the goodness-of-fit test. Also, you will learn how to conduct a chi-square test for association/independence to determine whether or not there is convincing evidence that two categorical variables are related. While this test is the same as the test for homogeneity in its mechanics, the hypotheses are different. Be sure to note the distinction!

Learning Targets:

_____ I can state appropriate hypotheses and compute the expected counts and chi-square statistic for a chi-square test based on data in a two-way table.

_____ I can state and check the Random, 10%, and Large Counts conditions for a chi-square test based on data in a two-way table.

_____ I can calculate the degrees of freedom and *P*-value for a chi-square test based on data in a two-way table.

_____ I can perform a chi-square test for homogeneity.

_____ I can perform a chi-square test for independence.

_____ I can choose the appropriate chi-square test in a given setting.

While You Read: Key Vocabulary and Concepts

expected counts:
conditions for a chi-square test based on data in a two-way table:
chi-square test for homogeneity:
chi-square test for independence:

After You Read: Check for Understanding

Concept 1: Expected Counts and the Chi-Square Statistic

While a one-way table can summarize data for a single categorical variable, a two-way table can be used to summarize data on the relationship between two categorical variables. When these data are produced using independent random samples from several populations or from a randomized comparative experiment, we can test whether or not the actual distribution of the categorical variable is the same for each population or treatment. If the data are produced using a single random sample from a population and classified according to two categorical variables, we can test whether or not there is a relationship between those variables. In each case, we must compare the observed counts to expected counts.

To determine an expected count, we use the general formula

$$\text{expected count} = \frac{\text{row total} \cdot \text{column total}}{\text{table total}}.$$

Then, just like we did with the goodness-of-fit test, we calculate the chi-square statistic using

$$\chi^2 = \sum \frac{(\text{observed count} - \text{expected count})^2}{\text{expected count}}.$$

Concept 2: Chi-Square Test for Homogeneity

To determine whether or not a distribution of a categorical variable differs for two or more populations or treatments, we use a chi-square test for homogeneity. This test is similar to the test for goodness-of-fit in the sense that we compare observed counts to expected counts using a chi-square test statistic. However, the hypotheses and degrees of freedom differ slightly.

1) **STATE the hypotheses you would like to test.**
   The null hypothesis says that the variable has the same distribution for all of the populations or treatments. The alternative hypothesis is that the distribution of that variable is not the same for all of the populations or treatments:
   H_0: There is no difference in the distribution of a categorical variable for several
      populations or treatments.
   H_a: There is a difference in the distribution of a categorical variable for several
      populations or treatments.

2) **PLAN: Choose the appropriate inference method and check the conditions.**
   Name: Chi-Square Test for Homogeneity.
   Conditions: The data must come from independent random samples or from groups in a randomized experiment. When sampling without replacement, check that the sample sizes are less than 10% of their corresponding population sizes. All expected counts must be at least 5.

3) **DO: If conditions are met, calculate a test statistic and *P*-value.**
   Compute the chi-square test statistic and find the *P*-value by using a chi-square distribution with (number of rows – 1)(number of columns – 1) degrees of freedom.

4) CONCLUDE by interpreting the results of your calculations in the context of the problem.
If the P-value < the stated significance level, you can conclude that you have significant evidence to reject the null hypothesis. If the P-value > the significance level, then you fail to reject the null hypothesis.

If you find sufficient evidence to reject the null hypothesis, you should perform a follow up analysis to determine the components that contributed the most to the chi-square statistic. That is, determine which observed categories differed the most from the expected values.

Check for Understanding:

_____ *I can state appropriate hypotheses and compute the expected counts and chi-square statistic for a chi-square test based on data in a two-way table.*

_____ *I can calculate the degrees of freedom and P-value for a chi-square test based on data in a two-way table.*

_____ *I can perform a chi-square test for homogeneity.*

A recent study tracked the television viewing habits of 100 randomly selected first-grade boys and 200 randomly selected first-grade girls. Each child was asked to identify which of 3 shows is their favorite TV show. The following table summarizes the results:

	Mickey Mouse	Doc McStuffins	Captain Underpants
Boys	20	30	50
Girls	70	80	50

Do these data provide convincing evidence that television preferences differ significantly for boys and girls? Use $\alpha = 0.01$.

Concept 3: Chi-Square Test for Independence

To determine whether or not two categorical variables are related in a population, we can use a chi-square test for independence. The mechanics of this test are almost the same as those for the test for homogeneity. The only difference is that the data come from a single random sample from the population of interest. The hypotheses are defined in terms of an association between the two categorical variables.

H_0: There is no association between two categorical variables in the population of interest.

H_a: There is an association between two categorical variables in the population of interest.

Check for Understanding:

_____ *I can perform a chi-square test for independence.*

A recent study looked into the relationship between political views and opinions about nuclear energy. A survey administered to 100 randomly selected adults asked their political leanings as well as their approval of nuclear energy. The results are below:

	Liberal	Conservative	Independent
Approve	10	15	20
Disapprove	9	2	16
No Opinion	8	2	18

Do these data provide convincing evidence that political leanings and views on nuclear energy are associated in the larger population of adults from which the sample was selected? Use $\alpha = 0.05$.

Section 12.1: Inference for Regression

Before You Read: Section Summary

When you construct a least-squares regression line based on sample data, your line is an approximation of the population (true) regression line. If you took a different sample and constructed a least-squares regression line, it is very likely you would end up with a slightly different line. In this section, you will learn about the sampling distribution of the sample slope b so that you can perform inference about the true slope of the regression line. Like you did with other inference procedures, you will start by learning how to check the conditions for performing inference. Then you will learn how to construct and interpret a confidence interval for the true slope, and how to perform a significance test about the true slope. You will also be re-introduced to computer output for a linear regression analysis. It is important that you be able to interpret this output as a number of AP exam questions involve standard computer output for regression.

Learning Targets:

_____ I can check the conditions for performing inference about the slope β of the population (true) regression line.

_____ I can interpret the values of a, b, s, and SE_b in context, and determine these values from computer output.

_____ I can construct and interpret a confidence interval for the slope β of the population (true) regression line.

_____ I can perform a significance test about the slope β of the population (true) regression line.

While You Read: Key Vocabulary and Concepts

sample regression line:
population (true) regression line:
sampling distribution of a slope:
conditions for regression inference:
t interval for the slope:
t test for the slope:

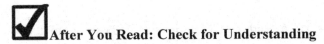**After You Read: Check for Understanding**

Concept 1: The Sampling Distribution of b

If the conditions for performing inference are met, we can use the slope b of the sample regression line $\hat{y} = a + bx$ to estimate or test a claim about the slope β of the population (true) regression line $\mu_y = \alpha + \beta x$. The required conditions are:

- **Linear**: There is a true linear relationship between the variables given by $\mu_y = \alpha + \beta x$.
  Is a scatterplot of the sample data linear?

- **Independent**: Individual observations are independent.
  If sampling without replacement, is the sample size less than 10% of the population?

- **Normal**: For each x-value, the response y follows a Normal distribution.
  Does a graph of the residuals exhibit strong skewness or other signs of non-Normality?

- **Equal SD**: At each x-value, the standard deviation σ of the responses y is the same.
  Is the amount of scatter above and below 0 on the residual plot roughly the same from the smallest to largest x-values?

- **Random**: The data are produced by a random sample or randomized experiment.

If we take repeated samples of the same size n from a population with a true regression line $\mu_y = \alpha + \beta x$ and determine the sample regression line $\hat{y} = a + bx$, the sampling distribution of the slope b will have the following characteristics:

1) The shape of the sampling distribution will be approximately Normal.

2) The mean of the sampling distribution is $\mu_b = \beta$.

3) The standard deviation of the sampling distribution of b is $\sigma_b = \dfrac{\sigma}{\sigma_x \sqrt{n}}$

   where σ is the standard deviation of the residuals and σ_x is the standard deviation of the explanatory variable.

To perform inference about the slope, we note that the sampling distribution of the standardized slope values has a t distribution with $n - 2$ degrees of freedom.

Also, since we don't know σ for the true regression line, we estimate the variability of the sampling distribution of b with the *standard error of the slope*

$$SE_b = \frac{s}{s_x \sqrt{n-1}}$$

Concept 2: Confidence Intervals for β

When we construct a least-squares regression line $\hat{y} = a + bx$ and the conditions noted above are met, b is our estimate of the true slope β. A level C confidence interval for the true slope has the form $b \pm t^*SE_b$ where t^* is the critical value for the t distribution with $n - 2$ degrees of freedom that has area C between $-t^*$ and t^*.

Check for Understanding:

_____ *I can construct and interpret a confidence interval for the slope β of the population (true) regression line.*

A study by *Consumer Reports* rated 10 randomly selected cereals on a 100-point scale (higher numbers are better) and recorded the number of grams of sugar in each serving. The data from the study are below:

Sugar	6.0	8.0	5.0	0.0	8.0	10.0	14.0	8.0	6.0	5.0
Rating	68.40	33.98	59.43	93.70	34.38	29.51	33.17	37.04	49.12	53.31

The LSRL for this data is $\hat{r} = 82.62 - 4.77(s)$ where r = rating and s = sugar.

Construct and interpret a 95% confidence interval for the true slope of the regression line. Assume the conditions for performing inference are met.

Concept 3: Significance Test for β

When the conditions for inference are met, not only can we estimate the true slope from b, we can also test whether or not a specified value for β is plausible. The process for testing a claim about a population (true) slope follows the same format used for other significance tests.

1) **STATE the parameter of interest and the hypotheses you would like to test.**

   The null hypothesis states that the population (true) slope is equal to a particular value (usually zero) while the alternative hypothesis is that the population (true) slope is greater than, less than, or not equal to that value:

   $H_0: \beta = 0$

   $H_a: \beta > 0$ OR $\beta < 0$ OR $\beta \neq 0$

   Define the parameter and state a significance level.

2) **PLAN: Choose the appropriate inference method and check the conditions.**

   Check the linear, independent, Normal, equal SD, and random conditions.

3) **DO: If conditions are met, calculate a test statistic and *P*-value.**

   Compute the t test statistic: $t = \dfrac{b - \text{hypothesized slope}}{SE_b}$

   Find the *P*-value by calculating the probability of observing a t statistic at least this extreme in the direction of the alternative hypothesis in a t distribution with $n - 2$ degrees of freedom.

4) **CONCLUDE by interpreting the results of your calculations in the context of the problem.**

   If the *P*-value is smaller than the stated significance level, you can conclude that you have sufficient evidence to reject the null hypothesis. If the *P*-value is larger than the significance level, then you fail to reject the null hypothesis.

Generally, we test whether or not the true slope is zero, which would indicate no linear relationship between x and y. If you want to test a null hypothesis other than zero, get the slope and standard error from computer output and use the formula to calculate the t statistic.

Like other inference situations, a significance test can tell us whether or not a claim about the parameter is plausible, while using a confidence interval can give us additional information about its true value.

Check for Understanding:

_____ *I can interpret the values of a, b, s, and SE$_b$ in context, and determine these values from computer output.*

_____ *I can perform a significance test about the slope β of the population (true) regression line.*

The study in the previous Check for Understanding was expanded to include a total of 77 randomly selected cereals. The scatterplot, residual plot, and computer output of the regression analysis are given here. A dotplot of the residuals (not shown here) shows no strong skewness or outliers.

```
Predictor        Coef      StDev      T            P
Constant         59.284    1.948      30.43        0.000
Sugar            -2.4008   0.2373     -10.12       0.000

s = 9.196        R-Sq = 57.7%        R-Sq(adj) = 57.1%
```

1) Use this output to determine the LSRL for the sample data.

2) Interpret the slope in the context of the situation.

3) Is there convincing evidence that the slope of the true regression line is less than zero? Use $\alpha = 0.01$.

Chapter Summary: Inference for Distributions of Categorical Data

In this chapter, you learned the inference procedures for distributions of categorical data. A chi-square goodness-of-fit test can be used to determine whether or not an observed distribution of a categorical variable differs from a hypothesized distribution. When examining the distribution of a single categorical variable in multiple populations or treatments, a test for homogeneity can be used to determine whether the distributions differ. Finally, we can use a test for independence to determine whether or not two categorical variables are related in a population. In each test, we use the chi-square test statistic to measure how much the observed counts differ from the expected counts. When the test provides significant evidence against the null hypothesis, we can use a follow-up analysis to determine which component(s) contributed the most to the test statistic.

In this chapter, you also learned how to apply your knowledge of inference to linear relationships. When you find a least-squares regression line for a set of sample data, you are constructing a model that approximates the true relationship between x and y. By considering the sampling distribution of b, you can construct a confidence interval for the slope of the true regression line as well as test claims about the slope.

How well do you understand each of the learning targets?

Learning Target	Got It!	Almost There	Needs Some Work
I can state appropriate hypotheses and compute the expected counts and chi-square test statistic for a chi-square test for goodness of fit.			
I can state and check the Random, 10%, and Large Counts conditions for performing a chi-square test for goodness of fit.			
I can calculate the degrees of freedom and P-value for a chi-square test for goodness of fit.			
I can perform a chi-square test for goodness of fit.			
I can conduct a follow-up analysis when the results of a chi-square test are statistically significant.			
I can 2tate appropriate hypotheses and compute the expected counts and chi-square test statistic for a chi-square test based on data in a two-way table.			
I can state and check the Random, 10%, and Large Counts conditions for a chi-square test based on data in a two-way table.			
I can calculate the degrees of freedom and P-value for a chi-square test for goodness of fit.			
I can perform a chi-square test for homogeneity.			
I can perform a chi-square test for independence.			
I can choose the appropriate chi-square test in a given setting.			
I can check the conditions for performing inference about the slope β of the population (true) regression line.			
I can interpret the values of a, b, s, and SE_b in context, and determine these values from computer output.			
I can construct and interpret a confidence interval for the slope β of the population (true) regression line.			
I can perform a significance test about the slope β of the population (true) regression line.			

Chapter 12 Multiple Choice Practice

Directions. Identify the choice that best completes the statement or answers the question. Check your answers and note your performance when you are finished.

1. To test the effectiveness of your calculator's random number generator, you randomly select 1000 numbers from a standard Normal distribution. You classify these 1000 numbers according to whether their values are at most –2, between –2 and 0, between 0 and 2, or at least 2. The results are given in the following table. The expected counts, based on the empirical rule, are given as well.

	At most -2	Between –2 and 0	Between 0 and 2	At least 2
Observed Count	18	492	468	22
Expected Count	25	475	475	25

To test to see if the distribution of observed counts differs significantly from the distribution of expected counts, we can use a χ^2 goodness of fit test. For this test, the test statistic has approximately a χ^2 distribution. How many degrees of freedom does this distribution have?
(A) 3
(B) 4
(C) 7
(D) 999
(E) 1000

2. Refer to problem 1. Which of the following is the component of the χ^2 statistic corresponding to the category "at most −2"?
(A) (43)(1000)/2000
(B) (43)(25)/1000
(C) 18/1000
(D) $(18 - 25)^2/25$
(E) $(18 - 25)^2/18$

3. Anne wants to know if males and females prefer different brands of frozen pizzas. She bakes four dozen pizzas made by each of four manufacturers, which she labels brands A, B, C, and D. She then selects a simple random sample of 48 students, records their gender, gives them one slice of each brand and asks which brand they like best. Here are her results:

	A	B	C	D	Total
Males	2	4	6	7	19
Females	11	5	6	7	29
Total	13	9	12	14	48

The appropriate null hypothesis for Anne's question in this problem is:
(A) There is an association between gender and preferred frozen pizza.
(B) Gender and pizza preference are independent.
(C) The distribution of preferred pizza for each gender is different.
(D) The observed count in each cell is equal to the expected count.
(E) The male and female subjects in this experiment have the same distribution of pizza brand preference.

4. Refer to problem 3. Are the conditions for a chi-square test of association/independence met?
   (A) Yes, because the sample size is greater than 30.
   (B) Yes, because a simple random sample was selected.
   (C) No, because the distribution for each gender is different.
   (D) No, because not all observed counts are greater than 5.
   (E) No, because 25% of expected counts are less than 5.

5. The table provided shows the individual components of the chi-square test of association/independence for a study done on amount of time spent at a computer and whether or not a person wears glasses.

| | | Wear Glasses? | |
		Yes	No
Amount of Screen time	**Above Average**	8.7	6.3
	Average	0.5	0.3
	Below Average	3.1	2.2

Which of the following statements is supported by the information in this table?
   (A) Above-average screen time individuals wore glasses much less often than expected.
   (B) Average screen time individuals wore glasses much less often than expected.
   (C) Below-average screen time individuals wore glasses about as often as expected.
   (D) You can't determine this without the original observed counts.
   (E) The chi-square statistic for this test is about 3.5.

6. A random sample of 200 Canadian students were asked about their hand dominance and whether they suffer from allergies. Here are the results:

| | | Allergies? | |
		Yes	No
Hand Dominance	**Ambidextrous**	12	7
	Left-handed	11	9
	Right-handed	95	66

What can you conclude about the relationship between hand dominance and allergies?
   (A) Using a test for association/independence, there is not convincing evidence ($P = 0.13$) to conclude that there is a relationship between hand dominance and allergies.
   (B) Using a test for association/independence, there is convincing evidence ($P = 0.87$) to conclude that there is a relationship between hand dominance and allergies.
   (C) Using a test for association/independence, there is not convincing evidence ($P = 0.87$) to conclude that there is a relationship between hand dominance and allergies.
   (D) Using a test for association/independence, there is not convincing evidence ($P = 0.13$) to conclude that there is a relationship between hand dominance and allergies.
   (E) We cannot perform a chi-square test on these data.

7. Can we predict annual household electricity costs in a specific region from the number of rooms in the house? Below is a scatterplot of annual electricity costs (in dollars) versus number of rooms for 30 randomly-selected houses in Michigan, along with computer output for linear regression of electricity costs on number of rooms.

Scatterplot of annual electricity cost vs. number of rooms

```
Predictor    Coef   SE Coef     T      P
Constant    406.9    164.8    2.47   0.020
Rooms       58.45    24.77    2.36   0.026

S = 246.735 R-Sq = 16.6%  R-Sq(adj) = 13.6%
```

Assume the conditions for inference have been met. If we test the hypotheses $H_0: \beta = 0$ vs. $H_a: \beta > 0$ at the $\alpha = 0.05$ level. Which of the following is the appropriate conclusion?

(A) Because the P-value of 0.020 is less than α, we reject H_0. There is convincing evidence of a linear relationship between annual electricity costs and number of rooms in the population of Michigan homes.

(B) Because the P-value of 0.020 is greater than α we fail to reject H_0. We do not have enough evidence to conclude that there is a linear relationship between annual electricity costs and number of rooms in the population of Michigan homes.

(C) Because the P-value of 0.026 is greater than α, we accept H_0. We have convincing evidence that there is not a linear relationship between annual electricity costs and number of rooms in the population of Michigan homes.

(D) Because the P-value of 0.026 is less than α, we accept H_0. We have convincing evidence that there is not a linear relationship between annual electricity costs and number of rooms in the population of Michigan homes.

(E) Because the P-value of 0.026 is less than α, we reject H_0. We have convincing evidence of a linear relationship between annual electricity costs and number of rooms in the population of Michigan homes.

8. Are high school students who like their English class more likely to enjoy their history class as well? Here is a residual plot for 30 randomly-selected students who were asked to rate how much they liked both English and history on a 0 to 5 scale (a higher rating means the student liked the subject more).

Residual plot for history rating vs. english rating

Which of the following conditions for inference does the residual plot suggest has not been satisfied?

(A) The data come from a random sample.

(B) Observations for each student are independent.

(C) The variance of residuals is roughly equal for each value of English rating.

(D) For each value of English rating, the distribution of history rating is roughly Normal.

(E) Mean History rating is a linear function of English rating.

9. Consider the output for the regression analysis on the situation from question 8.

```
Predictor     Coef   SE Coef      T       P
Constant    1.1867   0.5574     2.13    0.042
English     0.5254   0.1995     2.63    0.014

S = 1.37707   R-Sq = 19.8%   R-Sq(adj) = 17.0%
```

Assume the conditions for regression inference have been satisfied. What does the quantity R-Sq = 19.8% represent?
(A)   The correlation of history rating and English rating—a measure of the strength of the linear relationship between the two variables.
(B)   The average deviation of observed history ratings from the predicted history ratings, expressed as a percentage of the predicted history rating.
(C)   The average deviation of observed English ratings from the predicted English ratings, expressed as a percentage of the predicted English rating.
(D)   The percentage of variation in history rating that can be explained by the regression of history rating on English rating.
(E)   The LSRL is accurately predicts history rating 19.8% of the time.

10. Use the computer output shown in problem 9. Which of the following is the 95% confidence interval for the population slope?
(A) $1.1867 \pm 1.960(0.5574)$
(B) $1.1867 \pm 2.048(0.5574)$
(C) $0.5254 \pm 1.960(0.1995)$
(D) $0.5254 \pm 2.048(0.1995)$
(E) $0.5254 \pm 2.630(1.37707)$

Check your answers below. If you got a question wrong, check to see if you made a simple mistake or if you need to study that concept more. After you check your work, identify the concepts you feel very confident about and note what you will do to learn the concepts in need of more study.

#	Answer	Concept	Right	Wrong	Simple Mistake?	Need to Study More
1	A	Degrees of Freedom				
2	D	Chi-square Components				
3	B	Chi-square test of Independence				
4	E	Conditions for Chi-Square Procedures				
5	D	Follow-up Analysis				
6	C	Chi-square Conclusions				
7	E	Significance Test from Output				
8	C	Conditions for Inference				
9	D	Confidence Interval for Slope				
10	D	Conclusion from Significance Test				

FRAPPY! Free Response AP® Problem, Yay!

The following problem is modeled after actual Advanced Placement Statistics free response questions. Your task is to generate a complete, concise response in 15 minutes. After you generate your response, read over the solution and scoring guide. Score your response and note what, if anything, you would do differently to increase your own score.

A study was performed to determine whether or not the name of a course had an effect on student registrations. A statistics course in a large school district was given 4 different names in a course catalog. Each name corresponded to the exact same statistics course. A random sample of student registrations was recorded and the results are given below:

Course Name	Number of Registrations
Statistical Applications	25
Statistical Reasoning	22
Statistical Analysis	30
The Practice of Statistics	40
Total	117

Do these data suggest the name of the course has an effect on student registrations? Conduct an appropriate statistical test to support your conclusion. Use $\alpha = 0.05$.

FRAPPY! Scoring Rubric

The following problem is modeled after actual Advanced Placement Statistics free response questions. Your task is to generate a complete, concise response in 15 minutes. After you generate your response, read over the solution and scoring guide. Score your response and note what, if anything, you would do differently to increase your own score.

Intent of the Question

The primary goals of this question are to assess your ability to (1) state the appropriate hypotheses; (2) identify and compute the appropriate test statistic; (3) make a conclusion in the context of the problem.

Solution

The solution should contain:

- **Test and Hypotheses**: The test must be identified by name or formula as a chi-square goodness-of-fit test and hypotheses must be stated appropriately. H_0: *student registrations do not differ by course name* and H_a: *student registrations do differ by course name.*
- **Conditions**: Random sample is given. It is reasonable to believe that $117 < 10\%$ of all registrations for the course. All expected counts are 29.25, which is at least 5.
- **Mechanics**: $\chi^2 = 6.38$ and P-value $= 0.094$ with 3 degrees of freedom.
- **Conclusion**: Because the P-value is larger than the significance level of 0.05 we fail to reject the null hypothesis. We do not have convincing evidence to suggest the course name has an effect on the number of registrations.

Scoring

Each element scored as essentially correct (E), partially correct (P), or incorrect (I).

Hypotheses and Name is essentially correct if the hypotheses are written correctly and the response correctly identifies the test by name or formula. This part is partially correct if the test isn't identified or if the hypotheses are written incorrectly. Incorrect otherwise.

Conditions and Mechanics is essentially correct if the response correctly does 4 of the 5 following things: (1) checks the Normal condition, (2) checks the 10% condition, (3) checks the large counts condition, (4) correct test statistic, (5) correct P-value. This part is partially correct if 3 or more of those 3 things are done correctly. Incorrect otherwise.

Conclusion is essentially correct if the response correctly fails to reject the null hypothesis because the P-value is greater than a significance level of 0.05 and provides an interpretation in context. This part is partially correct if the response fails to justify the decision by comparing the P-value to a significance level OR if the conclusion lacks an interpretation in context. Incorrect otherwise.

Scoring

4   Complete Response

All three parts essentially correct

3   Substantial Response

Two parts essentially correct and one part partially correct

2   Developing Response

Two parts essentially correct and no parts partially correct

One part essentially correct and one or two parts partially correct

Three parts partially correct

1   Minimal Response

One part essentially correct and no parts partially correct

No parts essentially correct and two parts partially correct

My Score:
What I did well:
What I could improve:
What I should remember if I see a problem like this on the AP Exam:

FRAPPY! Free Response AP® Problem, Yay!

The following problem is modeled after actual Advanced Placement Statistics free response questions. Your task is to generate a complete, concise response in 15 minutes. After you generate your response, read over the solution and scoring guide. Score your response and note what, if anything, you would do differently to increase your own score.

Matthew is interested in purchasing a digital camera and notices that as each model's image quality (in megapixels) increases, the cost appears to increase linearly. A scatterplot and regression output of the megapixels vs. cost for seven randomly chosen camera models is below:

```
Regression Analysis: Cost versus Megapixels

Predictor       Coef      SE Coef    T       P
Constant       63.457     2.387     26.58   0.000
Speed          16.2809    0.8192    19.88   0.000

S = 3.087    R-Sq = 98.7%      R-Sq (adj) = 98.5%
```

(a) Using the regression output, write the equation of the fitted regression line in context.

(b) Interpret the slope and *y*-intercept in the context of the problem.

(c) Construct and interpret a 98% confidence interval for the slope. Assume the conditions for inference have been met.

FRAPPY! Scoring Rubric

Use the following rubric to score your response. Each part receives a score of "Essentially Correct," "Partially Correct," or "Incorrect." When you have scored your response, reflect on your understanding of the concepts addressed in this problem. If necessary, note what you would do differently on future questions like this to increase your score.

Intent of the Question

The primary goals of this question are to assess your ability to (1) interpret standard computer output; (2) interpret a linear model in context; (3) construct and interpret a confidence interval for the slope of a regression line;

Solution

(a) $\widehat{cost} = 63.453 + 16.2809(\text{megapixels})$

(b) Intercept = 63.457. This is the predicted cost when megapixels = 0.
    Slope = 16.2809. We predict a cost increase of $16.28 for each increase of 1 megapixel.

(c) 98% Confidence Interval: $16.2809 \pm 3.365(0.8192) = (13.52, 19.03)$.
    We are 98% confident the interval from 13.52 to 19.03 captures the true slope of the regression line for megapixels and cost.

Scoring:

Each element scored as essentially correct (E), partially correct (P), or incorrect (I).

Part (a) is Essentially correct if the equation is properly stated and variables are defined in the context of the problem. Partially correct if the equation is properly stated, but the variables are not defined or left as x and y.

Part (b) is Essentially correct if both the intercept and slope are identified and interpreted correctly. Partially correct if only one is properly identified and interpreted. Note, the slope must indicate a *predicted* increase.

Part (c) is Essentially correct if a correct interval is constructed (with formula shown) and interpreted in the context of the problem. Partially correct if supporting work is not provided or if the interpretation is incorrect or lacks context.

Scoring

4   Complete Response

All three parts essentially correct

3   Substantial Response

Two parts essentially correct and one part partially correct

2   Developing Response

Two parts essentially correct and no parts partially correct

One part essentially correct and one or two parts partially correct

Three parts partially correct

1   Minimal Response

One part essentially correct and no parts partially correct

No parts essentially correct and two parts partially correct

My Score:
What I did well:
What I could improve:
What I should remember if I see a problem like this on the AP Exam:

Chapter 12 Formula Sheet

Create a one-page summary of important concepts and formulas found in this chapter. This will serve as a valuable resource as you prepare for the AP Exam.

Chapter 12 Crossword Puzzle
INFERENCE FOR DISTRIBUTIONS AND RELATIONSHIPS

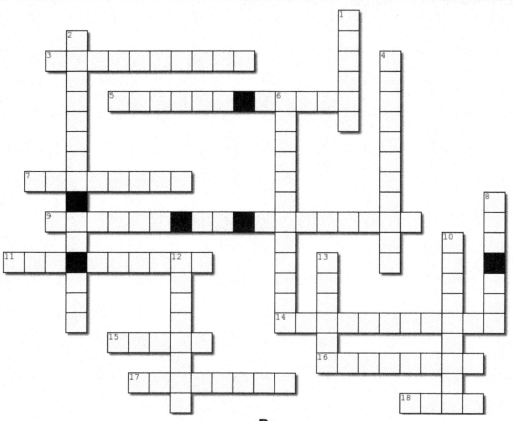

Across

3. To estimate the population (true) slope, we construct a _____ interval.

5. Chi-square distributions are a family of curves that are _____.

7. Type of categorical count gathered from a sample of data.

9. If a chi-square test rejects the null hypothesis, be sure to conduct a _____.

11. A ____-____ test statistic is used to test hypotheses about distributions of categorical data.

14. The x-variable is also known as the _____ variable.

15. To calculate a confidence interval, we must use the standard _____ of the slope.

16. Type of categorical count that we would see if the null hypothesis were true.

17. The difference: observed y - predicted y is called a _____.

18. The Greek letter we use to represent the slope of the population (true) regression line.

Down

1. When calculating chi-square statistics, observations should be expressed in _____ rather than percents.

2. This test is used to determine whether a population has a certain hypothesized distribution.

4. A chi-square test for _____ compares the distribution of a categorical variable for several populations or treatments.

6. To test whether there is an association between two categorical variables, use a chi-square test of association/____.

8. When comparing two or more categorical variables over multiple groups, arrange the data in a ____ ____table.

10. A follow-up analysis involves identifying the _____ that contributed the most to the chi-square statistic.

12. The y-variable is also known as the _____ variable.

13. When we construct a LSRL for a set of observed data, we construct a ____ regression line.

Chapter 1: Solutions

Introduction Concepts 1 and 2:
_____ *I can identify individuals and variables in a set of data.*

1) The individuals are the 6 students (James, Jen, …, Sharon).

2) Quantitative (discrete): ACT Score.
   Quantitative (continuous): Age.
   Categorical: Gender and Favorite Subject.

3) It appears the students who prefer math and science had higher scores on the ACT. However, we cannot infer there is a large difference between the scores of these students and those who do not prefer math and science.

Section 1.1 Concept 1:
_____ *I can make and interpret bar graphs for categorical data.*

1) Bar chart is shown below. It appears the majority of individuals prefer Goodbye Blue Monday and One Mean Bean. Very few people prefer the national chain.

2) Pie chart is shown below. The pie chart does not just show actual counts. Rather, it displays the percent of the total that preferred each coffee-shop. It is clear, again, from this chart that the overwhelming preference is for Goodbye Blue Monday, One Mean Bean, and The Ugly Mug with 70% of residents polled preferring them.

Category Name	Frequency	Relative Frequency
Goodbye Blue	75	30%
Ugly Mug	50	20%
Morning Joe's	38	15.2%
One Mean Bean	50	20%
Brewed own	25	10%
National Chain	12	4.8%
Total	250	100%

Coffee Shop Preferences

Section 1.1 Concept 2:

_____ *I can describe the nature of the association between two categorical variables.*

We suspect gender might influence coffee preference, so we'll compare the conditional distributions of coffee preference for men alone and women alone. We'll make a side-by-side bar graph to compare the preferences of males and females.

Preference	Male	Female
National Chain	17.8%	14.0%
One Mean Bean	2.8%	18.3%
The Ugly Mug	27.1%	5.4%
Goodbye Blue Monday	31.8%	19.4%
Home-brewed	18.7%	34.4%
Don't drink coffee	1.9%	8.6%

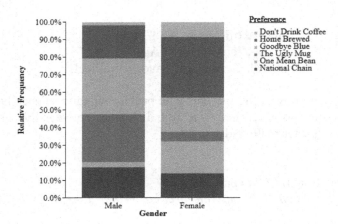

Based on the sample, it appears men prefer to get their coffee from The Ugly Mug and Goodbye Blue Monday while women are more likely (34.4% vs 18.7%) to home brew their coffee. There appears to be an association between gender and preference because the distribution of preference differs for the two genders, as seen in the fact that the segmented bar graphs differ for each gender.

Section 1.2 Concepts 1 and 2:

_____ *I can make and interpret dotplots and stemplots.*

1) The distribution of gas mileage appears to be fairly symmetric, is centered at about 37 mpg, and varies from 31.8 to 41 mpg. There do not appear to be any unusual observations.

2) Stemplot:

```
31 | 8
32 | 7
33 | 6
34 | 2 5
35 | 1
36 | 2 3 3 5 7 8 9 9
37 | 0 1 2 3 9
38 | 5
39 | 0 3 5 7 9
40 | 3 5
41 | 0 0
```

Key: 41 | 0 = 41.0 miles per gallon

Section 1.2 Concept 3:
_____ *I can make and interpret a histogram.*

1) Histograms may vary depending on "bin widths" and
    starting values. The distribution of mileage for the 50
    cars is fairly symmetric and unimodal. The center of
    the distribution is approximately 37 mpg, and the
    number of miles per gallon vary from 31 to 42. There
    do not appear to be any unusual observations.

2) To get your calculator to match the histogram you
    constructed by hand you will need to adjust the scale
    under window settings.

Section 1.3 Concepts 1 and 2:
_____ *I can calculate and interpret measures of center.*

1) The plot suggests the distribution of length of time to complete the logic puzzle is slightly skewed to
    the right. Therefore, the mean will probably be greater than the median because it tends to get pulled
    in the direction of the tail.

2) The average amount of time necessary to complete the logic puzzle was 32.67 seconds.

3) Median = 29 seconds. This is the "middle" time in the distribution. Half of the students took longer
    than 29 seconds to complete the puzzle and half took less than 29 seconds.

4) Because there is some skewness, the median would be a better measure as it is not affected by the tail
    or extreme values. It is a more accurate measure of center for this distribution.

Section 1.3 Concept 3:
_____ *I can calculate and interpret measures of variability.*

1) The distribution of book lengths (in pages) is fairly symmetric with a median of 330. There are
    outliers at the minimum of 170 and 242. $Q_1 = 314$, Median = 330, $Q_3 = 344$, and the maximum is 374
    pages.

2) The data have a mean of 316.27 pages and standard deviation 51.63 pages. Mrs. Molesky's favorite
    books tend to vary by about 52 pages from the mean of 316 pages.

Chapter 1 Crossword Puzzle
DATA ANALYSIS

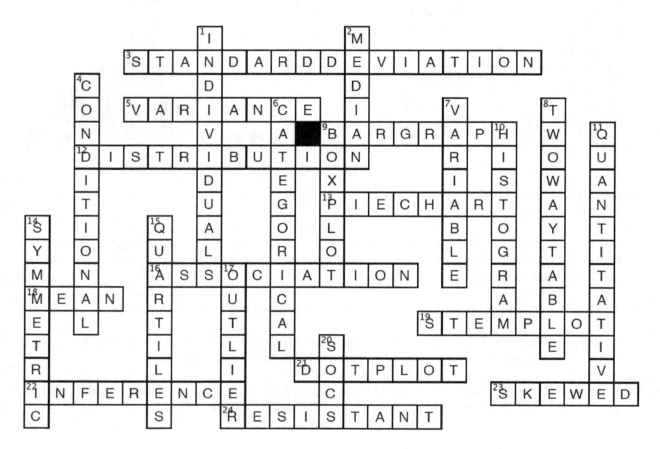

Across

3. The average distance of observations from their mean (two words) [STANDARDDEVIATION]
5. The average squared distance of the observations from their mean [VARIANCE]
9. Displays the counts or percents of categories in a categorical variable through differing heights of bars [BARGRAPH]
12. Tells you what values a variable takes and how often it takes these values [DISTRIBUTION]
13. Displays a categorical variable using slices sized by the counts or percents for the categories [PIECHART]
16. When specific values of one variable tend to occur in common with specific values of another [ASSOCIATION]
18. A measure of center, also called the average [MEAN]
19. A graphical display of quantitative data that involves splitting the individual values into two components [STEMPLOT]
21. One of the simplest graphs to construct when dealing with a small set of quantitative data [DOTPLOT]
22. Drawing conclusions beyond the data at hand [INFERENCE]
23. The shape of a distribution if one side of the graph is much longer than the other [SKEWED]
24. What we call a measure that is relatively unaffected by extreme observations [RESISTANT]

Down

1. The objects described by a set of data [INDIVIDUALS]
2. The midpoint of a distribution of quantitative data [MEDIAN]
4. A _____ distribution describes the distribution of values of a categorical variable among individuals who have a specific value of another variable. [CONDITIONAL]
6. A variable that places an individual into one of several groups or categories [CATEGORICAL]
7. A characteristic of an individual that can take different values for different individuals [VARIABLE]
8. When comparing two categorical variables, we can orgainze the data in a ___-___ _____. [TWOWAYTABLE]
9. A graphical display of the five-number summary [BOXPLOT]
10. A graphical display of quantitative data that shows the frequency of values in intervals by using bars [HISTOGRAM]
11. A variable that takes numerical values for which it makes sense to find an average [QUANTITATIVE]
14. The shape of a distribution whose right and left sides are approximate mirror images of each other [SYMMETRIC]
15. These values lie one-quarter, one-half, and three-quarters of the way up the list of quantitative data [QUARTILES]
17. A value that is at least 1.5 IQRs above the third quartile or below the first quartile [OUTLIER]
20. When exploring data, don't forget your ____ [SOCS]

Chapter 2: Solutions

Section 2.1 Concept 1:
_____ *I can find and interpret the percentile of an individual value in a distribution.*
_____ *I can estimate percentiles and individual values using a cumulative relative frequency graph.*

1) James earned a score of 33. His score is greater than or equal to 18 of the 23 students. Approximately 78% of students scored at or below 33 points.

2) Heather earned a score of 14. Her score is greater than or equal to 6 of the 23 students. Approximately 26% of students scored at or below 14 points.

3) Using the cumulative relative frequency graph, a score of 38 is at about the 80th percentile.

4) Q_1 is about 14 points, the median is about 25 points, and Q_3 is about 30 points.

Section 2.1 Concept 2:
_____ *I can find and interpret the standardized score (z-score) of an individual value in a distribution of data.*

1) Mean: $\overline{x} = 25.04$, Standard Deviation: $s_x = 14.20$

2) $z = \dfrac{45 - 25.04}{14.2} = 1.41$
Alyse's score falls 1.41 standard deviations above the mean Chapter 2 quiz score.

3) $z = \dfrac{2 - 25.04}{14.2} = -1.62$
Carl's score falls 1.62 standard deviations below the mean Chapter 2 quiz score.

4) First quiz: $z = \dfrac{45 - 25.04}{14.2} = 1.41$ Next quiz: $z = \dfrac{47 - 32}{6.5} = 2.31$
Alyse's standardized score is greater for the next quiz. She scored better relative to the mean on this quiz.

Section 2.1 Concept 3:
_____ *I can describe the effect of adding, subtracting, multiplying by, or dividing by a constant on the shape, center, and variability of a distribution of data.*

1) The distribution of scores is roughly symmetric, centered at a mean of 25.04 points. The scores have a minimum of 0 and a maximum of 50 (range = 50), with a standard deviation of 14.2 points.

2) If the teacher added 5 points to each score, the new distribution would still be symmetric. The mean score would increase by 5 to 30.04 points, and the variability would remain the same, with a standard deviation of 14.2 points.

3) If the teacher doubled the scores, the new distribution would still be symmetric. The mean score would double to 50.08 points, and the variability would double. The standard deviation would double to 28.4 points and the range would double to 100 points.

Section 2.2 Concept 1:
_____ *I can use a density curve to model distributions of quantitative data.*

1) The total area under the curve is 1.

2) 12% of scores fell between 28 and 40.

3) Because this curve is skewed left, the mean will be less than the median.

4) Because the total area = 1, the percent of scores that fall above 40 = $1 - 0.08 - 0.12 = 0.80$. 80% of the scores fall above 40.

Section 2.2 Concept 2:
_____ *I can find the proportion of values in a specified interval in a Normal distribution using Table A or technology.*

1)

Chapter 2 Test Scores

2) $P(78 < x < 83) = 0.34$, $P(83 < x < 93) = 0.475$. $P(78 < x < 93) = 0.34 + 0.475 = 81.5\%$

3) $z = \dfrac{90 - 83}{5} = 1.4$ $P(z > 1.40) = 1 - 0.9192 = 0.0808$.
    Approximately 8.08% of test scores were an "A".

4) $z = \dfrac{71 - 83}{5} = -2.4$ and $z = \dfrac{95 - 83}{5} = 2.4$ The area under the Normal curve between these two z-scores is $0.9918 - 0.0082 = 0.9836$. Approximately 98.36% of test scores fall between 71 and 95.

5) The 20th percentile corresponds to a z-score of about -0.84. To determine this value, solve
    $-0.84 = \dfrac{x - 83}{5}$ for x. $x = 83 - 0.84(5) = 78.8$.

Section 2.2 Concept 3:

_____ *I can determine whether a distribution of data is approximately Normal from graphical and numerical evidence.*

Number of push-ups

The quickest way to assess Normality is to construct a Normal probability plot. If the plot displays a linear pattern, the data can be assumed to be approximately Normal.

It appears the number of push-ups that the 23 students on the JV and High School basketball teams could do is approximately Normally distributed.

You could also justify this by counting how many scores fall within one, two, and three standard deviations of the mean and determining whether or not that reflects the empirical rule.

Mean: $\bar{x} = 25.04$, Standard Deviation: $s_x = 14.20$

Lower boundary	Upper boundary	Percent of Observations that fall in this interval	Percent expected to fall in this interval if the data are approximately normal:
$\bar{x} - 1\,s_x = 22.2$	$\bar{x} + 1\,s_x = 40.5$	$\dfrac{14}{23} \approx 60.8\%$	68%
$\bar{x} - 2\,s_x = 13.1$	$\bar{x} + 2\,s_x = 49.7$	$\dfrac{22}{23} \approx 95.6\%$	95%
$\bar{x} - 3\,s_x = 3.9$	$\bar{x} + 3\,s_x = 58.8$	$\dfrac{23}{23} = 100\%$	99.7%

These values adhere to the empirical rule fairly well! Keep in mind that you will rarely find a distribution that is perfectly Normal.

Chapter 2 Crossword Puzzle
MODELING DISTRIBUTIONS OF QUANTITATIVE DATA

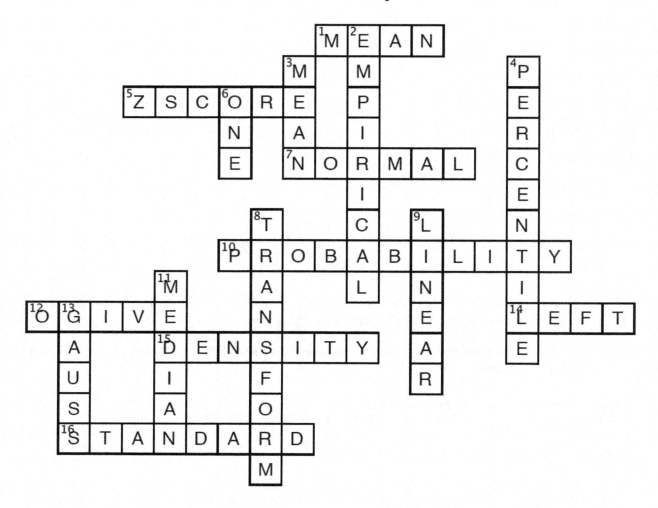

Across

1. The balance point of a density curve, if it were made of solid material [MEAN]
5. The standardized value of an observation [ZSCORE]
7. These common density curves are symmetric and bell-shaped [NORMAL]
10. A Normal _____ plot provides a good assessment of whether a data set is approximately Normally distributed [PROBABILITY]
12. Another name for a cumulative relative frequency graph [OGIVE]
14. The standard Normal table tells us the area under the standard Normal curve to the ___ of z [LEFT]
15. A ___ curve is a smooth curve that can be used to model a distribution [DENSITY]
16. This Normal distribution has mean 0 and standard deviation 1 [STANDARD]

Down

2. The ____ rule is also known as the 68-95-99.7 rule for Normal distributions [EMPIRICAL]
3. To standardize a value, subtract the ___ and divide by the standard deviation [MEAN]
4. The value with p percent of the observations less than it [PERCENTILE]
6. The area under any density curve is always equal to [ONE]
8. We ___ data when we change each value by adding a constant and/or multiplying by a constant. [TRANSFORM]
9. If a Normal probability plot shows a _____ pattern, the data are approximately Normal [LINEAR]
11. The point that divides the area under a density curve in half [MEDIAN]
13. This mathematician first applied Normal curves to data to errors made by astronomers and surveyors [GAUSS]

Chapter 3: Solutions

Section 3.1 Concept 1:
_____ *I can distinguish between explanatory and response variables for quantitative data.*

1) Explanatory: test anxiety   Response: performance on the test
2) Explanatory: volume of hippocampus   Response: verbal retention

Section 3.1 Concept 2:
_____ *I can make a scatterplot to display the relationship between two quantitative variables.*
_____ *I can describe the direction, form, and strength of a relationship displayed in a scatterplot and identify unusual features.*

The scatterplot displays a moderate, negative, linear relationship between anxiety and exam performance. As anxiety increases, exam performance decreases.

Section 3.1 Concept 3:
_____ *I can interpret the correlation.*

$r = -0.8185$. The linear relationship between anxiety and test score is a strong and negative.

Section 3.2 Concept 1, 2, and 3:
_____ *I can make predictions using regression lines, keeping in mind the dangers of extrapolation.*
_____ *I can calculate and interpret a residual*
_____ *I can interpret the slope and y intercept of a regression line.*
_____ *I can determine the equation of a least-squares regression line using technology or computer output.*

1) predicted score = 71.3 − 1.14(anxiety)

2) slope: $b = -1.14$. For each increase of one unit in anxiety scores, we the predicted exam score decreases by about 1.14 points.

3) predicted score = 71.3 − 1.14(15) = 54.2.

4) residual = actual − predicted = $y - \hat{y}$ = 60 − 54.2 = 5.8.

5) No, 35 is far greater than the maximum observed anxiety score. Extrapolation such as this could result in a poor prediction as we do not know if the linear model applies beyond the observed data. (For all we know, the exam scores could actually start to increase!)

Section 3.2 Concept 4:

_____ *I can construct and interpret residual plots to assess whether a regression model is appropriate.*

_____ *I can interpret the standard deviation of the residuals and r^2 and use these values to assess how well a least-squares regression line models the relationship between two variables.*

1) The residual plot does not show any obvious curved pattern. It appears the linear model may be appropriate for making predictions of exam scores.

2) $r = 0.8185$ and $r^2 = 0.67$.

Interpretation of r: The linear relationship between anxiety score and exam score is strong and negative.

Interpretation of r^2: Approximately 67% of the variability in predicted exam scores can be explained by the least-squares regression model of anxiety score on exam score.

Section 3.2 Concept 5:

_____ *I can determine the equation of a least-squares regression line using technology or computer output.*

1) predicted algae level = 42.8477 + 0.4762(temperature).

You could also write $\hat{y} = 42.8477 + 0.4762x$, where $\hat{y}$ = the predicted algae level and x = the temperature.

2) Slope: $b = 0.4762$. For each increase of 1-degree Fahrenheit, the predicted algae level increases by 0.4762 parts per million.

3) $r = \sqrt{0.917} = 0.957$. The linear relationship between temperature and algae level is strong and positive.

4) $s = 0.4224$. The actual algae levels typically vary by about 0.4224 units from the algae levels predicted by the least-squares regression line with x = temperature.

Section 3.3 Concept 1:

_____ *I can use transformations involving powers, roots, and logarithms to create a linear model that describes the relationship between two quantitative variables, and use the model to make predictions.*

Plot (diameter$^{0.7}$, length)

predicted length = 19.5(diameter)$^{0.7}$ +17

If diameter = 47mm,
predicted length = 19.5(47)$^{0.7}$ +17 = 305.74.

Section 3.3 Concept 2:

_____ *I can determine which of several models does a better job of describing the relationship between two quantitative variables.*

It is unclear which residual plot has the most random scatter. The model with the greatest value of r^2 is Model 3. Also notice that the scatterplot for Model 3 shows the most linear form.

Model 3: (log(police), log(crime)) is the most linear of the plots. Therefore, a power model may be the best choice to describe the relationship between police and crime.

$$\ln(\widehat{crime}) = 4.886 + 0.5365 \square \ln(police)$$

If a state has 25,400 police officers,

$$\ln(\widehat{crime}) = 4.886 + 0.5365 \square \ln(25.4)$$

$$\ln(\widehat{crime}) = 6.62144$$

crime = $e^{6.62144} \approx 751.03$ crimes

Chapter 3 Crossword Puzzle
EXPLORING TWO-VARIABLE QUANTITATIVE DATA

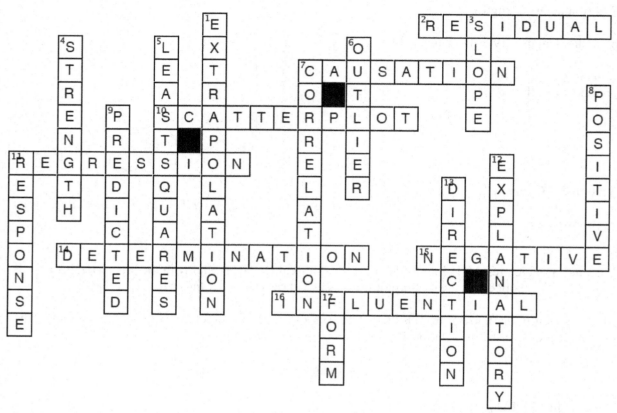

Across

2. the difference between an observed value of the response and the value predicted by a regression line [RESIDUAL]
7. Important note: Association does not imply _____. [CAUSATION]
10. graphical display of the relationship between two quantitative variables [SCATTERPLOT]
11. line that describes the relationship between two quantitative variables [REGRESSION]
14. the coefficient of _____ describes the fraction of variability in y values that is explained by least squares regression on x. [DETERMINATION]
15. A _____ association is defined when above average values of one variable are accompanied by below average values of the other. [NEGATIVE]
16. individual points that substantially change the correlation or slope of the regression line [INFLUENTIAL]

Down

1. the use of a regression line to make a prediction far outside the observed x values [EXTRAPOLATION]
3. the amount by which y is predicted to change when x increases by one unit [SLOPE]
4. The _____ of a relationship in a scatterplot is determined by how closely the point follow a clear form. [STRENGTH]
5. the ____-_____ regression line is also known as the line of best fit (2 words) [LEASTSQUARES]
6. an individual value that falls outside the overall pattern of the relationship [OUTLIER]
7. value that measures the strength of the linear relationship between two quantitative variables [CORRELATION]
8. A _____ association is defined when above average values of the explanatory are accompanied by above average values of the response [POSITIVE]
9. y-hat is the _____ value of the y-variable for a given x [PREDICTED]
11. variable that measures the outcome of a study [RESPONSE]
12. variable that may help explain or influence changes in another variable [EXPLANATORY]
13. The _____ of a scatterplot indicates a positive or negative association between the variables. [DIRECTION]
17. The ____ of a scatterplot is usually linear or nonlinear. [FORM]

Chapter 4: Solutions

Section 4.1 Concept 1:
_____ *I can identify the population and sample in a statistical study.*

Population: all sentences and words used in the popular Algebra 1 textbooks.
Sample: the sentences and words in the 10 randomly selected paragraphs.

Section 4.1 Concept 2:
_____ *I can describe how to select a simple random sample using slips of paper, technology, or a table of random digits.*

Assign each person a two-digit label 01-23. Read two-digit blocks across the random number table until 4 of the labels are selected, ignoring repeats and labels from 24-00.
The four selected are 19: Rohnkol, 22: Wilcock, 05: Buckley, 13: Lacey

Section 4.1 Concept 3:
_____ *I can explain how undercoverage, nonresponse, question wording, and other aspects of a sample survey can lead to bias.*

A practical problem with this survey is that recent graduates may not give truthful answers about whether or not they cheated on an exam their senior year. The actual proportion of students who cheated on at least one exam their senior year is most likely higher than the 64 percent observed in the study.

Section 4.2 Concept 1:
_____ *I can explain the concept of confounding and how it limits the ability to make cause-and-effect conclusions.*

1) This is an observational study since no treatment was imposed on the subjects. Test scores and shoe size were observed. No effort was made to influence either variable.
2) The explanatory variable would be the shoe size and response would be test score.
3) One possible confounding variable could be age of the students. Older students would have bigger feet, on average, and would most likely have higher test scores.

Section 4.2 Concept 2:
_____ *I can identify experimental units and treatments in an experiment.*
_____ *I can describe a completely randomized design for an experiment.*

1) Experimental units: Mr. Tyson's students
   Explanatory variable: listening to classical music (yes or no)
   Response variable: test scores

2) A potential confounding variable could be an existing musical preference based on test score. Perhaps higher performing students prefer listening classical music. Maybe students who listen to classical music have more resources/opportunities to score well than those who don't.

3) The 150 students should be randomly assigned to two groups. This could be accomplished by drawing names from a hat until 75 are in one group and 75 are in another. Both groups will receive the same instruction from Mr. Tyson. However, one group will be assigned to listen to classical music while studying and the other group will study in silence. All students will take the same assessment and their average results will be compared.

Section 4.2 Concept 3:
_____ *I can describe a randomized block design and a matched pairs design for an experiment and explain the purpose of blocking in an experiment.*

(Example Response)
Suppose Mr. Tyson suspects students enrolled in a music class may have higher scores than those who don't. In order to ensure not all students enrolled in a music class are assigned to listen to classical music (which could happen through random assignment), he should block by enrollment. He should block all students enrolled in a music class together and all students who are not enrolled in music should be blocked separately. Then, he should randomly assign half of the students in each block to listen to classical music while studying and the other half should study in silence. Then all students should take the same assessment and the results within each block should be compared.

Section 4.3 Concept 1:
_____ *I can explain the concept of sampling variability when making an inference about a population and how sample size affects sampling variability.*

1) No. It is unlikely the true average amount of change carried by all AP Statistics students is $0.42. Different samples of size 50 would produce different average amounts.

2) A random sample of 200 students would be more likely to give an estimate closer to the truth, because larger random samples tend to produce more precise estimates than smaller random samples.

Chapter 4 Crossword Puzzle
COLLECTING DATA

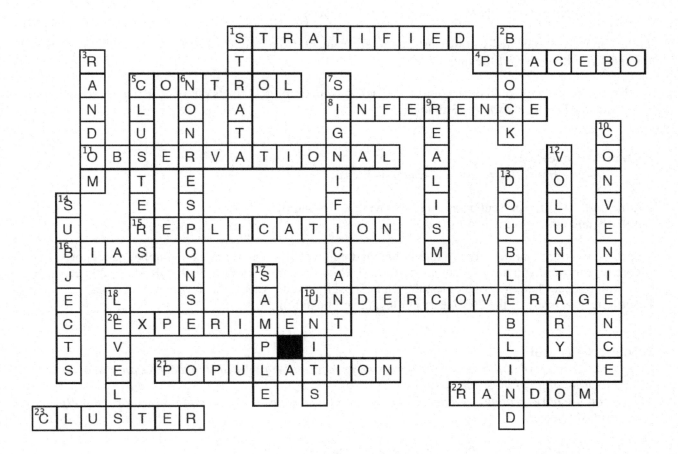

Across

1. a _____ random sample consists of separate simple random samples drawn from groups of similar individuals [STRATIFIED]
4. a "fake" treatment that is sometimes used in experiments [PLACEBO]
5. the effort to minimize variability in the way experimental units are obtained and treated [CONTROL]
8. the process of drawing a conclusion about the population based on a sample [INFERENCE]
11. this type of student can not be used to establish cause-effect relationships [OBSERVATIONAL]
15. the practice of using enough subjects in an experiment to reduce chance variation [REPLICATION]
16. a study that systematically favors certain outcomes shows this [BIAS]
19. this occurs when some groups in the population are left out of the process of choosing the sample [UNDERCOVERAGE]
20. a study in which a treatment is imposed in order to observe a reaspnse [EXPERIMENT]
21. the entire group of individuals about which we want information [POPULATION]
22. a simple _____ sample consists of individuals from the population, each of which has an equally likely chance of being chosen [RANDOM]
23. a _____ sample consists of a simple random sample of small groups from a population [CLUSTER]

Down

1. groups of similar individuals in a population [STRATA]
2. a group of experimental units that are similar in some way that may affect the response to the treatments [BLOCK]
3. the rule used to assign experimental units to treatments is ____ assignment [RANDOM]
5. smaller groups of individuals who mirror the population [CLUSTERS]
6. this occurs when an individual chosen for the sample can't be contacted or refuses to participate [NONRESPONSE]
7. an observed effect that is too large to have occurred by chance alone [SIGNIFICANT]
9. a lack of ____ in an experiment can prevent us from generalizing the results [REALISM]
10. a sample in which we choose individuals who are easiest to reach [CONVENIENCE]
12. a ____ response sample consists of people who choose themselves by responding to a general appeal [VOLUNTARY]
13. neither the subjects nor those measuring the response know which treatment a subject received (two words) [DOUBLEBLIND]
14. when units are humans, they are called [SUBJECTS]
17. the part of the population from which we actually collect information [SAMPLE]
18. another name for treatments [LEVELS]
19. the individuals on which an experiement is done are experimental ____ [UNITS]

Chapter 5: Solutions

Section 5.1 Concept 1:

_____ *I can interpret probability as a long-run relative frequency.*

1) If you were to repeatedly draw cards, with replacement, from a shuffled deck, you would draw a jack, queen, or king 23% of the time.

2) No. Although we would expect to draw a jack, queen, or king 23 times out of 100, but we are not guaranteed to do so *exactly* 23 times.

Section 5.1 Concept 2:

_____ *I can use simulation to model a random process.*

Let the digits 01-95 represent a passenger showing up for the flight.
Let 96-99 and 00 represent a "no show".

Select 12 two-digit numbers from a line of the random number table or a random number generator. Ignore repeats until you have 12 numbers selected. Count how many times 96, 97, 98, 99, or 00 occurs. If these values occur less than two times, the flight is overbooked. Repeat this procedure 20 times. Determine how many of the 20 trials result in an overbooked flight.

Section 5.1 Concept 1:

_____ *I can give a probability model for a random process with equally likely outcomes and use it to find the probability of an event.*
_____ *I can use basic probability rules, including the complement rule and addition rule for mutually exclusive events.*

1) There are 52 possible outcomes. Each outcome has a probability of 1/52.

2) $P(A) = 4/52 = 0.0769$. $P(B) = 13/52 = 0.25$.

3) $P(A^C) = 1 - P(A) = 48/52 = 0.9231$.

4) No, A and B are not mutually exclusive because a card can be both an Ace and a heart.

Section 5.2 Concept 2:

_____ *I can use a two-way table or Venn diagram to model a random process and calculate probabilities involving two events.*
_____ *I can apply the general addition rule to calculate probabilities.*

1) Use a two-way table to display the sample space.

	A	A^C
B	1	12
B^C	3	36

2)

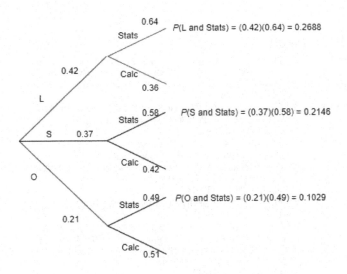

3) $P(A \cup B) = P(A) + P(B) - P(A \text{ and } B) = 4/52 + 13/52 - 1/52 = 16/52 = 0.3077$

Section 5.3 Concept 1:
_____ *I can calculate and interpret conditional probabilities.*
_____ *I can determine if two events are independent.*

If A and B are independent, $P(A) = P(A \mid B)$.
$P(A) = 120/200 = 0.60$ and $P(A \mid B) = 80/140 = 0.5714$.
Because these probabilities are not the same, A and B are not independent.

Section 5.3 Concept 2:
_____ *I can use a tree diagram to model a random process involving a sequence of outcomes and can calculate probabilities.*
_____ *I can use the general multiplication rule to calculate probabilities.*

```
                        0.64
                              Stats    P(L and Stats) = (0.42)(0.64) = 0.2688
                        Stats
              0.42
                        Calc
                              0.36
          L
                        0.58    P(S and Stats) = (0.37)(0.58) = 0.2146
                  Stats
            S   0.37
                        Calc 0.42

          O
                        0.49    P(O and Stats) = (0.21)(0.49) = 0.1029
                  Stats
              0.21
                        Calc 0.51
```

$P(\text{Statistics}) = 0.2688 + 0.2146 + 0.1029 = 0.5863$

Section 5.3 Concept 3:
_____ *I can use a tree diagram to model a random process involving a sequence of outcomes and can calculate probabilities.*

$P(\text{Lakeville} \mid \text{Statistics}) = P(\text{Lakeville and Statistics}) / P(\text{Statistics})$
$$= 0.2688 / 0.5863 = 0.4585$$

Chapter 5 Crossword Puzzle
PROBABILITY

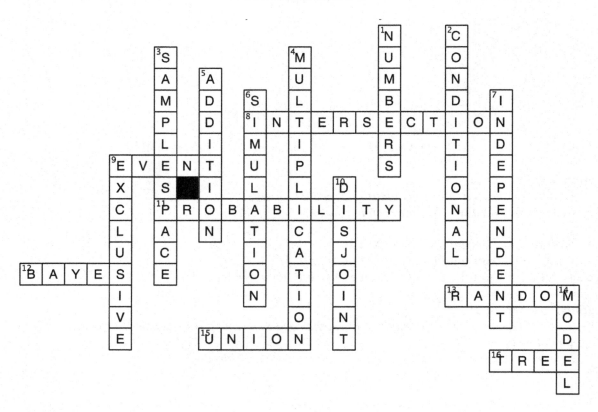

Across

8. The collection of outcomes that occur in both of two events. [INTERSECTION]
9. A collection of outcomes from a chance process. [EVENT]
11. The proportion of times an outcome would occur in a very long series of repetitions. [PROBABILITY]
12. _____ Theorem can be used to find probabilities that require going "backward" in a tree diagram. [BAYES]
13. In statistics, this doesn't mean "haphazard." It means "by chance." [RANDOM]
15. The collection of outcomes that occur in either of two events. [UNION]
16. A _____ diagram can help model chance behavior that involves a sequence of outcomes. [TREE]

Down

1. The law of large _____ states that the proportion of times an outcome occurs in many repetitions will approach a single value. [NUMBERS]
2. The probability that one event happens given another event is known to have happened. [CONDITIONAL]
3. The set of all possible outcomes for a chance process (two words). [SAMPLESPACE]
4. The probability that two events both occur can be found using the general _____ rule. [MULTIPLICATION]
5. P(A or B) can be found using the general _____ rule. [ADDITION]
6. The imitation of chance behavior, based on a model that reflects the situation. [SIMULATION]
7. The occurrence of one event has no effect on the chance that another event will happen. [INDEPENDENT]
9. Another term for disjoint: Mutually _____. [EXCLUSIVE]
10. Two events that have no outcomes in common and can never occur together. [DISJOINT]

Chapter 6: Solutions

Section 6.1 Concept 1:

_____ *I can use the probability distribution of a discrete random variable to calculate the probability of an event.*

_____ *I can make a histogram to display the probability distribution of a discrete random variable and describe its shape.*

Consider two 4-sided dice, each having sides labeled 1, 2, 3, 4. Let X = the sum of the numbers that appear after a roll of the dice.

1) X is a discrete random variable. We are most likely to roll a sum of 5 and least likely to roll a sum of **2 or 8**.

		First roll			
		1	2	3	4
	1	2	3	4	5
Second	2	3	4	5	6
roll	3	4	5	6	7
	4	5	6	7	8

X	2	3	4	5	6	7	8
$P(X)$	1/16	2/16	3/16	4/16	3/16	2/16	1/16

2) Yes, we should be surprised. In 10 rolls we would expect to see a sum of 3 or less about once or twice because $10\left(\dfrac{1}{16}+\dfrac{2}{16}\right)=1.875$.

Section 6.1 Concept 2:
_____ *I can calculate and interpret the mean (expected value) of a discrete random variable.*
_____ *I can calculate and interpret the standard deviation of a discrete random variable.*
_____ *I can use the probability distribution of a continuous random variable (uniform or Normal) to calculate the probability of an event.*

1) $E(Y) = 0(0.155) + 1(0.195) + 2(0.243) + 3(0.233) + 4(0.174) = 2.076$.
    If many, many plays of this game are randomly selected, the average number of goals per game will be about 2.076.

    $\sigma_Y^2 = (0 - 0.076)^2(0.155) + \cdots + (4 - 2.076)^2(0.174) = 1.7382$

    $\sigma_Y = \sqrt{1.7382} = 1.3184$.

    If many, many plays of this game are randomly selected, the number of goals per game typically varies by about 1.3184 from the mean of 2.076.

2) The weights of toddler boys follow an approximately Normal distribution with mean 34 pounds and standard deviation 3.5 pounds. Suppose you randomly choose one toddler boy and record his weight. What is the probability that the randomly selected boy weighs less than 31 pounds?

    Using Table A: $z = \dfrac{31 - 34}{3.5} = -0.8571$. $P(z < -0.8571) = 0.1956$.

    Using Technology: Let X = the weight of a randomly selected boy.
    $P(X < 31) =$ Normalcdf(lower: -1000, upper: 31, mean: 34, SD: 3.5) $= 0.1957$.

Section 6.2 Concept 1:
_____ *I can describe the effect of adding or subtracting a constant or multiplying or dividing by a constant on the probability distribution of a random variable.*

The shape of the distribution of Y will be slightly skewed to the right because the probability distribution of X is slightly skewed to the right.

$\mu_Y = 1.5(\mu_X) - 2 = -0.35$.
If many, many tosses are randomly selected, the average profit per toss will be about $-\$0.35$.
$\sigma_Y = 1.5(\sigma_X) = 1.4145$.
If many, many tosses are randomly selected, the average profit per toss will typically vary by about $\$1.4145$ from the mean of $-\$0.35$.

Section 6.2 Concept 2:
_____ *I can calculate the mean and standard deviation of the sum or difference of random variables.*

1) $\mu_{total} = 1.4 + 1.2 + 0.9 + 1 = 3.3$ min

    $\sigma_{total} = \sqrt{0.1^2 + 0.4^2 + 0.8^2 + 0.7^2} = \sqrt{1.3} \approx 1.14$ min

2) $\mu_{Doug-Alan} = 1 - 1.4 = -0.4$ min

    If many, many days are randomly selected, Doug will be faster than Alan by about 0.4 min, on average.

    $\sigma_{Doug-Alan} = \sqrt{0.7^2 + 0.1^2} \approx 0.7071$

    If many, many days are randomly selected, the difference (Doug – Alan) in time needed to check their homework will typically vary by 0.7071 min from the mean difference of 0.4 min.

Section 6.2 Concept 3:
_____ *I can find probabilities involving the sum or difference of independent Normal random variables.*

1) $\mu_{\text{Molesky}-\text{Liberty}} = 110 - 100 = 10$ and $\sigma_{\text{Molesky}-\text{Liberty}} = \sqrt{10^2 + 8^2} = \sqrt{164} \approx 12.81$

2) Find $P(\text{Molesky} - \text{Liberty} < 0)$.

Using Table A: $z = \dfrac{0 - 10}{12.81} = -0.78$. $P(z < -0.78) = 0.2177$.

Using Technology: $P(\text{Molesky} - \text{Liberty} < 0) = \text{Normalcdf(lower: } -1000, \text{ upper: } 0, \text{ mean: } 10, \text{ SD: } 12.81) = 0.2175$.

There is about a 21.75% chance Mr. Molesky will finish before Mr. Liberty on any given day.

Section 6.3 Concept 1:
_____ *I can determine whether the conditions for a binomial setting have been met.*
_____ *I can calculate and interpret probabilities involving binomial random variables.*

1) Show that X is a binomial random variable.
   B: Success = heart, Failure = not a heart
   I: Each draw is independent because cards are replaced and the deck is shuffled
   N: There are $n = 10$ observations in each game
   S: $P(\text{heart}) = 0.25$ in each draw.

2) $P(X < 4) = P(X = 0) + P(X = 1) + P(X = 2) + P(X = 3)$

   Using the formula: $P(X < 4) = \binom{10}{0}(0.25)^0 (0.75)^{10} + \cdots + \binom{10}{3}(0.25)^3 (0.75)^7 = 0.7759$

   Using Technology: $P(X < 4) = \text{binomcdf}(n: 10, p: 0.25, x: 3) = 0.7759$

Section 6.3 Concept 2:
_____ *I can calculate and interpret the mean and standard deviation of a binomial random variable.*
_____ *I can use the Normal approximation to the binomial distribution to calculate probabilities, when appropriate.*

1) Show that X is approximately a binomial random variable.
   X is approximately binomial with $n = 500$ and $p = 0.72$. Because $np = 500(0.72) = 360 \geq 10$ and $n(1 - p) = 500(0.28) = 140 \geq 10$, we can approximate X with a Normal distribution.

2) Use a Normal approximation to find the probability that 400 or more students would give their teacher a positive rating in this sample.

   $\mu_X = np = 500(0.72) = 360$

   $\sigma_X = \sqrt{np(1 - p)} = \sqrt{500(0.72)(0.18)} \approx 10.04$

   We want to calculate $P(X \geq 400)$.

   Using Table A: $z = \dfrac{400 - 360}{10.04} = 3.98$. $P(z \geq 3.98)$ is less than 0.0002.

   Using Technology: $P(X \geq 400) = \text{Normalcdf(lower: } 400, \text{ upper: } 1000, \text{ mean: } 360, \text{ SD: } 10.04) = 0.000034$

Section 6.3 Concept 3:

_____ *I can calculate and interpret probabilities involving geometric random variables.*
_____ *I can calculate and interpret the mean and standard deviation of a geometric distribution.*

1) Show that X is a geometric random variable.
   - There are two outcomes (Success: ring or Failure: no ring).
   - Each box is independent, meaning, knowing one box has a ring would give no information about any other box.
   - The probability of a ring in any given box is 0.2.
   - We are interested in how long it will take to find a ring.

2) Using the formula: $P(X = 7) = 0.8^6(0.2) = 0.0524$
   Using technology: geometpdf(p: 0.2, x: 7) = 0.0524

3) $P(X < 4) = P(X = 1) + P(X = 2) + P(X = 3)$

   Using the formula: $P(X < 4) = (0.2) + (0.8)(0.2) + (0.8)^2(0.2) = 0.488$

   Using Technology: $P(X < 4) =$ geometcdf(p: 0.2, x: 3) = 0.488

4) $E(X) = \dfrac{1}{0.2} = 5$ boxes.

5) $\sigma_X = \dfrac{\sqrt{1-p}}{p} = \dfrac{\sqrt{1-0.2}}{0.2} = 4.472$

   If many, many cereal boxes were randomly selected, the number of boxes it would take to get the first ring would typically vary by about 4.472 boxes from the mean of 5 boxes.

Chapter 6 Crossword Puzzle
RANDOM VARIABLES AND PROBABILITY DISTRIBUTIONS

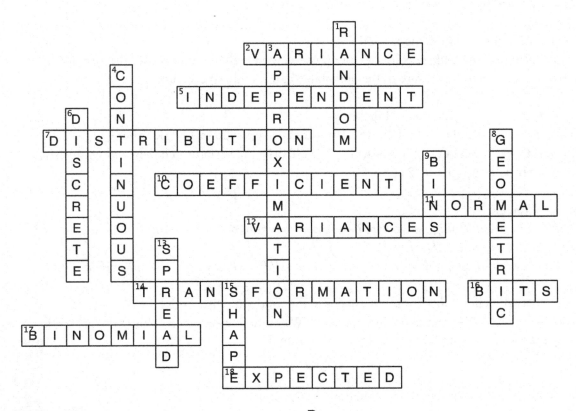

Across

2. The average of the squared deviations of the values of a variable from its mean. [VARIANCE]
5. Random variables are _____ if knowing whether an event in X has occurred tells us nothing about the occurrence of an event involving Y. [INDEPENDENT]
7. The probability _____ of a random variable gives its possible values and their probabilities. [DISTRIBUTION]
10. The number of ways of arranging k successes among n observations is the binomial _____. [COEFFICIENT]
11. The sum or difference of independent Normal random variables follows a _____ distribution. [NORMAL]
12. When you combine independent random variable, you always add these. [VARIANCES]
14. A linear _____ occurs when we add/subtract and multiply/divide by a constant. [TRANSFORMATION]
16. An easy way to remember the requirements for a geometric setting. [BITS]

Down

1. A _____ variable takes numerical values that describe the outcomes of some chance process. [RANDOM]
3. When n is large, we can use a Normal _____ to determine probabilities for binomial settings. [APPROXIMATION]
4. A random variable that takes on all values in an interval of numbers. [CONTINUOUS]
6. A random variable that takes a fixed set of possible values with gaps between. [DISCRETE]
8. A _____ setting arises when we perform independed trials of the same chance process and record the number of trials until a particular outcome occurs. [GEOMETRIC]
9. An easy way to remember the requirements for a binmial setting. [BINS]
13. Adding a constant to each value of a random variable has no effect on the shape or _____ of the distribution. [SPREAD]
15. Multiplying each value of a random variable by a constant has no effect on the _____ of the distribution. [SHAPE]

Chapter 7: Solutions

Section 7.1 Concept 1:

_____ *I can distinguish between a parameter and a statistic.*

1) *Population*: All males with high blood pressure
   Parameter: Mean arterial pressure (μ) for all males with high blood pressure (the population).
   Statistic: Mean arterial pressure of the 500 males in the study (the sample).

2) *Population*: All 16- to 24-year old drivers
   Parameter: Proportion (p) of all 16- to 24-year old drivers who text while driving.
   Statistic: Proportion of the 1500 16- to 14-year old drivers that indicated they text while driving.
   (Sample proportion = $\hat{p} = 0.12$).

Section 7.1 Concept 2:

_____ *I can distinguish among the distribution of a population, the distribution of a sample and the sampling distribution of a statistic.*

_____ *I can create a sampling distribution using all possible samples from a small population.*

A breakfast cereal includes marshmallow shapes in the following distribution: 10% stars, 10% crescent moons, 20% rockets, 40% astronauts, 20% planets. We are interested in examining the proportion of rockets in a random sample of 2000 marshmallows from the cereal.

1) The population distribution of marshmallow shapes is shown at the right.

2) Here is the distribution of sample data we would expect to see ($n = 2000$).

   We would expect to see about 400 rockets because $2000(0.2) = 400$.

3) The sampling distribution would be fairly symmetric with mean 0.2 and standard deviation 0.009, like shown below.

Section 7.2 Concept 1:

_____ *I can calculate the mean and standard deviation of the sampling distribution of a sample proportion* $\hat{p}$ *and interpret the standard deviation.*

_____ *I can determine if the sampling distribution of* $\hat{p}$ *is approximately Normal.*

Suppose your job at a potato chip factory is to check each shipment of potatoes for quality assurance. Further, suppose that a truckload of potatoes contains 95% that are acceptable for processing. If more than 10% are found to be unacceptable in a random sample, you must reject the shipment. To check, you randomly select and test 250 potatoes. Let $\hat{p}$ be the sample proportion of unacceptable potatoes.

1) The mean of the sampling distribution of $\hat{p}$ is 0.05.

2) $np = 12.5 \geq 10$ and $n(1 - p) = 237.5 \geq 10$. Because $250 < 10\%$ of all potatoes the standard deviation of

the sampling distribution of $\hat{p}$ is approximately $\sigma_{\hat{p}} = \sqrt{\dfrac{0.05(1 - 0.05)}{250}} = 0.0137$.

3) Because both np and $n(1 - p)$ are at least 10, the sampling distribution is approximately Normal. Because 0.10 is more than 3 standard deviations above the mean, it is unlikely we would observe a sample proportion greater than 10%. It is not likely we would reject the truckload based on a sample of 250 potatoes if 95% were truly acceptable.

$P(\hat{p} > 0.10) \approx 0$

| 0.0089 | 0.0226 | 0.0363 | 0.05 | 0.0637 | 0.0774 | 0.0911 |

Section 7.2 Concept 2:

_____ *I can use a Normal distribution to calculate probabilities involving* $\hat{p}$, *if appropriate.*

- Shape: Because both $np = 650$ and $n(1 - p) = 350$ are greater than 10, we can assume the sampling distribution of $\hat{p}$ is approximately Normal.

- Center: The mean of the sampling distribution of $\hat{p}$ is 0.65.

| 0.605 | 0.62 | 0.635 | 0.65 | 0.665 | 0.68 | 0.695 |

- Variability: Because $1000 < 10\%$ of the population of all high school students, the standard deviation

of the sampling distribution of $\hat{p}$ is approximately $\sigma_{\hat{p}} = \sqrt{\dfrac{0.65(1 - 0.65)}{1000}} \approx 0.015$.

The sampling distribution of $\hat{p}$ is approximately Normal with mean 0.65 and standard deviation 0.015. We want to fine the probability that the random sample will result in a value of $\hat{p}$ that is between $0.65 - 0.03 = 0.62$ and $0.65 + 0.03 = 0.68$.

$P(0.62 \leq \hat{p} \leq 0.68) = \text{Normalcdf(lower: 0.62, upper: 0.68, mean: 0.65, SD: 0.015)} \approx 0.9545$.

Section 7.2 Concept 3:

_____ *I can calculate the mean and standard deviation of the sampling distribution of a difference in sample proportions $\hat{p}_1 - \hat{p}_2$ and interpret the standard deviation.*

_____ *I can determine if the sampling distribution of $\hat{p}_1 - \hat{p}_2$ is approximately Normal.*

_____ *I can use a Normal distribution to calculate probabilities involving $\hat{p}_1 - \hat{p}_2$, if appropriate.*

1) The shape of the sampling distribution is approximately Normal because
$n_W\, p_W = (50)(0.45) = 22.5 \geq 10$,
$n_W (1 - p_W) = (50)(1 - 0.45) = 27.5 \geq 10$,
$n_E\, p_E = (50)(0.4) = 20 \geq 10$, and
$n_E (1 - p_E) = (50)(1 - 0.4) = 30 \geq 10$.

2) The mean of the sampling distribution is $0.45 - 0.40 = 0.05$.

3) Because $50 < 10\%$ of all students at West High (it's a large high school) and $50 < 10\%$ of all students at East High (it is also a large high school) the standard deviation of the sampling distribution is

approximately $\sigma_{\hat{p}_W - \hat{p}_E} = \sqrt{\dfrac{0.45(1-0.45)}{50} + \dfrac{0.4(1-0.4)}{50}} \approx 0.0987$.

4) $P(\hat{p}_E > \hat{p}_W)$ is equivalent to $P(\hat{p}_W < \hat{p}_E) = P(\hat{p}_W - \hat{p}_E < 0)$.

Based on a Normal distribution with a mean of 0.05 and a standard deviation of 0.0987:

$P(\hat{p}_W - \hat{p}_E < 0) = \text{Normalcdf(lower: } -1000, \text{ upper: } 0, \text{ mean: } 0.05, \text{ SD: } 0.0987) \approx 0.3062$.

Section 7.3 Concept 1:

_____ *I can calculate the mean and standard deviation of the sampling distribution of a sample mean $\bar{x}$ and interpret the standard deviation.*

_____ *I can use a Normal distribution to calculate probabilities involving $\bar{x}$, if appropriate.*

1) P(a randomly chosen 5$^\text{th}$ grader will take more than 2.5 minutes)

Using Table A: $z = \dfrac{2.5 - 2}{0.8} = \mathbf{0.625}$ $P(z > 0.625) = 0.2659$

Using Technology: $P(x > 2.5) = \text{Normalcdf(lower: } 2.5, \text{ upper: } 1000, \text{ mean: } 2, \text{ SD: } 0.8) = 0.2660$.

2) The sampling distribution of $\bar{x}$ will
   - have a shape that is Normal because the shape of the population is Normal,
   - have a mean of 2 minutes, the same as the mean of the population, and
   - because $20 < 10\%$ of the population of all 5th graders, the standard deviation is approximately
   $\dfrac{0.8}{\sqrt{20}} \approx 0.179$.

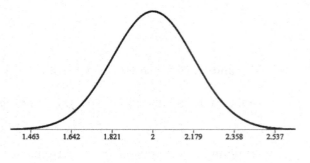

$P(\bar{x} > 2.5)$:

Using Table A: $z = \dfrac{2.5 - 2}{0.1789} = \mathbf{2.795}$ $P(z > 2.795) = 0.0026$

Using Tech: $P(\bar{x} > 2.5) = \text{Normalcdf(lower: } 2.5, \text{ upper: } 1000, \text{ mean: } 2, \text{ SD: } 0.179) \approx 0.0026$.

Section 7.3 Concept 2:

_____ *I can use a Normal distribution to calculate probabilities involving $\bar{x}$, if appropriate.*

The sampling distribution of $\bar{x}$ will

- be approximately Normal because although the shape of the population is unknown, the sample size is large ($n = 250 \geq 30$).
- have a mean of 188, the same as the mean of the population, and
- because 250 < 10% of the population of all adult men, the standard deviation is approximately $\dfrac{41}{\sqrt{250}} \approx 2.593$.

180.221   182.814   185.407   188   190.593   193.186   195.779

$P(\bar{x} > 193)$:

Using Table A: $z = \dfrac{193-188}{2.593} = 1.928$ $P(z > 193) = 0.0269$.

Using Tech: $P(\bar{x} > 193) = \text{Normalcdf(lower: 193, upper: 1000, mean: 188, SD: 2.593)} = 0.0269$

Section 7.3 Concept 3:

_____ *I can calculate the mean and standard deviation of the sampling distribution of a difference in sample means $\bar{x}_1 - \bar{x}_2$ and interpret the standard deviation.*

_____ *I can determine if the sampling distribution of $\bar{x}_1 - \bar{x}_2$ is approximately Normal.*

_____ *I can use a Normal distribution to calculate probabilities involving $\bar{x}_1 - \bar{x}_2$, if appropriate.*

1) The shape of the sampling distribution of $\bar{x}_W - \bar{x}_E$ is approximately Normal because both sample sizes are large ($n_W = 50 \geq 30$ and $n_E = 50 \geq 30$).

2) The mean of the sampling distribution of $\bar{x}_W - \bar{x}_E$ is $95 - 55 = 40$ minutes.

3) Because 50 < 10% of all students at West High (it's a large high school) and 50 < 10% of all students at East High (it is also a large high school) the standard deviation of the sampling distribution is approximately $\sigma_{\bar{x}_W - \bar{x}_E} = \sqrt{\dfrac{25^2}{50} + \dfrac{35^2}{50}} \approx 6.083$ minutes.

4) $P(\bar{x}_E > \bar{x}_W)$ is equivalent to $P(\bar{x}_W < \bar{x}_E) = P(\bar{x}_W - \bar{x}_E < 0)$.

Based on a Normal distribution with a mean of 40 and a standard deviation of 6.083:

$P(\bar{x}_W - \bar{x}_E < 0) = \text{Normalcdf(lower: } -1000, \text{ upper: } 0, \text{ mean: } 40, \text{ SD: } 6.083) \approx 0.$

It is nearly impossible to select two random samples from these schools (each of size 50) for which the sample mean amount of time spent on homework for the East High sample is greater than that of the West High sample.

Chapter 7 Crossword Puzzle
SAMPLING DISTRIBUTIONS

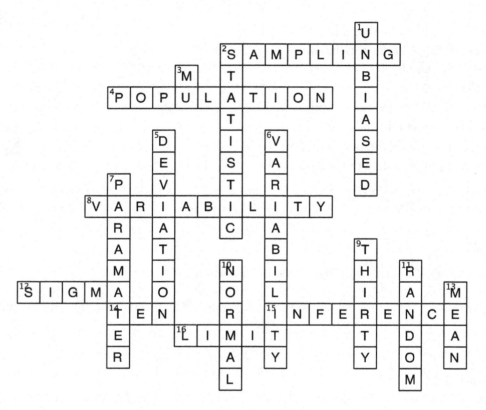

Across

2. _____ distribution: the distribution of values taken by the statistic in all possible samples of the same size from the population [SAMPLING]
4. _____ distribution: the distribution of all values of a variable in the population [POPULATION]
8. _____ of a statistic is described by the spread of the sampling distribution [VARIABILITY]
12. Greek letter used for the population standard deviation [SIGMA]
14. the Normal approximation for the sampling distribution of a sample proportion can be used when both the number of successes and failures are greater than _____ [TEN]
15. sampling distributions and sampling variability provide the foundation for performing _____ [INFERENCE]
16. central _____ theorem tells us if the sample size is large, the sampling distribution of the sample mean is approximately Normal, regardless of the shape of the population [LIMIT]

Down

1. a statistic is an _____ estimator if the mean of the sampling distribution is equal to the true value of the parameter being estimated. [UNBIASED]
2. a number, computed from sample data, that estimates a parameter [STATISTIC]
3. Greek letter used for the population mean [MU]
5. standard _____ : measure of spread of a sampling distribution [DEVIATION]
6. sampling _____ notes the value of a statistic may be different from sample to sample [VARIABILITY]
7. a number that describes a population [PARAMATER]
9. the rule of thumb for using the central limit theorem - the sample size should be greater than _____ [THIRTY]
10. when the sample size is large, the sampling distribution of a sample proportion is approximately _____ [NORMAL]
11. to draw a conclusion about a population parameter, we can look at information from a _____ sample [RANDOM]
13. center of a sampling distribution [MEAN]

Chapter 8: Solutions

Section 8.1 Concept 1:
_____ *I can interpret a confidence level in context.*
_____ *I can interpret a confidence interval in context.*

1) We are 90% confident the interval from 19.10 to 20.74 captures the true mean contents of a "20 oz." bottle of water.

2) If we were to collect many random samples of 50 "20 oz." water bottles from the population of all water bottles and construct a confidence interval for the mean contents in the same manner, 90% of the intervals would capture the true mean contents.

3) The average contents for the sample was 19.92 oz. Because 20 oz. is in the interval, we do not have evidence to suggest the population mean is less or greater than 20 oz.

Section 8.1 Concept 2:
_____ *I can describe how the sample size and confidence level affect the margin of error.*
_____ *I can explain how practical issues like nonresponse, undercoverage, and response bias can affect the interpretation of a confidence interval.*

1) The width of the confidence interval would decrease because decreasing the confidence level decreases the margin of error.

2) The width of the confidence interval would decrease because increasing the sample size decreases the margin of error.

3) The margin of error does not account for the fact that adults who are at home in the late-morning may more likely to be homemakers and, therefore more likely to bake at least twice a week. The true proportion of adults who bake at home may be less than that observed in the sample.

Section 8.2 Concepts 1 and 2:
_____ *I can state and check the Random, 10%, and Large Counts conditions for constructing a confidence interval for a population proportion.*
_____ *I can construct and interpret a confidence interval for a population proportion.*

State: 90% CI for p = the true proportion of adults who can roll their tongue.
Plan: One-sample z interval for p.
- Random: We have a random sample of adults.
- 10%: $300 < 10\%$ of all adults.
- Large Counts: The number of successes and failures are both at least 10 ($68 \geq 10$ and $232 \geq 10$).

Do: 95% CI $= 0.23 \pm 1.645\sqrt{\dfrac{0.23(0.77)}{300}} = (0.1869, \ 0.2664)$

Conclude: We are 90% confident the interval from 0.19 to 0.27 captures the true proportion of adults who can roll their tongue.

Section 8.2 Concept 3:

_____ *I can determine the sample size required to obtain a C% confidence interval for a population proportion with a specified margin of error.*

$$1.96\sqrt{\frac{0.5(0.5)}{n}} \le 0.02 \Rightarrow \sqrt{\frac{0.5(0.5)}{n}} \le 0.0102 \Rightarrow \frac{0.25}{n} \le 0.000104$$

$$n \ge 2401$$

She would need at least 2401 adults to estimate the proportion who can roll their tongues with 95% confidence and a margin of error of at most 2%.

Section 8.3 Concept 1:

_____ *I can determine whether the conditions are met for doing inference about a difference between two proportions.*

_____ *I can construct and interpret a confidence interval for a difference between two proportions.*

State: 95% confidence interval for $p_{1990} - p_{2010}$ where p_{1990} = the true proportion of adults that smoke in 1990 and p_{2010} = the true proportion of adults that smoke in 2010.

Plan: Two-sample z interval for $p_{1990} - p_{2010}$.

- Random: We have two independent random samples
- 10%: 1500 < 10% of all adults in 1990 and 2000 < 10% of all adults in 2010.
- Large Counts: There are at least 10 successes in each sample (551 in 1990 and 652 in 2010) and more than 10 failures in each sample (949 in 1990 and 1348 in 2010)

Do: $\hat{p}_{1990} = \frac{551}{1500} = 0.367$ and $\hat{p}_{2010} = \frac{652}{2000} = 0.326$

95% CI: $(0.367 - 0.326) \pm 1.96\sqrt{\frac{0.367(1-0.367)}{1500} + \frac{0.326(1-0.326)}{2000}} = (0.0094,\ 0.0732)$

Conclude: We are 95% confident the interval from 0.0094 to 0.0732 captures the true difference in the proportions of adults who smoked in 1990 and in 2010. Since 0 is not contained in this interval, we can conclude the proportion of adults who smoked in 1990 was greater than in 2010.

Chapter 8 Crossword Puzzle
ESTIMATING PROPORTIONS WITH CONFIDENCE

Across

2. The large _____ condition says that the number of successes and failures must be at least 10. (**counts**)

4. We can decrease the width of a confidence interval by _____ the sample size. (**increasing**)

6. When selecting two random samples for the purpose of statistical inference, the two samples must be _____. (**independent**)

7. A single value used to estimate a parameter is called a _____ estimator. (**point**)

8. The margin of error consists of a _____ value and the standard error of the sampling distribution. (**critical**)

9. A _____ interval provides an estimate for a population parameter. (**confidence**)

11. The confidence _____ is the success rate of the method in repeated random sampling. (**level**)

13. We can construct an interval that is less wide by _____ the confidence level. (**decreasing**)

14. The conclusion should always be written in terms of the population _____. (**parameter**)

Down

1. When you draw a conclusion about a population based upon a sample you are performing statistical _____. (**inference**)

3. The 10% condition applies when sampling _____. (**without replacement**)

5. To estimate with confidence, the estimate should be based upon a _____ sample. (**random**)

10. The 10% condition says that the size of the sample must be less than 10% of the size of the _____. (**population**)

12. A confidence interval consists of an estimate, plus or minus the margin of _____. (**error**)

Chapter 9: Solutions

Section 9.1 Concept 1:

_____ *I can state appropriate hypotheses for a significance test about a population parameter.*

1) The parameter of interest is p = the true proportion of hearts in the "chute" of cards.
2) H_0: $p = 0.25$ vs. H_a: $p > 0.25$
3) The sample proportion is $7/12 = 0.0583$. It is possible to be dealt 7 hearts in 12 cards, however it is very unlikely. We would expect about 3 hearts when dealt 12 cards.

Section 9.1 Concept 2:

_____ *I can interpret a P-value in context.*
_____ *I can make an appropriate conclusion for a significance test.*

1) If the null hypothesis is true, the proportion of hearts in the "chute" would be 0.25.
2) Assuming the proportion of hearts in the "chute" is 0.25, there is a 0.4% chance we would observe 7 or more hearts when 12 cards are randomly selected. This is highly unlikely.
3) Because it is so unlikely that we would observe 7 or more hearts when dealt 12 cards from a fair chute (less than a 5% chance), we have evidence to suggest there may be more hearts than usual in the chute.

Section 9.1 Concept 3:

_____ *I can interpret a Type I error and a Type II error in context, and give a consequence of each error in a given setting.*

1) A Type I error would occur if we found convincing evidence that the proportion of hearts in the chute is greater than 0.25 when, in reality, the proportion of hearts is 0.25. We were just dealt an unusual hand.
2) A Type II error would occur if we did not find convincing evidence that the proportion of hearts in the chute is greater than 0.25 when, in reality, the proportion of hearts is actually greater than 0.25.

Section 9.2 Concept 1:

_____ *I can state and check the Random, 10%, and Large Counts conditions for performing a significance test about a population proportion.*
_____ *I can calculate the standardized test statistic and P-value for a test about a population proportion.*
_____ *I can perform a significance test about a population proportion.*

State: H_0: $p = 0.214$ versus H_a: $p > 0.214$, where p = the true proportion of passages that follow the speech pattern in the work in question.

Plan: z test for one proportion
- Random: We have a random sample of passages from the work in question.
- 10%: $439 < 10\%$ of all passages of Plato's work.
- Large Counts: The number of successes (136) and failures (303) are both at least 10.

Do: $\hat{p} = \dfrac{136}{439} = 0.3098$. $\quad z = \dfrac{0.3098 - 0.214}{\sqrt{\dfrac{0.3098(1 - 0.3098)}{439}}} = 4.89$

P-value = $P(z > 4.89) = 0.000001$

Conclude:

Because the P-value is less than 5%, we reject H_0. We have convincing evidence that the true proportion of passages that follow the speech pattern in the work in question is greater than 0.214.

Section 9.2 Concept 2:

_____ *I can use a confidence interval to make a conclusion for a two-sided test about a population parameter.*

State: 99% CI for p = the true proportion of teens who text while driving.

Plan: z CI for one proportion
- Random: We have a random sample of 27 teenage drivers.
- 10%: 27 < 10% of all teenage drivers
- Large Counts: The number of successes (15) and failures (12) are both at least 10.

Do:

$$0.56 \pm 2.576\sqrt{\dfrac{0.56(0.44)}{27}} = (0.3092,\ 0.8019)$$

Conclude:

We are 99% confident the interval from 0.31 to 0.80 captures the true proportion of teens who text while driving. Because 0.77 is in this interval, we do not have evidence to suggest the true proportion is different than 77%.

Section 9.2 Concept 3:

_____ *I can interpret the power of a significance test and describe what factors affect the power of a test.*

1) If the true proportion of processors that use more than 70 watts of power in the batch is $p = 0.04$ watts, there is a 0.12 probability that the quality control engineer will find convincing evidence for H_a: $p > 0.03$.

2) Decrease. A smaller significance level makes it harder to reject H_0 when H_a is true.

3) Increase. A larger sample size gives more information about the true proportion p.

4) Increase. It is easier to detect a bigger difference between the null and alternative parameter value.

Section 9.3 Concept 1:
_____ *I can perform a significance test to compare two proportions.*

State:

H_0: $p_N = p_S$

H_a: $p_N > p_S$

where p_N = the true proportion of low-income students at Lakeville North and p_S = the true proportion of low-income students at Lakeville South.

Plan: 2-proportion z-test

- Random: We have two independent random samples.
- 10%: 120 < 10% of all students that attend Lakeville North and
  150 < 10% of all students at Lakeville South.

- Large Counts: $\hat{p}_C = \dfrac{28+30}{120+150} = \dfrac{58}{270} = 0.215$

  $n_1\hat{p} = 120(0.215) = 25.8$

  $n_1(1-\hat{p}_C) = 120(1-0.215) = 94.2$

  $n_2\hat{p}_C = 150(0.215) = 32.25$

  $n_2(1-\hat{p}_C) = 150(1-0.215) = 117.75$

  These expected counts are all at least 10.

Do: $\hat{p}_N = \dfrac{28}{120} = 0.233$ and $\hat{p}_S = \dfrac{30}{150} = 0.2$

$z = \dfrac{0.233-0.2}{\sqrt{\dfrac{0.215(1-0.215)}{120} + \dfrac{0.215(1-0.215)}{150}}} = 0.663$

P-value: $P(z > 0.663) = 0.2537$

Conclude:

Because the P-value is greater than $\alpha = 0.05$, we fail to reject the null hypothesis. We do not have convincing evidence to conclude that the proportion of low-income students at Lakeville North is greater than the proportion of low-income students at Lakeville South.

Chapter 9 Crossword Puzzle
TESTING CLAIMS ABOUT PROPORTIONS

Across

1. If the P-value is greater than the significance level, we _____ to reject the null hypothesis. (**fail**)

4. Conclusions should always be written in _____. (**context**)

6. If an observed difference is too small to have occurred due to chance alone, the difference is statistically _____. (**significant**)

11. Hypotheses always refer to the _____. (**population**)

12. If we reject the null hypothesis when it is actually true, we commit a Type I error. (**error**)

14. Always check the _____ before carrying out an inference procedure. (**conditions**)

15. The statements a statistical test is designed to compare. (**hypotheses**)

16. The probability that we would observe a statistic as least as extreme as the one observed assuming the null is true. (**p value**)

Down

2. Reject the null hypothesis if the P-value is _____ than the significance level. (**less**)

3. The test _____ is a standardized value that assesses how far the estimate is from the hypothesized parameter. (**statistic**)

5. We can use a _____ test to compare the observed data with a hypothesis about a population. (**significance**)

7. The _____ hypothesis is the claim about the population we are finding evidence for. (**alternative**)

8. The _____ hypothesis is the claim for which we are seeking evidence against. (**null**)

9. The probability that a significance test will reject the null when a particular alternative value of the parameter is true. (**power**)

10. If we calculate a very small P-value, we have evidence to _____ the null hypothesis. (**reject**)

13. The Greek letter used to designate the significance level. (**alpha**)

Chapter 10: Solutions

Section 10.1 Concepts 1 and 2:

_____ *I can determine the critical value for calculating a C% confidence interval for a population mean using a table or technology.*

1) $t^* = 1.330$

2) $t^* = 1.984$

3) $t^* = 2.756$

Section 10.1 Concept 3:

_____ *I can construct and interpret a confidence interval for a population mean.*

State: 95% CI for μ = the true mean amount of sugar for all soft drinks from this manufacturer.

Plan:

- Random: A random sample was selected.

- 10%: 8 < 10% of all soft drinks from this manufacturer.

- Normal / Large Sample: The shape of the distribution of the population is not provided and the sample size is small. We must look at the distribution of the sample.

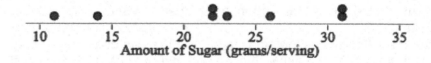

The dotplot shows no strong skewness and no outliers. The Normal/Large Sample condition is met.

Do: $22.5 \pm 2.365 \dfrac{7.191}{\sqrt{8}} = (16.488,\ 28.512)$

Conclude:

We are 95% confident the interval from 16.488 to 28.512 captures the true mean amount of sugar for this manufacturer's soft drinks.

Section 10.2 Concept 1:

_____ *I can construct and interpret a confidence interval for a difference between two means.*

State:

95% CI for $\mu_1 - \mu_2$ = the true difference in mean weight loss where μ_1 = the mean weight loss for the new diet and μ_2 = the mean weight loss for the current diet.

Plan:

- Random: Patients were randomly assigned to each treatment.
- 10%: Does not apply because no random sampling took place.
- Normal / Large Samples: $n_1 = 100$ and $n_2 = 100$ are both at least 30.

Do: $(9.3 - 7.4) \pm 1.990\sqrt{\dfrac{4.7^2}{100} + \dfrac{4^2}{100}} = (0.672,\ 3.128)$ with df = 99 (using df = 80).

Using technology: (0.683, 3.117), df = 193.06

Conclude:

We are 95% confident the interval from 0.68 to 3.12 captures the true difference in mean weight loss for the two diets. Because 0 is not contained in this interval, we have evidence to suggest the new diet is more effective than the current diet.

Section 10.2 Concept 2:

_____ *I can construct and interpret confidence intervals for a mean difference.*

State:

95% CI for μ_{diff} = the true mean difference in the number of presses (Caffeine – Placebo)

Plan:

- Random: The treatment order was randomly assigned to the subjects.
- 10%: Not needed because no random sampling took place.
- Normal/Large Sample: Because the shape of the distribution of the population is unknown and the number of differences is small, we will look at the distribution of the 11 differences. Here are the differences:

Subject	# of Presses Caffeine	# of Presses Placebo	Difference Caffeine – Placebo
1	251	201	50
2	284	262	22
3	300	283	17
4	321	290	31
5	240	259	−19
6	294	291	3
7	377	354	23
8	345	346	−1
9	303	283	20
10	340	361	−21
11	408	411	−3

Here is a dotplot of the differences:

The distribution of the difference in the number of presses (Caffeine – Placebo) shows no strong skewness and contains no outliers.

Do: The mean of the differences is $\bar{x}_{\text{diff}} = 11.09$. The standard deviation of the differences is $s_{\text{diff}} = 21.52$.

$$11.09 \pm 2.228\left(\frac{21.52}{\sqrt{11}}\right) = (-3.37, 25.55)$$

Conclude:

I am 95% confident that the interval from −3.37 to 25.55 contains the true mean difference in the number of presses (Caffeine – Placebo).

Chapter 10 Crossword Puzzle
ESTIMATING MEANS WITH CONFIDENCE

Across

5. For two sample problems, the data may arise from two _____ in a randomized experiment. (**groups**)

7. In a one-sample problem, df = the _____ _____ minus 1. (**sample size**)

10. The 10% condition should be checked when the sample(s) are selected _____ _____. (**without replacement**)

11. This type of data result from recording two values of the same quantitative variable for each individual. (**paired**)

12. The Normal/Large Sample condition is met for inference about the difference of means if both sample sizes are at least _____. (**thirty**)

Down

1. The margin of error in a confidence interval consists of a critical value and standard _____ of the statistic. (**error**)

2. A particular t distribution is specified by its _____ of freedom. (**degrees**)

3. A confidence interval is used to _____ an unknown population parameter. (**estimate**)

4. The margin of error decreases as the sample size _____. (**increases**)

6. If all else remains the same and the sample size is quadrupled, the margin of error will be cut in _____. (**half**)

8. To perform two-sample inference procedures, the random samples must be _____. (**independent**)

9. The margin of error is larger for higher _____ levels. (**confidence**)

Chapter 11: Solutions

Section 11.1 Concept 1:

_____ *I can state and check the Random, 10%, and Normal/Large Sample conditions for performing a significance test about a population mean.*

_____ *I can perform a significance test about a population mean.*

State:

H_0: $\mu = 8.9$ versus H_a: $\mu \neq 8.9$ where $\mu =$ the true mean ratio for all fossils at the Minnesota Iron Range site.

Plan: t test for μ

- Random: The researchers are willing to view the humerus bones they found as a random sample of all such humerus bones.
- 10%: $41 < 10\%$ of the population of all humerus bones in this area.
- Normal/Large Sample: $n = 41 \geq 30$

Do: $\bar{x} = 9.27$, $s_x = 1.198$, $n = 41$

Standardized Test Statistic: $t = \dfrac{9.27 - 8.9}{1.198 / \sqrt{41}} = 1.97$

P-value $= 0.056$

Conclude:

Because the P-value is greater than 0.05, we fail to reject the null hypothesis. There is not convincing evidence to suggest these bones have a ratio different than 8.9.

Section 11.1 Concept 2:

_____ *I can use a confidence interval to make a conclusion for a two-sided test about a population mean.*

The 99% confidence interval does not include 20 ounces as a plausible value, so the manufacturer should reject the null hypothesis. There is convincing evidence that the true mean content for all 20-ounces of bottle cleaner is not 20 ounces.

Section 11.2 Concept 1:

_____ *I can calculate the standardized test statistic and P-value for a test about a difference between two means.*

_____ *I can perform a significance test about a difference between two means.*

State:

H_0: $\mu_B = \mu_G$

H_a: $\mu_B > \mu_G$

Where μ_B = the true mean short-term memory score for all boys and μ_G = the true mean short-term memory score for all girls.

Plan: t test for a difference in means

- Random: A random sample of 200 boys and an independent random sample of 150 girls were selected.

- 10%: 200 < 10% of all boys and 150 < 10% of all girls.

- Normal / Large Sample: $n_B = 200$ and $n_G = 150$ are both at least 30.

Do: $t = \dfrac{48.9 - 48.4}{\sqrt{\dfrac{12.96}{200} + \dfrac{11.85}{150}}} = 0.375$ and the P-value = 0.354

Conclude:

Because the P-value 0f 0.354 is greater than $\alpha = 0.05$, we fail to reject the null hypothesis. There is not convincing evidence that the boys have better short-term memory than the girls.

Section 11.2 Concept 2:

_____ *I can perform a significance test about a mean difference.*

State:

H_0: $\mu_{\text{diff}} = 0$

H_a: $\mu_{\text{diff}} > 0$

μ_{diff} = the true mean difference in the number of presses (Caffeine – Placebo)

Plan:

- Random: The treatment order was randomly assigned to the subjects.
- 10%: Not needed because no random sampling took place.
- Normal/Large Sample: Because the shape of the distribution of the population is unknown and the number of differences is small, we will look at the distribution of the 11 differences. Here are the differences:

Subject		1	2	3	4	5	6	7	8	9	10	11
# of Presses	Caffeine	251	284	300	321	240	294	377	345	303	340	408
	Placebo	201	262	283	290	259	291	354	346	283	361	411
Difference	Caffeine – Placebo	50	22	17	31	–19	3	23	–1	20	–21	–3

Here is a dotplot of the differences:

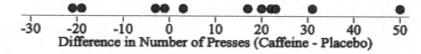

Difference in Number of Presses (Caffeine - Placebo)

The distribution of the difference in the number of presses (Caffeine – Placebo) shows no strong skewness and contains no outliers.

Do: The mean of the differences is $\bar{x}_{\text{diff}} = 11.09$.

The standard deviation of the differences is $s_{\text{diff}} = 21.52$.

$$t = \frac{11.09 - 0}{\frac{21.52}{\sqrt{11}}} = 1.709 \qquad P\text{-value} = 0.059.$$

Conclude:

Because the P-value (0.059) is greater than the significance level ($\alpha = 0.05$), we fail to reject H_0. There is not convincing evidence that the true mean difference (Caffeine – Placebo) in the number of presses for subjects like these is greater than 0.

Chapter 11 Crossword Puzzle
TESTING CLAIMS ABOUT MEANS

Across

2. _____ result from recording two values of the same quantitative variable for each individual or pair of similar individuals. (**paired data**)

4. If the P-value is _____ than the significance level, we fail to reject the null hypothesis. (**greater**)

5. To draw a conclusion about a test compare the _____ to the significance level. (**p-value**)

6. In a significance test for a _____ in means, the data may come from two groups in a randomized experiment. (**difference**)

9. If the P-value is less than the _____ _____ then reject the null hypothesis. (**significance level**)

10. A 95% confidence interval about a mean will give consistent results as a _____ test. (**two-sided**)

13. When stating the hypotheses, always define the _____ of interest. (**parameter**)

14. We can increase the _____ of a test by increasing the sample size. (**power**)

Down

1. In a one-sample t test, the _____ _____ _____ = n - 1. (**degrees of freedom**)

3. We can ___ the probability of type II error by increasing the sample size. (**decrease**)

7. When performing inference for a difference in means, if two samples are selected they must be _____. (**independent**)

8. For paired data, use _____ _____ t procedures. (**one sample**)

11. When performing inference about one or two samples, the sample(s) must be selected at _____. (**random**)

12. If the sample size(s) are small, look at a _____ of the sample data. There should be no strong skewness or outliers. (**graph**)

Chapter 12: Solutions

Section 12.1 Concept 1:

_____ *I can state appropriate hypotheses and compute the expected counts and chi-square test statistic for a chi-square test for goodness of fit.*

H_0: Each number on the die is equally likely to be rolled.
H_a: Each number on the die is not equally likely to be rolled.

If the die was fair, we would expect each number to be rolled $300(1/6) = 50$ times.

$$\chi^2 = \frac{(42-50)^2}{50} + \frac{(55-50)^2}{50} + \frac{(38-50)^2}{50} + \cdots + \frac{(44-50)^2}{50}$$

$$\chi^2 = 10.28$$

Section 12.1 Concept 2:

_____ *I can state and check the Random, 10%, and Large Counts conditions for performing a chi-square test for goodness of fit.*
_____ *I can calculate the degrees of freedom and P-value for a chi-square test for goodness of fit.*
_____ *I can perform a chi-square test for goodness of fit.*
_____ *I can conduct a follow-up analysis when the results of a chi-square test are statistically significant.*

State:
    H_0: Each value has an equal probability (1/6) of occurring
    H_a: At least one value does not have a 1/6 chance of occurring

Plan: Chi-Square Test for Goodness of Fit
  • Random: We have a random sample of 300 die rolls.
  • 10%: Not needed, because we did not sample without replacement.
  • Large Counts: All expected counts (50) are greater than 5.

Do: $\chi^2 = 10.28$. With df = 5, the *P*-value will be between 0.05 and 0.10.

Conclude: Because the *P*-value is greater than $\alpha = 0.05$, we fail to reject the null hypothesis. We do not have convincing evidence to conclude that the die is not fair.

Section 12.2 Concept 1:

_____ *I can state appropriate hypotheses and compute the expected counts and chi-square statistic for a chi-square test based on data in a two-way table.*
_____ *I can calculate the degrees of freedom and P-value for a chi-square test based on data in a two-way table.*
_____ *I can perform a chi-square test for homogeneity.*

	Mickey Mouse	**Doc McStuffins**	**Captain Underpants**
Boys	20 (30)	30 (36)	50 (33.3)
Girls	70 (60)	80 (73.3)	50 (66.6)

Do these data provide convincing evidence that television preferences differ significantly for boys and girls?

State:

     H_0: The distribution of preferences is the same for boys and girls.

     H_a: The distributions of preference are not the same.

Plan: Chi-Square Test for Homogeneity

- Random: We have a random sample of 100 first-grade boys and an independent random sample of 200 first-grade girls.
- 10%: 100 < 10% of all first-grade boys and 200 < 10% of all first-grade girls.
- Large Counts: All expected counts are greater than 5. The smallest is 30.

Do: $\chi^2 = 19.32$. With df = 2, the P-value ≈ 0

Conclude:

Because the P-value of approximately 0 is less than 0.01, we reject the null hypothesis. We have convincing evidence to conclude that the distribution of preferences for boys and girls are not the same.

Follow-up Analysis: This table gives the observed count, followed by the expected count in parentheses, followed by the component of the Chi-Square Test Statistic.

	Mickey Mouse	**Doc McStuffins**	**Captain Underpants**
Boys	20 (30), 3.33	30 (36), 1	50 (33.3), **8.34**
Girls	70 (60), 1.67	80 (73.3), 0.61	50 (66.6), **4.17**

This follow-up analysis suggests the biggest difference occurs in the preferences for Captain Underpants, with more boys and fewer girls preferring that show than expected.

Section 12.2 Concept 2:

_____ *I can perform a chi-square test for independence*

State:

     H_0: There is no association between political leanings and views on nuclear energy.

     H_a: There is an association between political leanings and views on nuclear energy.

Plan: Chi-Square Test for Association/Independence.

	Liberal	**Conservative**	**Independent**
Approve	10 (12.15)	15 (8.55)	20 (24.3)
Disapprove	9 (7.29)	2 (5.13)	16 (14.58)
No Opinion	8 (7.56)	2 (5.32)	18 (15.12)

- Random: We have a single random sample of 100 adults.
- 10%: 100 < 10% of all adults.
- Large Counts: All expected counts are at least 5. The smallest is 5.13.

Do: $\chi^2 = 11.10$. With df = 4, the P-value = 0.025.

Conclude: Because the P-value of 0.025 < α = 0.05, we reject the null hypothesis. There is convincing evidence that there is an association between political leanings and views on nuclear energy.

Follow-up Analysis: This table gives the observed count, followed by the expected count in parentheses, followed by the component of the Chi-Square Test Statistic.

	Liberal	Conservative	Independent
Approve	10 (12.15), 0.38	15 (8.55), **4.86**	20 (24.3), 0.76
Disapprove	9 (7.29), 0.40	2 (5.13), 1.91	16 (14.58), 0.14
No Opinion	8 (7.56), 0.03	2 (5.32), 2.07	18 (15.12), 0.55

A follow-up analysis suggests the biggest difference occurs with more Conservatives approving of nuclear energy than expected.

Section 12.3 Concept 1:

_____ *I can construct and interpret a confidence interval for the slope β of the population (true) regression line.*

State: 95% CI for β
Plan: Conditions for inference are met.
Do: $-4.77 \pm 2.306(1.0105) = (-7.10, -2.44)$

Conclude: We are 95% confident the interval from −7.10 to −2.44 captures the true slope of the regression line.

Section 12.3 Concept 2:

_____ *I can interpret the values of a, b, s, and SE_b in context, and determine these values from computer output.*
_____ *I can perform a significance test about the slope β of the population (true) regression line.*

1) predicted rating score = 59.284 − 2.4008(sugar)

2) slope: $b = -2.400$. For each increase of 1g of sugar, the average rating score decreases by approximately 2.4 points.

3)
State: $H_0: \beta = 0$
      $H_a: \beta < 0$
      where β = the slope of the population regression line relating y = rating score to x = amount of sugar.
Plan: t test for β
   - Linear: The scatterplot suggests that the relationship is linear.
   - Independent: 77 < 10% of all types of cereal.
   - Normal: A dotplot of the residuals shows no strong skewness or outliers.
   - Equal SD: The scatter of the points around the line residual = 0 appears to be the same at all x-values.
   - Random: The 77 types of cereal were randomly selected.

Do: According to the computer output, $t = -10.12$ and the P-value = 0.000.

Conclude: Because the P-value is less than $\alpha = 0.01$, we reject the null hypothesis. There is convincing evidence to conclude that the slope of the true regression line is less than zero.

Chapter 12 Crossword Puzzle
INFERENCE FOR DISTRIBUTIONS AND RELATIONSHIPS

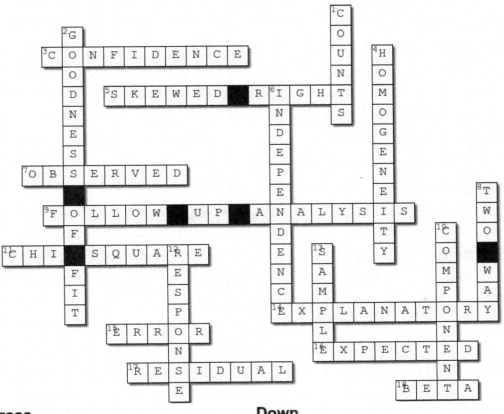

Across

3. To estimate the population (true) slope, we construct a _____ interval. (**confidence**)

5. Chi-square distributions are a family of curves that are _____. (**skewed right**)

7. Type of categorical count gathered from a sample of data. (**observed**)

9. If a chi-square test rejects the null hypothesis, be sure to conduct a _____. (**follow up analysis**)

11. A ___-____ test statistic is used to test hypotheses about distributions of categorical data. (**chi square**)

14. The x-variable is also known as the _____ variable. (**explanatory**)

15. To calculate a confidence interval, we must use the standard _____ of the slope. (**error**)

16. Type of categorical count that we would see if the null hypothesis were true. (**expected**)

17. The difference: observed y - predicted y is called a _____. (**residual**)

18. The Greek letter we use to represent the slope of the population (true) regression line. (**beta**)

Down

1. When calculating chi-square statistics, observations should be expressed in _____ rather than percents. (**counts**)

2. This test is used to determine whether a population has a certain hypothesized distribution. (**goodness of fit**)

4. A chi-square test for _____ compares the distribution of a categorical variable for several populations or treatments. (**homogeneity**)

6. To test whether there is an association between two categorical variables, use a chi-square test of association/_____. (**independence**)

8. When comparing two or more categorical variables over multiple groups, arrange the data in a _____ _____ table. (**two way**)

10. A follow-up analysis involves identifying the _____ that contributed the most to the chi-square statistic. (**component**)

12. The y-variable is also known as the _____ variable. (**response**)

13. When we construct a LSRL for a set of observed data, we construct a _____ regression line. (**sample**)

Preparing for the AP® Statistics Examination

After studying and working on statistics all year, you will have a chance to take the AP® Statistics Exam in May. Not only will you be able to apply all that you have learned, you will also have an opportunity to earn college credit for your efforts. If you earn a "passing score" on the exam, you may be eligible to receive AP® credit at a college or university. This means you will have demonstrated a level of knowledge equivalent to that of students completing an introductory statistics course. You may gain credit hours, advanced placement in a course sequence, and possibly a savings in tuition! For these reasons, it is to your advantage to do your best on the exam. Hopefully this guide has helped you understand the concepts in AP® Statistics. Not only is a strong conceptual understanding necessary, but you must also plan and prepare for the exam itself. This section is designed to help you get ready for the exam. Best of luck in your studies!

The number of students taking the AP® Statistics Exam has been increasing in recent years. In 2019, over 225,000 students took the exam and earned scores between 1 and 5.

Score	Qualification	Translation
1	No recommendation	No credit, but you're still better off after having taken the course!
2	Possibly qualified	Credit? Probably not.
3	Qualified	Maybe college credit
4	Well qualified	Most likely college credit
5	Extremely well qualified	Statistical rock star…woohoo!

Of those 2019 test takers, 59.2% earned a score of 3 or higher and have a good chance of earning college credit. And just think, the majority of students taking the exam probably didn't prepare as much as you did! After working through this Strive Guide along with your textbook, you are well poised to earn a high score on the exam!

Exam Prep Sections

1. The AP® Statistics Exam Format
2. Sample Schedule
3. Test Taking Tips
4. Updated TPS6e AP® Exam Tips by Chapter
5. Planning Your Exam Preparation and Review
6. Practice Exams

Section 1 – The AP® Statistics Exam Format

The AP® Statistics Exam is divided into two sections. The first section consists of 40 multiple-choice questions and the second section consists of 6 free-response questions. Each section counts for 50% of the total exam score.

Section I: Multiple Choice   **90 minutes**   **50% of exam score**

You will have 90 minutes to complete the 40-question multiple-choice section of the exam. Each question has five answer choices (A-E), only one of which is correct. Each correct answer earns you one point, while each question answered incorrectly (or left blank) earns you no points. It is in your best interest to answer every question, even if you need to make an educated guess! The questions will cover all of the topics and skills from the course and may require some calculation. Some may require interpreting a graph or reflecting on a given situation. Keep in mind you have just over 2 minutes per question. Don't feel it is necessary to work the questions in order. A good strategy is to work all of the ones you feel are easy and then go back to the ones that might take a little more time. Be sure to keep an eye on the clock!

The composition of the Multiple Choice section is based on both content and skills. Here are the numbers of questions for each unit and skill category.

Exam Weighting for the Multiple-Choice Section of the AP Exam

Units	Number of questions
1: Exploring One-Variable Data	6-9
2: Exploring Two-Variable Data	2-3
3: Collecting Data	5-6
4: Probability, Random Variables, and Probability Distributions	4-8
5: Sampling Distributions	3-5
6: Inference for Categorical Data: Proportions	5-6
7: Inference for Quantitative Data: Means	4-7
8: Inference for Categorical Data: Chi-Square	1-2
9: Inference for Quantitative Data: Slopes	1-2

Skills	Number of questions
Skill 1: Selecting Statistical Methods	6-9
Skill 2: Data Analysis	6-9
Skill 3: Using Probability and Simulation	12-16
Skill 4: Statistical Argumentation	10–14

Section II: Free Response   **90 minutes**   **50% of exam score**

The second section of the exam is made up of 6 free-response questions including one "investigative task." You will have 90 minutes to complete this section of the exam. You should allow about 25 minutes for the investigative task, leaving just over 12 minutes for each of the other questions. These questions are designed to measure your statistical reasoning and communication skills and are graded on the following 0-4 scale.

   4 = Complete Response {NO statistical errors and clear communication}
   3 = Substantial Response {Minor statistical error/omission or fuzzy communication}
   2 = Developing Response {Important statistical error/omission or lousy communication}
   1 = Minimal Response {A "glimmer" of statistical knowledge related to the problem}
   0 = Inadequate Response {Statistically dangerous to self and others}

Each problem is graded holistically by the AP® Statistics Readers, meaning your entire response to the problem and all its parts is considered before a score is assigned. Be sure to keep an eye on the clock so you can provide at least a basic response to each question!

Here is a breakdown of the structure of the second section of the exam.

   Part A: Questions 1–5   65 minutes   37.5% of exam score
   Part B: Question 6 (Investigative task)   25 minutes   12.5% of exam score

The composition of the Free Response section is based on skills. The first 5 free-response questions (Part A) include:
   • One multi-part question focusing primarily on Collecting Data (Skill Category 1)
   • One multi-part question focusing primarily on Exploring Data (Skill Category 2)
   • One multi-part question focusing primarily on Probability and Sampling Distributions (Skill Category 3)
   • One question focusing primarily on Inference (Skill Categories 1, 3, 4)
   • One question focusing on two or more skill categories

The sixth free-response question (Part B) is the Investigative Task, which assesses multiple skill categories and content areas, focusing on applying the skills and content in new contexts or non-routine ways.

Section 2 – Sample Schedule

This section presents a general outline to help you prepare and review for the AP® Statistics Exam. Every student has their own routine and method of studying. Consider these suggestions as you work through the course and create a plan to maximize your chance of earning a 3 or higher on the exam.

1. *At the start of your AP Statistics course*
   During the first few weeks of the school year, familiarize yourself with the course framework and AP® Statistics Exam format. It has been said that any student can hit a target that is clear and holds still for them. The course framework clearly indicates the topics you will study and skills you need to master. Both the course framework and exam format are explained in the next few sections. Additional information on the exam can be found on the College Board's AP® Central website.

2. *During your AP Statistics course*
   As you work through each chapter, be sure to read the textbook and do all assigned practice problems. Use this guide to help organize your notes, define key terms, and practice important concepts. Each chapter in this guide includes practice multiple choice and free-response questions. Be sure to try all of them and note any concepts that give you difficulty.

3. *Six weeks before the exam*
   About six weeks before the exam, begin planning for your review and preparation. If you are currently taking more than one AP® course, be sure you understand when each exam will be given and plan accordingly.

4. *Four weeks before the exam*
   In early April, you should be wrapping up your studies in the course. This is a good time to attempt a practice test. Your teacher may provide one and/or you may want to take one of the practice exams in this section. Be sure to note any concepts that give you difficulty so you can tailor your preparation and review for the actual exam. There are still several weeks of class left and plenty of time for you to review, practice, and solidify your understanding of the key concepts in the course.

5. *The week before the exam*
   The week before the exam, you should be done with your studies and should practice, practice, practice! Take this time to refresh your memory on the key concepts and review the topics that gave you the most trouble during the year. Take another practice test to get used to the exam format. Allow 90 minutes for the multiple-choice section and 90 minutes for the free-response section. Use only the formulas and tables provided on the actual exam.

6. *The day of the exam*
   You have prepared and reviewed as much as possible and are ready for the exam! Make sure you get a good night's sleep, eat a good breakfast the morning of the exam, and check that your calculator is working. Bring several pencils, a clean eraser, and arrive at your exam site early. Good luck!

Section 3 – Test Taking Tips

Once you have mastered all of the concepts and have built up your statistical communication skills, you are ready to begin reviewing for the actual exam. The following tips were written by your textbook's author, Daren Starnes, and a former AP® Statistics teacher, Sanderson Smith, and are used with permission.

General Advice

Relax, and take time to think! Remember that everyone else taking the exam is in a situation identical to yours. Realize that the problems will probably look considerably more complicated than those you have encountered in other math courses. That's because a statistics course is, necessarily, a "wordy" course.

Read each question carefully before you begin working. This is especially important for problems with multiple parts or lengthy introductions. Underline key words, phrases, and information as you read the questions.

Look at graphs and displays carefully. For graphs, note carefully what is represented on the axes, and be aware of number scale. Some questions that provide tables of numbers and graphs relating to the numbers can be answered simply by "reading" the graphs.

About graphing calculator use: As noted throughout this guide, your graphing calculator is meant to be a tool and is to be used sparingly on some exam questions. Your brain is meant to be your primary tool. Don't waste time punching numbers into your calculator unless you're sure it is necessary. Entering lists of numbers into a calculator can be time-consuming, and certainly doesn't represent a display of statistical intelligence. Do not write directions for calculator button-pushing on the exam and avoid calculator syntax, such as *normalcdf* or *1-PropZTest*.

Multiple-choice questions:
- Examine the question carefully. What statistical topic is being tested? What is the purpose of the question?
- Read carefully. After deciding on an answer, make sure you haven't made a careless mistake or an incorrect assumption.
- If an answer choice seems "too obvious," think about it. If it's so obvious to you, it's probably obvious to others, and chances are good that it is not the correct response.
- Since there is no penalty for a wrong answer or skipped problem, it is to your advantage to attempt every question or make an educated guess, if necessary.

Free-response questions:
- Do not feel it necessary to work through these problems in order. Question 1 is meant to be straightforward, so you may want to start with it. Then move to another problem that you feel confident about. Whatever you do, don't run out of time before you get to Question 6. This Investigative Task counts almost twice as much as any other question.
- Read each question carefully, sentence by sentence, and underline key words or phrases.
- Decide what statistical concept/idea is being tested. This will help you choose a proper approach to solving the problem.
- You don't have to answer a free-response question in paragraph form. Sometimes an organized set of

bullet points or an algebraic process is preferable. NEVER leave "bald answers" or "just numbers" though!

- ALWAYS answer each question in context.
- The amount of space provided on the free-response questions does not necessarily indicate how much you should write.
- If you cannot get an answer to part of a question, make up a plausible answer to use in the remaining parts of the problem.

On problems where you have to produce a graph:

- Label and scale your axes! Do not copy a calculator screen verbatim onto the exam.
- Don't refer to a graph on your calculator that you haven't drawn. Transfer it to the exam paper. Remember, the person grading your exam can't see your calculator!

Communicate your thinking clearly.

- Organize your thoughts before you write, just as you would for an English paper.
- Write neatly. The AP® Readers cannot score your solution if they can't read your writing!
- Write efficiently. Say what needs to be said, and move on. Don't ramble.
- The burden of communication is on you. Don't leave it to the reader to make inferences.
- When you finish writing your answer, look back. Does the answer make sense? Did you address the context of the problem?

Follow directions. If a problem asks you to "explain" or "justify," then be sure to do so.

- Don't "cast a wide net" by writing down everything you know, because you will be graded on everything you write. If part of your answer is wrong, you will be penalized.
- Don't give parallel solutions. Decide on the best path for your answer, and follow it through to the logical conclusion. Providing multiple solutions to a single question is generally not to your advantage. You will be graded on the lesser of the two solutions. Put another way, if one of your solutions is correct and another is incorrect, your response will be scored "incorrect."

Remember that your exam preparation begins on the first day of your AP® Statistics class. Keep in mind the following advice throughout the year.

- READ your statistics book. Most AP® Statistics Exam questions start with a paragraph that describes the context of the problem. You need to be able to pick out important statistical cues. The only way you will learn to do that is through hands-on experience.
- PRACTICE writing about your statistical thinking. Your success on the AP® Statistics Exam depends not only on how well you can "do" the statistics, but also on how well you explain your reasoning.
- WORK as many problems as you can in the weeks leading up to the exam.

Section 4 – Updated TPS6e AP® Exam Tips by Chapter

These AP® Statistics Exam tips will look familiar from reading *The UPDATED Practice of Statistics,* 6th edition. We have included them here as a valuable review as you prepare for the AP® Statistics Exam

Chapter 1 Data Analysis

- If you learn to distinguish categorical from quantitative variables now, it will pay big rewards later. You will be expected to analyze categorical and quantitative variables correctly on the AP® Statistics exam.
- When comparing groups of different sizes, be sure to use relative frequencies (percents or proportions) instead of frequencies (counts) when analyzing categorical data. Comparing only the frequencies can be misleading, as in this setting. There are many more people who never use snowmobiles among the non-environmental club members in the sample (445) than among the environmental club members (212). However, the percentage of environmental club members who never use snowmobiles is much higher (69.5% to 36.4%). Finally, make sure to avoid statements like "More club members never use snowmobiles" when you mean "A greater percentage of club members never use snowmobiles."
- Always be sure to include context when you are asked to describe a distribution. This means using the variable name, not just the units the variable is measured in.
- If you're asked to make a graph on a free-response question, be sure to label and scale your axes. Unless your calculator shows labels and scaling, don't just transfer a calculator screenshot to your paper.
- The formula sheet provided with the AP® Statistics exam also gives the sample standard deviation in the equivalent form $s_x = \sqrt{\dfrac{1}{n-1}\sum\left(x_i - \overline{x}\right)^2}$.
- You may be asked to determine whether a quantitative data set has any outliers. Be prepared to state and use the rule for identifying outliers.
- Use statistical terms carefully and correctly on the AP® Statistics exam. Don't say "mean" if you really mean "median." Range is a single number; so are Q_1, Q_3, and *IQR*. Avoid poor use of language, like "the outlier *skews* the mean" or "the median is in the middle of the *IQR*." Skewed is a shape and the *IQR* is a single number, not a region. If you misuse a term, expect to lose some credit.

Chapter 2 Modeling Distributions of Quantitative Data

- Students often do not get full credit on the AP® exam because they only use option (ii) with "calculator-speak" to show their work on Normal calculation questions—for example, normalcdf(−1000,6,6.84,1.55). This is *not* considered clear communication. To get full credit, follow the two-step process above, making sure to carefully label each of the inputs in the calculator command if you use Step 2: normalcdf(lower: −1000, upper: 6, mean: 6.84, SD:1.55).
- As noted previously, to make sure that you get full credit on the AP® Statistics exam, do not use "calculator-speak" alone—for example, invNorm(0.90,6.84,1.55). This is *not* considered clear communication. To get full credit, follow the two-step process above, making sure to carefully label each of the inputs in the calculator command if you use technology in Step 2: invNorm(area: 0.90, mean: 6.84, SD:1.55).

- Never say that a distribution of quantitative data *is* Normal. Real-world data always show at least slight departures from a Normal distribution. The most you can say is that the distribution is "approximately Normal."
- Normal probability plots are not included on the AP® Statistics Course Framework. However, these graphs are very useful for assessing Normality. You may use them on the AP® Statistics exam if you wish—just be sure that you know what you're looking for.

Chapter 3   Exploring Two-Variable Quantitative Data

- When you are asked to *describe* the association shown in a scatterplot, you are expected to discuss the direction, form, and strength of the association, along with any unusual features, *in the context of the problem.* This means that you need to use both variable names in your description.
- If you are asked to make a scatterplot, be sure to label and scale both axes. *Don't* just copy an unlabeled calculator graph directly onto your paper.
- When asked to interpret the slope or *y* intercept, it is very important to include the word *predicted* (or equivalent) in your response. Otherwise, it might appear that you believe the regression equation provides actual values of *y*.
- When displaying the equation of a least-squares regression line, the calculator will report the slope and intercept with much more precision than we need. There is no firm rule for how many decimal places to show for answers on the AP® Statistics exam. Our advice: decide how much to round based on the context of the problem you are working on.

Chapter 4   Collecting Data

- If you're asked to describe how the design of a sample survey leads to bias, you're expected to do two things: (1) describe how the members of the sample might respond differently from the rest of the population, and (2) explain how this difference would lead to an underestimate or overestimate. Suppose you were asked to explain how using your statistics class as a sample to estimate the proportion of all high school students who own a graphing calculator could result in bias. You might respond, "This is a convenience sample. It would probably include a much higher proportion of students with a graphing calculator than in the population at large because a graphing calculator is required for the statistics class. So this method would probably lead to an overestimate of the actual population proportion."
- If you are asked to identify a possible confounding variable in a given setting, you are expected to explain how the variable you choose (1) is associated with the explanatory variable and (2) is associated with the response variable.
- If you are asked to describe a completely randomized design, stay away from flipping coins. For example, suppose we ask each student in the caffeine experiment (page 279) to toss a coin. If it's heads, then the student will drink the cola with caffeine. If it's tails, then the student will drink the caffeine-free cola. As long as all 20 students toss a coin, this is still a completely randomized design. Of course, the two groups are unlikely to contain exactly 10 students because it is unlikely that 20 coin tosses will result in a perfect 50-50 split between heads and tails.

    The problem arises if we try to force the two groups to have equal sizes. Suppose we continue to have students toss coins until one of the groups has 10 students and then place the remaining students in the other group. In this case, the last two students in line are very likely to end up in the same group. However, in a completely randomized design, the last two subjects should only have a 50% chance of ending up in the same group.

- Don't mix the language of experiments and the language of sample surveys or other observational studies. You will lose credit for saying things like "use a randomized block design to select the sample for this survey" or "this experiment suffers from nonresponse because some subjects dropped out during the study."

Chapter 5 Probability

- On the AP® Statistics exam, you may be asked to describe how you will perform a simulation using rows of random digits. If so, provide a clear enough description of your process for the reader to get the same results from *only* your written explanation. Remember that every label needs to be the same length. In the golden ticket lottery example (page 334), the labels should be 01 to 95 (all two digits), not 1 to 95. When sampling without replacement, be sure to mention that repeated numbers should be ignored.

- Many probability problems involve simple computations that you can do on your calculator. It may be tempting to just write down your final answer without showing the supporting work. Don't do it! A "naked answer," even if it's correct, will usually be penalized on a free-response question.

- You can write statements like $P(A \mid B)$ if events A and B are clearly defined in a problem. Otherwise, it's probably easier to use contextual labels, like $P(I \mid F)$, as in the example on page 361. Or you can just use words: $P(\text{Instagram} \mid \text{Facebook})$.

Chapter 6 Random Variables and Probability Distributions

- If the mean of a random variable has a non-integer value but you report it as an integer, your answer will not get full credit.

- If you are asked to calculate the mean or standard deviation of a discrete random variable on a free response question, you must show numerical values substituted into the appropriate formula, as in the examples on pages 395 and 397.   Feel free to use ellipses (…) if there are many terms in the summation, as we did. You may then use the method described in Technology Corner 13 to perform the calculation with 1-Var Stats. Writing only 1-Var Stats L1, L2 and then giving the correct values of the mean and standard deviation will not earn credit for showing work. Also, be sure to avoid incorrect notation when labeling these parameters.

- Students often do not get full credit on the AP® Statistics exam because they only use option (ii) with "calculator-speak" to show their work on Normal calculation questions—for example, normalcdf(68,70,64,2.7). This is not considered clear communication. To get full credit, follow the two-step process on page 401, making sure to carefully label each of the inputs in the calculator command if you use technology in Step 2: normalcdf(lower:68, upper:70, mean:64, SD: 2.7).

- Don't rely on "calculator speak" when showing your work on free response questions. Writing binompdf(5,0.25,3) = 0.08789 will *not* earn you full credit for a binomial probability calculation. At the very least, you must indicate what each of those calculator inputs represents. For example, "binompdf(trials:5,p:0.25,x value:3) = 0.08789."

Chapter 7   Sampling Distributions

- Many students lose credit on the AP® Statistics exam when defining parameters because their description refers to the sample instead of the population or because the description isn't clear about which group of individuals the parameter is describing. When defining a parameter, we suggest including the word *all* or the word *true* in your description to make it clear that you aren't referring to a sample statistic.

- Terminology matters. Never just say "the distribution." Always say "the distribution of [blank]," being careful to distinguish the distribution of the population, the distribution of sample data, and the sampling distribution of a statistic. Likewise, don't use ambiguous terms like "sample distribution," which could refer to the distribution of sample data or to the sampling distribution of a statistic. You will lose credit on free response questions for misusing statistical terms.

- Make sure to understand the difference between accuracy and precision when writing responses on the AP® Statistics Exam. Many students use "accurate" when they really mean "precise." For example, a response that says "increasing the sample size will make an estimate more accurate" is incorrect. It should say that increasing the sample size will make an estimate more precise. If you can't remember which term to use, don't use either of them. Instead, explain what you mean without using statistical vocabulary.

- Notation matters. The symbols $\hat{p}$, $\bar{x}$, n, p, μ, σ, $\mu_{\hat{p}}$, $\sigma_{\hat{p}}$, $\mu_{\bar{x}}$, and $\sigma_{\bar{x}}$ all have specific and different meanings. Either use notation correctly—or don't use it at all. You can expect to lose credit if you use incorrect notation.

- Many students lose credit on probability calculations involving $\bar{x}$ because they forget to divide the population standard deviation by $\sqrt{n}$. Remember that averages are less variable than individual observations!

Chapter 8   Estimating Proportions with Confidence

- When interpreting a confidence interval, make sure that you are describing the parameter and not the statistic. It's wrong to say that we are 95% confident the interval from 0.613 to 0.687 captures the proportion of U.S. adults who *admitted* they would experience financial difficulty. The "proportion who *admitted* they would experience financial difficulty" is the sample proportion, which is known to be 0.65. The interval gives plausible values for the proportion who *would admit* to experiencing some financial difficulty if asked.

- On a given problem, you may be asked to interpret the confidence interval, the confidence level, or both. Be sure you understand the difference: the confidence interval gives a set of plausible values for the parameter and the confidence level describes the overall capture rate of the method.

- If a free response question asks you to construct and interpret a confidence interval, you are expected to do the entire four-step process. That includes clearly defining the parameter, identifying the procedure, and checking conditions.

- You can use your calculator to compute a confidence interval on the AP® Statistics exam. But there's a risk involved. If you just give the calculator answer with no work, you'll get either full credit for the "Do" step (if the interval is correct) or no credit (if it's wrong). If you opt for the calculator-only method, be sure to complete the other three steps, including identifying the procedure (e.g., one-sample z interval for p) and give the interval in the Do step (e.g., 0.19997 to 0.26073).

- Many students lose credit when defining parameters in an experiment by describing the sample proportion rather than the true proportion. For example, "the true proportion of the men who *had* surgery and survived 20 years" describes $\hat{p}_S$, not p_S.

- The formula for the two-sample z interval for $p_1 - p_2$ often leads to calculation errors by students. As a result, your teacher may recommend using the calculator's 2-PropZInt feature to compute the confidence interval on the AP® Statistics exam. Be sure to name the procedure (two-sample z interval for $p_1 - p_2$) in the "Plan" step and give the interval $(-0.311, 0.116)$ in the "Do" step.

Chapter 9   Testing Claims About Proportions

- Hypotheses always refer to a population, not to a sample. Be sure to state H_0 and H_a in terms of population parameters. It is *never* correct to write a hypothesis about a sample statistic, such as H_0: $\hat{p} = 0.80$ or H_a: $\overline{x} \neq 31$.

- We recommend that you follow the two-sentence structure from the example (page 591) when writing the conclusion to a significance test. The first sentence should give a decision about the null hypothesis—reject H_0 or fail to reject H_0—based on an explicit comparison of the P-value to a stated significance level. The second sentence should provide a statement about whether or not there is convincing evidence for H_a in the context of the problem.

- Notice that we did not include an option (ii) to "Use technology to find the desired area without standardizing" when performing the Normal calculation in part (b) of the example. That's because you are always required to give the standardized test statistic and the P-value when performing a significance test on the AP® Statistics exam.

- When a significance test leads to a fail to reject H_0 decision, as in the example (page 606), be sure to interpret the results as "We don't have convincing evidence for H_a." Saying anything that sounds like you believe H_0 is (or might be) true will lead to a loss of credit. For instance, it would be *wrong* to conclude, "There is convincing evidence that the true proportion of blemished potatoes is 0.08." And don't write responses as text messages, like "FTR the H_0."

- You can use your calculator to carry out the mechanics of a significance test on the AP® Statistics exam. But there's a risk involved. If you give just the calculator answer with no work, and one or more of your values are incorrect, you will probably get no credit for the "Do" step. If you opt for the calculator-only method, be sure to name the procedure (one-sample z test for a proportion) and to report the test statistic ($z = 1.15$) and P-value (0.1243).

- When making a conclusion in a significance test, be sure that you are describing the parameter and not the statistic. In the example on page 609, it's wrong to say that we have convincing evidence that the proportion of students at Yanhong's school who *said* they have never smoked differs from the CDC's claim of 0.68. The "proportion who *said* they have never smoked" is the sample proportion, which is known to be 0.60. The test gives convincing evidence that the proportion of all students at Yanhong's school who *would say* they have never smoked a cigarette differs from 0.68.

- The formula for the two-sample z statistic for a test about $p_1 - p_2$ often leads to calculation errors by students. As a result, your teacher may recommend using the calculator's 2-PropZTest feature to perform calculations on the AP® Statistics exam. Be sure to name the procedure (two-sample z interval for $p_1 - p_2$) in the "Plan" step and report the standardized test statistic ($z = 1.17$) and P-value (0.2427) in the "Do" step.

Chapter 10   Estimating Means with Confidence

- If a question on the AP® Statistics exam asks you to construct and interpret a confidence interval, all the conditions should be met. However, you are still required to state the conditions and show evidence that they are met—including a graph if the sample size is small and the data are provided.
- It is not enough just to make a graph of the data on your calculator when assessing Normality. You must *sketch* the graph on your paper to receive credit. You don't have to draw multiple graphs—any appropriate graph will do.
- The formula for the two-sample t interval for $\mu_1 - \mu_2$ often leads to calculation errors by students. Also, the interval produced by technology is narrower than the one calculated using the conservative method. As a result, your teacher may recommend using the calculator's 2-SampTInt feature to compute the confidence interval. Be sure to name the procedure (two-sample t interval for $\mu_1 - \mu_2$) in the "Plan" step and give the interval (3.9362, 17.724) and df (55.728) in the "Do" step.

Chapter 11   Testing Claims About Means

- It is not enough just to make a graph of the data on your calculator when assessing Normality. You must *sketch* the graph on your paper and make an appropriate comment about it to receive credit. You don't have to draw more than one graph—a single appropriate graph will do.
- Remember: If you give just calculator results with no work, and one or more values are wrong, you probably won't get any credit for the "Do" step. If you opt for the calculator-only method, name the procedure (one-sample t test for μ) and report the test statistic ($t = -0.94$), degrees of freedom (df = 14), and P-value (0.1809).
- The formula for the two-sample t statistic for a test about $\mu_1 - \mu_2$ often leads to calculation errors by students. Also, the P-value from technology is smaller and more accurate than the one obtained using the conservative method. As a result, your teacher may recommend using the calculator's 2-SampTTest feature to perform calculations. Be sure to name the procedure (two-sample t test for $\mu_1 - \mu_2$) in the "Plan" step and to report the standardized test statistic ($t = 1.60$), P-value (0.0644), and df (15.59) in the "Do" step.

Chapter 12   Inference for Distributions and Relationships

- The formula for the chi-square test statistic is included on the formula sheet that is provided on the AP® Statistics exam. However, it doesn't include the word *count*:

$$\chi^2 = \sum \frac{(\text{Observed} - \text{Expected})^2}{\text{Expected}}$$

We included the word *count* to emphasize that you must use the observed and expected counts—not the observed and expected proportions—when calculating the chi-square test statistic.

- When checking the Large Counts condition, be sure to examine the *expected* counts, not the observed counts. Make sure to write and label the expected counts on your paper or you won't receive credit. And never round them to the nearest integer!

- You can use your calculator to carry out the mechanics of a significance test on the AP® Statistics exam. But there's a risk involved. If you just give the calculator answer with no work, and one or more of your values is incorrect, you will likely get no credit for the "Do" step. We recommend writing out the first few terms of the chi-square calculation followed by ". . . ". This approach might help you earn partial credit if you enter a number incorrectly. Be sure to name the procedure (chi-square test for goodness of fit) and to report the test statistic ($\chi^2 = 11.2$), degrees of freedom (df = 3), and P-value (0.011).

- As with chi-square tests for goodness of fit, the expected counts should *not* be rounded to the nearest whole number. While an observed count of entrées ordered must be a whole number, an expected count need not be a whole number. The expected count gives the average number of entrées ordered if H_0 is true and the random assignment process is repeated many times.

- In the "Do" step, you aren't required to show every term in the chi-square test statistic. Writing the first few terms of the sum followed by ". . ." is considered as "showing work." We suggest that you do this and then let your calculator tackle the computations.

- You can use your calculator to carry out the mechanics of a significance test on the AP® Statistics exam. But there's a risk involved. If you just give the calculator answer without showing work, and one or more of your entries is incorrect, you will likely get no credit for the "Do" step. We recommend writing out the first few terms of the chi-square calculation followed by ". . .". This approach may help you earn partial credit if you enter a number incorrectly. Be sure to name the procedure (χ^2 test for homogeneity) and to report the test statistic ($\chi^2 = 18.279$), degrees of freedom (df = 4), and P-value (0.0011).

- Many students lose credit on the AP® Statistics exam because they don't write down the expected counts in their response. It isn't enough to claim that all the expected counts are at least 5. You must provide clear evidence.

- When the P-value is very small, the calculator will report it using scientific notation. Remember that P-values are probabilities and must be between 0 and 1. If your calculator reports the P-value with a number that appears to be greater than 1, look to the right, and you will see that the P-value is being expressed in scientific notation. If you claim that the P-value is 4.82, you will certainly lose credit.

- When you see a list of data values on an exam question, wait a moment before typing the data into your calculator. Read the question through first. Often, information is provided that makes it unnecessary for you to enter the data at all. This can save you valuable time on the AP® Statistics exam.

Section 5 – Planning Your Exam Preparation and Review

This book has been designed to help you identify your statistical areas of strength and areas in which you need improvement. If you have been working through the checks-for-understanding, multiple-choice questions, FRAPPYs, and vocabulary puzzles for each chapter, you should have an idea which topics are in need of additional study or review.

The practice tests that are included in the section of the book are designed to help you get familiar with the format of the exam as well as check your understanding of the key concepts in the course. Plan on taking both of these tests as part of your preparation and review.

Allow yourself 90 minutes for each section of the test and be sure to check your answers in the provided keys. For each question you missed, determine whether it was a simple mistake or whether you need to go back and study that topic again. After you complete the tests, continue practicing problems before the exam date.

The best preparation for the exam (other than having a solid understanding of statistics) is to practice as many multiple-choice and free-response questions as possible. Ask your teacher or refer to the College Board's AP Central website for additional resources to help you with this!

Section 6 – Practice Exams

Use the following two practice exams to help you prepare for the AP® Statistics Exam. Allow yourself 90 minutes for the multiple-choice questions, take a break, and then allow yourself 90 minutes for the free-response section. When you finish, correct your exam and note any areas in need of improvement. Answers for each exam are included in the answer key.

PRACTICE TEST #1

SECTION I
Time—1 hour and 30 minutes
Number of questions—40
Percent of total score—50

Directions: Solve each of the following problems, using the available space for scratch work. Decide which of the given choices is best and fill in the corresponding circle on the answer sheet. No credit will be given for anything written in the test book. Do not spend too much time on any one problem.

1. A statistics class wants to estimate the average number of tattoos worn by motorcyclists in their city. At a rally attended by many motorcyclists in their city, the class randomly selects 30 rally attendees and asks each attendee how many tattoos they wear. Which of the following describes the sample and the population to which it would be most reasonable for the class to generalize the results?

   (A) The sample is the 30 rally attendees, and the population is all the motorcyclists in their city.
   (B) The sample is the 30 rally attendees, and the population is all rally attendees.
   (C) The sample is all rally attendees, and the population is all motorcyclists in their city.
   (D) The sample is all rally attendees, and the population is the 30 rally attendees.
   (E) The sample is the average number of tattoos that all rally attendees have, and the population is all rally attendees.

2. An agricultural station is testing the yields for six different varieties of seed corn. The station has four large fields available, which are located in four distinctly different parts of the county. The agricultural researchers consider the climatic and soil conditions in the four parts of the county as being unequal but are reasonably confident that the land in each field is fairly uniform. The researchers divide each field into six sections and then randomly assign one variety of corn seed to each section in that field. This procedure is done for each field. At the end of the growing season, the corn will be harvested, and the yield measured in tons per acre will be compared. Which one of the following statements about the design is correct?

   (A) This is an observational study since the researchers are watching the corn grow.
   (B) This a block design with fields as blocks and seed types as treatments.
   (C) This is a block design with seed types as blocks and fields as treatments.
   (D) This is a completely randomized design since the six seed types were randomly assigned to the four fields.
   (E) This is a completely randomized design with 24 treatments—6 seed types and 4 fields.

3. A large high school offers AP Statistics and AP Calculus. Among the seniors in this school, 65% take AP Statistics, 45% take AP Calculus, and 30% take both. If a senior from this school is randomly selected, what is the probability they are in AP Statistics or AP Calculus, but not both?

    (A)   35%
    (B)   50%
    (C)   70%
    (D)   75%
    (E)   80%

4. An avid football fan wonders if there is an association between how many penalties a team commits and how many points they score. The fan collects data on the number of penalties and the total points scored in the first three weeks of a recent National Football League (NFL) season for all 32 teams. The scatterplot below shows the results of the study, and the LSRL is included on the graph.

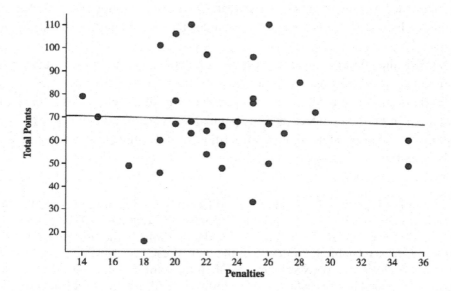

    Based on the scatterplot, which statement is **FALSE**?

    (A)   The point at (35, 60) is an outlier in regression.
    (B)   The residual plot of this data would show random scatter.
    (C)   There is a weak association between penalties and total points among these NFL teams.
    (D)   There is a slightly negative association between penalties and total points among these NFL teams.
    (E)   The point at (35, 50) has more leverage than the point at (18, 18).

5. Traffic engineers studied the traffic patterns of two busy intersections on opposite sides of town at rush hour. At the first intersection, the average number of cars waiting to turn left was 17 with a standard deviation of 4 cars. At the second intersection, the average number of cars waiting to turn left was 25 cars with a standard deviation of 7 cars. The report combined the mean number of cars at both intersections. Assuming that the number of cars waiting to turn left at each intersection is independent, what is the standard deviation of the total number of cars waiting to make a left turn at the two intersections?

   (A) $\sqrt{11}$
   (B) $\sqrt{33}$
   (C) $\sqrt{65}$
   (D) 8
   (E) 11

6. Two drugs are available to treat the flu. Adiflu is effective in curing 80% of flu cases, but results in unpleasant side effects for 45% of individuals who take it. Beneflu cures 55% of flu cases but results in unpleasant side effects for 25% of individuals who take it. Suppose 70 people take Adiflu and 90 people take Beneflu. What is the expected number of people who will experience unpleasant side effects?

   (A) 37.6
   (B) 54
   (C) 58
   (D) 105.5
   (E) 110.5

7. A pharmaceutical company has developed a new medication to lower a person's cholesterol. The advertisement for the new drug cites the results of an experiment comparing the drug with a placebo, stating that the cholesterol level had been lowered by an average of 13.2 mg/l with a P-value < 0.01. Which one of the following best explains the meaning of P-value?

   (A) There was a less than 1% difference in the mean cholesterol levels between those taking the placebo and those taking the new medication using the same experimental method.
   (B) Less than 1% of the people who were given the new cholesterol-reducing drug experienced any serious side effects.
   (C) Assuming that the placebo is equally as effective as the medication, we would have obtained a difference such as this or greater, in less than 1% of samples by random chance.
   (D) All but 1% of the people who were given the experimental drug experienced a drop of 13.2 mg/l when compared to the placebo group.
   (E) The difference in the mean cholesterol levels between those taking the placebo and those taking the medication was not significant at the 1% level.

8. A simple random sample of 100 batteries is selected from a process that produces batteries with a mean lifetime of 32 hours and a standard deviation of 3 hours. Thus, the standard deviation of the sampling distribution of the mean, $\sigma_{\bar{x}}$, is equal to 0.3. If the sample size had been 400, how would the value of $\sigma_{\bar{x}}$ change?

   (A) It is one-fourth as large as when $n = 100$.
   (B) It is one-half as large as when $n = 100$.
   (C) It is twice as large as when $n = 100$.
   (D) It is four times as large as when $n = 100$.
   (E) The value of $\sigma_{\bar{x}}$ does not change.

9. A poll of 83 AP Statistics students asked, "How many hours a week do you spend studying statistics?" The results are summarized in the computer output below.

Variable	N	Mean	Median	TrMean		StDev
Hours	83	8.5	7.2	7.38		4.9
	Minimum	Maximum	Q1	Q3		
Hours	0.00	25.00	5	12		

   If a boxplot of this data was constructed, according to the $1.5 \times IQR$ rule, what data points would be marked as outliers?

   (A) Any points greater than 10.5
   (B) Any points greater than 17
   (C) Any points greater than 17.7
   (D) Any points greater than 22.5
   (E) Any points greater than 25

10. A child psychologist claims the mean attention span for a 1-year old is 12 seconds. An advocacy group claims exposure to a popular cartoon results in a decrease in attention span. To investigate this claim, which of the following hypotheses would be appropriate?

    (A) $H_0: \mu < 12$ and $H_a: \mu = 12$
    (B) $H_0: \mu > 12$ and $H_a: \mu = 12$
    (C) $H_0: \mu = 12$ and $H_a: \mu < 12$
    (D) $H_0: \mu = 12$ and $H_a: \mu > 12$
    (E) $H_0: \mu = 12$ and $H_a: \mu \neq 12$

11. Prospective sales people for a high-tech company are now being offered a sales training program before they start working for the company. Previous data indicates that the mean number of sales per month for those who did not participate in the program is 28. To determine whether the sales-training program is effective, a random sample of 32 new sales personnel is given the training. The company is interested in assessing whether the sales program significantly increases the mean monthly sales as there will be a considerable investment in time and money to conduct the training program. The null and alternative hypotheses would be $H_0: \mu = 28$ and $H_a: \mu > 28$. Which of the following describes a Type II error?

   (A) The company finds convincing evidence that sales have increased when, in fact, they have. The company implements the sales program and recovers the cost of the training program.
   (B) The company finds convincing evidence that sales have increased when, in fact, they have not increased. The company implements the sales program and doesn't recover its costs for the training.
   (C) The company finds no convincing evidence that sales have increased when, in fact, they have not increased. The company does not implement the sales program and doesn't waste the money on training.
   (D) The company finds no convincing evidence that sales have increased when, in fact, they have. The company does not implement the sales program and misses out on a chance to increase sales.
   (E) The company takes more samples to ensure that they make the correct decision.

12. Researchers wanted to know if playing soft music improved students' performance on tests. Twelve students worked a complicated paper-and-pencil maze while listening to music and again while not listening to music. The order of music and non-music was randomly decided, and the mazes were completed one week apart. The time to complete each maze (in seconds) was recorded and the results are shown in the following table.

Subject	1	2	3	4	5	6	7	8	9	10	11	12
Time with music	83	79	73	76	75	79	74	67	80	69	71	63
Time without music	89	82	85	82	81	90	75	69	74	82	78	68

Which one of the following test procedures would be the most appropriate in order determine if there is a significant difference in average time to complete the maze?

   (A) A chi-square test for independence.
   (B) A two-sample test for a difference in proportions.
   (C) A t test on the slope of the regression line.
   (D) A two-sample t test for a difference in means.
   (E) A matched pairs t test for a mean difference.

13. A cereal manufacturer is packaging collectible cards from a popular movie in each box of cereal. One card, a holographic card of a memorable scene, is more rare than the others and occurs in only 3% of boxes. Which of the following represents the probability that the fifth box you purchase will contain your first holographic card?

(A) $\binom{5}{1}(0.97)^4(0.03)^1$

(B) $(0.97)^4(0.03)^1$

(C) $(0.97)^1(0.03)^4$

(D) $1 - (0.97)^5$

(E) $1 - (0.03)^5$

14. A local bridge club has 120 members. A cumulative relative frequency graph of their ages is shown in the figure below. Approximately how many of the bridge club members are more than 80 years of age?

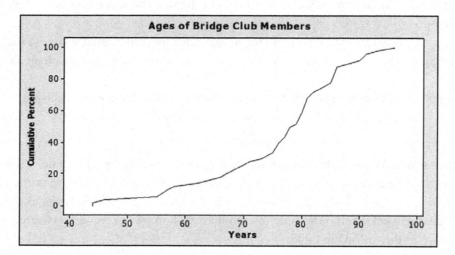

(A)   42

(B)   50

(C)   70

(D)   85

(E)   92

15. A study tested a recently advertised claim that a newly developed "gas pill" boosts mileage when added to a tank of gas. Ten randomly selected new cars were used in the study and would be run over an identical course twice, once with the additive and once without the additive. The order of the two treatments (pill and no pill) was randomized. Each car's tank was filled with a standard gasoline and one of the treatments applied. The car was then driven until the tank was empty. The car's tank was then refilled with the same standard gasoline and the process repeated for the other treatment. Professional drivers drove over the same course at identical speeds and did not know which treatment was used. The miles per gallon for each car were calculated under both treatments. Let μ_1 is the mean mileage for all cars that would be driven without the gas pill and μ_2 is the mean mileage for all cars that would be driven with the gas pill. The 95% confidence interval for the mean difference is given by (–0.13, 1.73).

Based on the information, which one of the following statements is TRUE?

(A)   Ninety-five percent of the time, the confidence interval will contain 0.
(B)   A two-sample t test should have been used instead of a paired t test.
(C)   The true mean mileage is higher for cars without the additive than those with the additive since the mean difference is positive.
(D)   The sample size is too small to draw any conclusions.
(E)   Since the interval contains 0, we cannot conclude that using the gas pill made a difference in mileage.

16. A shipping department of a large company claims they have 5 shipments returned per day, on average. The finance department believes it is more than 5. The finance department selects 100 days at random and records how many returned shipments there were each day. With all conditions for inference met, a significance test resulted in a P-value of 0.106.

For a significance level of $\alpha = 0.05$, which of the following is a correct conclusion?

(A)   The P-value is less than 0.05, and the null hypothesis is rejected. There is convincing statistical evidence that the true mean is more than 5.
(B)   The P-value is less than 0.05, and the null hypothesis is not rejected. There is not convincing statistical evidence that the true mean is less than 5.
(C)   The P-value is greater than 0.05, and the null hypothesis is rejected. There is not convincing statistical evidence that the true mean is more than 5.
(D)   The P-value is greater than 0.05, and the null hypothesis is not rejected. There is convincing statistical evidence that the true mean is 5.
(E)   The P-value is greater than 0.05, and the null hypothesis is not rejected. There is not convincing statistical evidence that the true mean is more than 5.

17. Eight people who suffer from hay fever volunteer to test a new medication that will relieve the symptoms. The last names of the volunteers are

(1) Rodriguez, (2) Liu, (3) Brown, (4) Kim, (5) Harris, (6) Munoz, (7) Klein, (8) Scott

Four of the volunteers will receive the new medication, while the other four will receive a placebo as part of a double-blind experiment. Starting at the left of the list of random numbers below and reading from left to right, assign the four people to be given the medication.

07119 97336 71048 08178 77233 13916 47564 81056 97025 85977 29372

The four people assigned to the treatment group are

(A)   Rodriguez, Liu, Brown, Klein
(B)   Liu, Harris, Klein, Scott
(C)   Rodriguez, Brown, Munoz, Klein
(D)   Rodriguez, Brown, Klein, Scott
(E)   Rodriguez, Kim, Klein, Scott

18. A farmer randomly sampled 46 sheep from a very large herd to construct a 95% confidence interval to estimate the mean weight of wool (in pounds) from a sheep in her herd. The interval obtained was (23.7, 33.6). If the farmer had used a 90% confidence interval instead, the confidence interval would have been which of the following?

(A)   Narrower and the resulting estimate would have been more precise.
(B)   Narrower and the resulting estimate would have been less precise.
(C)   Narrower but the precision cannot be determined.
(D)   Wider and the resulting estimate would have been more precise.
(E)   Wider and the resulting estimate would have been less precise.

19. Company A has 500 employees and Company B has 5000 employees. Union negotiators want to compare the salary distributions for the two companies. Which one of the following would be the most useful for accomplishing this comparison?

(A)   Dotplots for A and B drawn on the same scale.
(B)   Back-to-back stemplots for A and B.
(C)   Two frequency histograms for A and B drawn on the same scale.
(D)   Two relative-frequency histograms for A and B drawn on the same scale.
(E)   A scatterplot of A versus B.

20. Most flights at airports leave at their posted departure time. The frequency table below summarizes the times in the last month at a major airport where flights have been delayed past their posted departure time. The delays occurred for a variety of reasons—mechanical problems with the plane, congestion on the tarmac, the previous flight at a gate was late in leaving, weather, etc.

Delay Time	Frequency
Less than 10 minutes	11
At least 10 but less than 20 minutes	37
At least 20 but less than 30 minutes	33
At least 30 but less than 40 minutes	30
At least 40 but less than 50 minutes	26
At least 50 but less than 60 minutes	14
At least 60 but less than 70 minutes	6
At least 70 minutes	3

Which one of the following represents possible values for the median and mean delay times for flights from this major airport?

(A)   Median = 27 minutes and mean = 24 minutes
(B)   Median = 29 minutes and mean = 29 minutes
(C)   Median = 29 minutes and mean = 32 minutes
(D)   Median = 31 minutes and mean = 35 minutes
(E)   Median = 35 minutes and mean = 39 minutes

21. A national tabloid newspaper wants to estimate the true proportion of all people who believe that life exists elsewhere in the universe. What is the least number of people that should be sampled in order to estimate the true proportion of those who believe that life exists elsewhere within 0.04 of the real answer with 95% confidence? Past data indicate that 30% of the general population holds this belief.

(A)   11
(B)   356
(C)   505
(D)   610
(E)   711

22. Consumers frequently complain that there is a large variation in prices charged by different pharmacies for the same medication. A survey of a large sample of the pharmacies in a major city revealed that the prices charged for one bottle containing 50 tablets of a popular pain reliever were approximately normally distributed. The charge of $10.48 for this bottle was at the 90th percentile and 20% of the bottles cost less than $8.61. What are, respectively, the approximate mean and standard deviation of the price distribution for bottles containing 50 tablets of the pain reliever in this major city?

    (A) $9.35 and $0.88
    (B) $9.41 and $2.67
    (C) $9.55 and $0.88
    (D) $9.55 and $1.70
    (E) $9.73 and $1.70

23. The fertilizers often contain nitrogen, phosphate, and potassium to encourage fruit production. A study of the effect of various amounts of nitrogen on the yield, measured in pounds per plant, of 10 plots of tomato plants resulted in the following computer output:

Predictor	Coef	SE Coef	T	P
Constant	10.100	0.7973	12.67	0.000
Nitrogen	1.150	0.1879	6.12	0.000

    S = 0.8404   R-Sq = 82.4%   R-Sq(adj) = 80.2%

    Which of the following would represent a 99% confidence interval to estimate the true slope of the regression line of yield on nitrogen? Assume all conditions for inference are met.

    (A) $1.150 \pm 3.355(0.8404)$

    (B) $1.150 \pm 3.169\left(\dfrac{0.8404}{\sqrt{10}}\right)$

    (C) $1.150 \pm 6.120(0.1879)$

    (D) $1.150 \pm 3.355(0.1879)$

    (E) $1.150 \pm 3.169(0.1879)$

24. Flossing helps prevent tooth decay and gum disease. Yet reports suggest millions of Americans never floss. You are planning a sample survey to determine the proportion of the students at your high school who never floss. Which of the following will result in the largest margin of error?

    (A) A sample size of 200 and a confidence level of 95%
    (B) A sample size of 200 and a confidence level of 96%
    (C) A sample size of 200 and a confidence level of 99%
    (D) A sample size of 300 and a confidence level of 96%
    (E) A sample size of 300 and a confidence level of 99%

25. A statistics class took a random sample of students at their large high school to find the proportion of those who claimed to be vegetarians. This class found 12 out of the 150 students questioned were vegetarians. Another statistics class in a different large high school took a similar random sample of the students at its school and found that 10 out of 90 claimed to be vegetarians. Which one of the following represents the approximate 90% confidence interval for the difference between the proportions of students of the two schools that would claim to be vegetarians?

(A) $-0.031 \pm 1.645 \left(\frac{(0.08)(0.92)+(0.111)(0.889)}{\sqrt{150+90}} \right)$

(B) $-0.031 \pm 1.645 \left(\frac{(0.08)(0.92)}{\sqrt{150}} + \frac{(0.111)(0.889)}{\sqrt{90}} \right)$

(C) $-0.031 \pm 1.645 \left(\sqrt{\frac{(0.08)(0.92)}{150} + \frac{(0.111)(0.889)}{90}} \right)$

(D) $-0.031 \pm 1.960 \left(\frac{(0.08)(0.92)}{\sqrt{150}} + \frac{(0.111)(0.889)}{\sqrt{90}} \right)$

(E) $-0.031 \pm 1.960 \left(\sqrt{\frac{(0.08)(0.92)}{150} + \frac{(0.111)(0.889)}{90}} \right)$

26. A study performed by a psychologist determined that a person's score on a resiliency test is linearly related to the person's score on an inventory measuring the person's overall health. The equation of the least-squares regression line is $\widehat{resiliency} = -49 + 1.8(health)$. What is the residual for an individual with an overall health score of 110 and a resiliency score of 140?

(A) −30
(B) −9
(C) 9
(D) 30
(E) 149

27. A large sales company recruits many graduating students from universities for its workforce. Thirty percent of those hired for management positions come from private universities and colleges and the rest from public colleges and universities. It is very expensive and time-consuming to train new managers, so the company is examining its retention rate (those still working for the company after six years) of these hires. Over the past six years, 35% of those managers who were hired from private schools had left for other jobs, while 20% of those from public schools had done so. What is the probability that a randomly selected person, who left the company within the past six years, was hired from a private university or college?

(A) 0.105
(B) 0.4286
(C) 0.2308
(D) 0.35
(E) 0.2450

28. In a recent social research poll, 4800 randomly selected adults aged 18 to 26 were asked to record the number of hours they spent watching television and the number of non-work-related hours they spent surfing the Web during a typical week. Parallel boxplots of the data are given below.

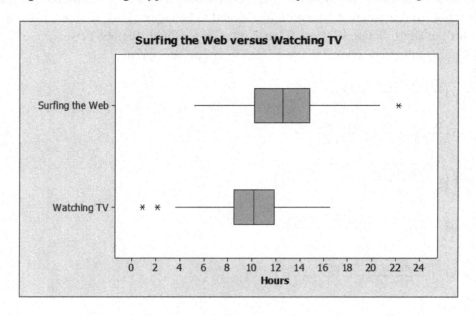

Based on the plots, which one of the following statements is **FALSE**?

(A)   The range of the distribution of hours spent surfing the Web is higher than the range for the distribution of hours spent watching television.

(B)   On average, adults aged 18 to 26 spent more time surfing the Web than watching television.

(C)   The median number of hours spent surfing the Web is higher than the median number of hours spent watching television.

(D)   The *IQR* for hours spent surfing the Web is smaller than the *IQR* for hours spent watching TV.

(E)   Both distributions have at least one outlier.

29. Three distributions are shown below. One represents the distribution of original values, one represents the approximate sampling distribution of means for samples of size $n = 5$, and one is the approximate sampling distribution of means for samples of size 20. If the distributions are ordered by original, means for $n = 5$, and means for $n = 20$, which of the following gives the correct order?

(A)   A, B, C
(B)   B, A, C
(C)   B, C, A
(D)   C, A, B
(E)   C, B, A

30. A dice game pays a player $5 for rolling a 3 or a 5 with a single die. The player has to pay $2 if any other number is rolled. If a person plays the game 30 times, what is the approximate probability that the person will win at least $15?

(A)   0.0030
(B)   0.0643
(C)   0.2767
(D)   0.3085
(E)   0.3910

31. A study is conducted to determine the effectiveness of mental exercises on short-term memory. A randomized comparative experiment is conducted, and the number of items recalled on a short-term memory test is recorded for 25 individuals who practiced mental exercises and 35 individuals who did not. The individuals who practiced mental exercises recalled 16.0 items on average with a variance of 6.25. The individuals that did not do any mental exercises recalled 12.5 items on average with a variance of 7.29. Assuming the conditions for inference are met, which expression shows the correct standard error for a two-sample t interval for a difference in means?

(A) $\sqrt{6.25 + 7.29}$

(B) $\sqrt{\dfrac{6.25}{25} + \dfrac{7.29}{35}}$

(C) $\sqrt{6.25 - 7.29}$

(D) $\sqrt{\dfrac{6.25}{25} - \dfrac{7.29}{35}}$

(E) $\sqrt{\dfrac{6.25}{60} + \dfrac{7.29}{60}}$

32. In a random sample of older patients at a large medical practice, the age of a patient and a measure of that patient's hearing loss were recorded. The correlation between age and hearing loss of the patients in the sample was found to be 0.7. Which one of the following would be a correct statement if the age of a patient were used to predict the amount of hearing loss for a patient?

(A) About 49% of the variation in age can be explained by the least-squares regression line using hearing loss as the explanatory variable.

(B) About 49% of the variation in hearing loss can be explained by the least-squares regression line using age as the explanatory variable.

(C) About 70% of the variation in hearing loss can be explained by the least-squares regression line using age as the explanatory variable.

(D) About 70% of a person's hearing loss can be explained by age, according to the regression line relating hearing loss and age.

(E) About 70% of the time, age will correctly predict the amount of hearing loss.

33. There are an ever-increasing number of sources for getting the daily news—traditional newspapers, online, radio, nightly television newscasts, comedy shows, cell phones, podcasts, etc. In a recent telephone survey, 3204 randomly selected adults were asked to cite their primary source of daily news. Four in 10 adults said that they read a newspaper, either in print or online, almost every day. A 98% confidence interval to estimate the true proportion of adults who would read either a print newspaper or its online equivalent for their daily news is given by (0.38, 0.42). Which of the following is a correct interpretation of the confidence level?

   (A) Ninety-eight percent of all samples of this size would yield a confidence interval of (0.38, 0.42).
   (B) There is a 98% chance that the true proportion of readers who would read either a print newspaper or its online equivalent for their daily news is in the interval (0.38, 0.42).
   (C) The procedure used to generate this interval will capture the true proportion of readers who would read either a print newspaper or its online equivalent for their daily news in 98% of samples.
   (D) Ninety-eight percent of all of the samples of size 3204 lie in the confidence interval (0.38, 0.42).
   (E) There is a 98% chance that a randomly selected reader is one of the 40% who would read a print newspaper or its online equivalent for their daily news.

34. A school counselor believes that students who enroll in a fine arts class (like band, orchestra, or choir) are more likely to participate in a fine arts activity (such as the school musical, play, or speech). The table below shows data that were collected from a random sample of high school students in a large city.

| | | Class | | | |
		Band	Orchestra	Choir	Total
Activity	One-Act Play	42	21	5	68
	Musical	120	59	10	189
	Speech	20	10	15	45
	Total	182	90	30	302

What is the expected count for the cell for the musical and orchestra?

   (A) 59

   (B) $\dfrac{(59)(90)}{302}$

   (C) $\dfrac{(59)(189)}{302}$

   (D) $\dfrac{(90)(189)}{302}$

   (E) $\dfrac{(59)(302)}{189}$

35. A tax assessor has developed a model to predict the value (in thousands of dollars) of a home based on the square footage of the home. The accompanying computer printout summarizes the findings.

Variable	Coef	SE	T	P
CONSTANT	35.70032	6.9533214	13.049	0.0237
SQFEET	0.14875	0.0030725	4.014	0.0017

Based on the information, which of the following is the best interpretation for the slope of the least-squares regression line?

(A)   Each additional square-foot increase in the size of the house will increase the predicted home value by approximately $35.70.

(B)   Each additional square-foot increase in the size of the house will increase the predicted home value by approximately $14.88.

(C)   Each additional square-foot increase in the size of the house will increase the predicted home value by approximately $148.75.

(D)   Each additional 1000 square-foot increase in the size of the house will increase the predicted home value by approximately $35,700.32.

(E)   Each additional square-foot increase in the size of the house will increase the predicted home value by approximately $35.70.

36. Emily, a superintendent of a school district, is interested in discovering student opinions about the quality of extracurricular activities, such as clubs and athletics, offered at the various campuses. The district has 2 high schools, 4 middle schools, and 10 elementary schools. To obtain a sample of district students, Emily first selects a random sample of students from each high school, then from each middle school, then from each elementary school. What type of sampling procedure did she implement?

(A) A simple random sample
(B) A stratified random sample
(C) A cluster sample
(D) A systematic random sample
(E) A convenience sample

37. A certain candy has different color wrappers for various holidays. During holiday #1 the candy wrappers are 50% red and 50% green. During holiday #2 the wrapper colors are 30% red, 30% silver, and 40% pink. Fifty pieces of candy are randomly selected from the holiday #1 distribution and 50 pieces of candy are randomly selected from the holiday #2 distribution. Respectively, what is the expected number and standard deviation of the total number of red wrappers from both holiday distributions?

(A)   40, 23
(B)   40, 4.796
(C)   40, 6.776
(D)   80, 4.796
(E)   80, 6.776

38. A city manager is interested in how a certain program helped change the city's distribution of household income. The manager selects a random sample of 1758 households and obtains their household income information. The results were compared to a similar poll of 1494 randomly selected households in 2015. The table below summarizes the data for household income.

Household Income	Current	2015
Under $30,000	196	184
$30,000 – under $50,000	414	316
$50,000 – under $75,000	488	382
At least $75,000	660	612

A chi-square test was performed, which resulted in a P-value of 0.0760. Which of the following conclusions is correct?

(A) At the 5% level of significance, there is sufficient evidence that the distribution of household income has not changed since 2015.

(B) At the 5% level of significance, there is sufficient evidence that the distribution of household income has changed since 2015.

(C) At the 5% level of significance, there is sufficient evidence to conclude that an association exists between the year and the distribution of household income.

(D) At the 10% level of significance, there is sufficient evidence that the distribution of household income has not changed since 2015.

(E) At the 10% level of significance, there is sufficient evidence that the distribution of household income has changed since 2015.

39. A pharmaceutical company wants to test two new acid reflux medications, A and B, to see which is most effective in relieving the reflux in the shortest amount of time. The researchers plan to give the two medications in three dosages: 50 mg, 100 mg, and 150 mg. They have 120 volunteers available for the study. For this part of the study, researchers think that the weight of the patient might play a role in the incidence of reflux disease. Volunteers are separated into 20 groups—the six heaviest, the next six heaviest, and so on, down to the six lightest. Within each group of six, three are randomly assigned to medication A and three to medication B. Within each medication group of three, one is randomly assigned to each dosage. Which one of the following statements best describes this experiment?

(A) There are two treatments, participants were blocked on weight, and the response variable is time until pain relief is achieved.

(B) There are two treatments, participants were blocked on dosage, and the response variable is time until pain relief is achieved.

(C) There are three treatments, participants were blocked on medication A and B, and the response variable is proportion of participants who achieved pain relief.

(D) There are six treatments, participants were blocked on weight, and the response variable is time until pain relief is achieved.

(E) There are six treatments, participants were blocked on weight, and the response variable is proportion of participants who achieved pain relief.

40. Researchers plan to conduct a study of cell phone usage among middle school children. They will select a simple random sample of children and record the number of hours that each of the children spends on their cell phones each week. The researchers will report the sample mean as a point estimate for the population mean. Which of the following statements is correct for the sample mean as a point estimator?

    (A)   A sample of size 30 will produce a more biased estimator than a sample of size 60.
    (B)   A sample of size 30 will produce a less biased estimator than a sample size of 60.
    (C)   A sample of size 30 will produce more variability of the estimator than a sample of size 50.
    (D)   A sample of size 30 will produce less variability of the estimator than a sample of size 60.
    (E)   A sample of size 30 will produce a biased estimator, but a sample size of 60 will produce an unbiased estimator.

PRACTICE TEST #1

SECTION II
Part A
Questions 1-5
Spend about 1 hour and 5 minutes on this part of the exam.
Percent of Section II score—75

Directions: Show all your work. Indicate clearly the methods you use, because you will be scored on the correctness of your methods as well as on the accuracy and completeness of your results and explanations.

1. A journalist is writing an article about what movie genre—horror, action/adventure, or comedy—that teen and adult moviegoers prefer. The journalist selects a systematic random sample of 80 moviegoers at the local movie theater during a day when over 1600 moviegoers attended the theater. The segmented bar graph below shows the movie genre preferences of the people included in the sample.

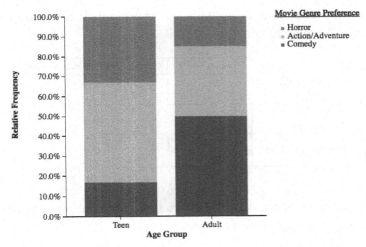

(a) Describe the association between movie genre preference and age group.

(b) The journalist used a systematic random sample to collect the 80 responses. Describe how this process may have been implemented in this context.

(c) The journalist's sample consisted of 60 teens and 20 adults. Use the following grid to sketch a mosaic plot of movie genre preference among teens and adults based on the graph in part (a).

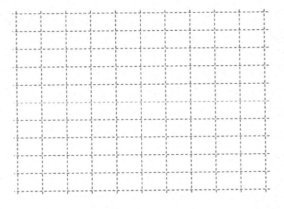

2. A graduate student who is studying dentistry is interested in comparing three different types of toothbrushes. The student recruited 60 volunteers to participate in the study. The volunteers will be divided evenly among three groups, where each group will use one of the three types of toothbrushes twice a day. The student will measure the amount of plaque on each subject's teeth before and after the treatment. Plaque is a substance that grows on teeth that causes cavities and gum disease.

    (a) Describe a process that the student can use in order to randomly assign the treatments to the subjects in this study.

    (b) Why is it important that the student implements random assignment in this experiment?

    (c) If the student finds statistically significant evidence that the subjects in one treatment group have less plaque than the other groups, on average, would the student be able to conclude that the toothbrush caused the reduction of plaque? Explain your answer.

3. A candy manufacturer is marketing a gift box containing four chocolate creams and five pieces of fudge. The manufacturing process for each candy and each empty box is designed with the specifications shown in the table below.

	Mean (oz.)	Standard Deviation (oz.)
One chocolate cream	3	0.2
One piece of fudge	4	0.3
The empty box	3	0.1

    The weights of the chocolate creams, the pieces of fudge, and the empty boxes are independent and each distribution of weight is approximately normal.

    (a) What are the mean and standard deviation of the weight of the full box of candy?

    (b) What is the probability that a randomly selected full box of candy will weigh less than 34 ounces?

    (c) What is the probability that at least one of three randomly selected full boxes of candy will weigh less than 34 ounces?

4. A gluten free diet is a diet that excludes certain grains, such as wheat, barley, and rye. Certain health problems require individuals to eat a gluten-free diet. A group of researchers reviewed a database with information from large-scale national surveys used to investigate the health and diet of American adults. In 2010, the researchers found that 0.5% of 2105 randomly selected survey participants were eating a GF diet. By 2014, they found that 2% of 1757 randomly selected survey participants were on a GF diet.

Do the data provide convincing statistical evidence, at the level of = 0.05, that there has been an increase in the proportion of American adults who eat a GF diet?

5. A large city wants to set up a citywide program to recycle newspapers, glass, and plastics as a way to reduce the amount of landfill, preserve the environment, and ultimately save the city some money. An analyst for one of the companies interested in bidding on the recycling contract has computed that they would be able to make a profit if the mean weekly household contribution to recycling exceeds 20 pounds. If this company can make a profit, then it is financially feasible for them to spend the money necessary to build a recycling plant, set up a collection system, and hire the necessary workers. In order to test the hypotheses, $H_0: \mu = 20$ and $H_a: \mu > 20$, the analyst will track the recycling contribution of a random sample of households over a 6-week period.

(a) What type of study design—experiment, prospective observational study, or retrospective observational study—will the analyst use? Explain your answer.

(b) The company is concerned about a Type II error. Describe the economic consequences to the company if a Type II error occurs.

(c) The analyst performs a statistical test with a significance level of 0.01 with a sample size of 100 randomly selected households. The power of this statistical test against an alternative of $\mu = 25$ was calculated to be 0.72. Interpret this value in context.

SECTION II
Part B
Question 6
Spend about 25 minutes on this part of the exam.
Percent of Section II score—25

Directions: Show all your work. Indicate clearly the methods you use, because you will be scored on the correctness of your methods as well as on the accuracy and completeness of your results and explanations.

6. Suppose that in soccer, in games where the teams are not evenly matched, the better team has a 72% probability of scoring the first goal in overtime of any game. If a team has six overtime games, and is considered the better team in all of them, what is the probability that this team will score the first overtime goal in at least five out of these six games? Answer the question using simulation.

    (a) Describe the design of a simulation using the table of random digits below to estimate the desired probability.

    (b) Using the random number table below, perform 12 trials of the simulation. Make your procedure clear by marking on or above the table so that someone can follow what you did. Make a table of your results. From your simulation, determine the estimated probability of scoring the first overtime goal in at least five of the six games.

84177 06757 17613 15582 51506 81435 41050 92031 06449 05059

59884 31180 53115 84469 94868 57967 05811 84514 75011 13006

63395 55041 15866 06589 13119 71020 85940 91932 09488 74987

54355 52704 90359 02649 47496 71567 94268 08844 26294 64759

08989 57024 97284 00637 89283 03514 59195 07635 03309 72605

29357 23737 67881 03668 33876 35841 52869 23114 15864 38942

(c) Below are two simulations of 200 trials each for the playing of six overtime games. One represents a team that is fairly evenly matched with its opponent, and the other represents a team that is better than its opponent. Which distribution represents which team? Explain your reasoning.

Distribution A

Distribution B

Answer Key for Practice Test 1
Part I Multiple Choice Section Solutions

Problem	Answer	Explanation
1	B	The sample is the 30 selected individuals at the rally. The population is all those at the rally. Although the students want to estimate the average number of tattoos that motorcyclists in the city have, they did not select their sample from the entire city, but only those at the rally.
2	B	Because the four fields are different and we want to account for these differences we will block by field and plant all six varieties of seed in each field. The varieties of seed corn are the treatments that are being applied to the fields.
3	B	 		Stats	Not Stats
Calc	0.30	0.15
Not Calc	0.35	0.20 | P(Calc and not Stat OR Stat and not Calc) $= 0.35 + 0.15 = 0.50$
4	A	To be an outlier in regression, the point should have a large residual compared to the other points. The point at (35, 60) has a small residual, so it is not an outlier in regression.
5	C	Because the number of cars at the two intersections are independent, we add the variances: $\sigma_T = \sqrt{4^2 + 7^2} = \sqrt{65}$
6	A	Expected number of individuals with side effects from Adiflu + expected number of individuals with side effects from Beneflu = $(0.8)(0.45)(70) + (0.55)(0.25)(90) = 37.575$
7	C	The P-value is the probability of obtaining a sample statistic at least as extreme as that found in the experiment (a difference of 13.2), given that the placebo is equally as effective as the medication.
8	B	Because $\sigma_{\bar{x}} = \dfrac{\sigma}{\sqrt{n}}$, multiplying the sample size by 4 would divide the standard deviation of the sampling distribution for the mean by $\sqrt{4n} = 2\sqrt{n}$. Therefore, quadrupling the sample size will cut the standard deviation in half.

9	D	A data point is an outlier if it lies above $Q_3 + 1.5(IQR)$ or below $Q_1 - 1.5(IQR)$. The lower bound is $Q_1 - 1.5(IQR) = 5 - 1.5(12 - 5) = -5.5$. Because negative data points are impossible in this context, there cannot be any low outliers. The upper bound is $Q_3 + 1.5(IQR) = 12 + 1.5(12 - 5) = 22.5$. Any point above this value is an outlier.
10	C	The null hypothesis always includes an equal sign. The one-sided alternative hypothesis in this case is less than 12 seconds.
11	D	A Type II error occurs when we fail to reject a null hypothesis when the alternative hypothesis is true. In this case, that would indicate that we fail to reject H_0: $\mu = 28$ (sales have not increased), when, in fact, $\mu > 28$. Thus, the company concludes that average sales per month have not increased when they actually have. The company loses the chance to make more money.
12	E	There are two measurements on each subject (time with music versus time without music). Each subject serves as his or her own control. This is a matched pairs experiment.
13	B	This is a geometric distribution with $P(\text{success}) = 0.03$. Because the fifth customer is the "first success", we have four failures and then a success, so $P(X = 5) = (0.97)^4(0.03)^1$.
14	A	Mark a vertical line at 80 years on the x-axis. At the point where this line intersects the cumulative relative frequency graph, make a horizontal line. This is about the 65% mark. This means that 65% of the all members are less than 80 years of age. Therefore 35% are at least 80 years of age and $0.35(120) = 42$ members.
15	E	(A) False. The confidence interval either contains 0 or it does not. (B) False. The data are clearly paired. (C) False. Even though the mean difference is positive, the confidence interval contains negative values that are plausible for the true mean difference in gas mileage based on the sample data. (D) False. A sample of size 10 can be sufficient to make a conclusion. (E) True. Because the confidence interval contains zero, there is no statistically significant difference between the additive and the non-additive. We cannot conclude that the pill is effective in improving gas mileage.

16	E	Because the *P*-value is greater than the significance level (0.106 > 0.05), we fail to reject the null hypothesis. We cannot find convincing evidence for the alternative with high *P*-values. The finance department does not have convincing statistical evidence that the average number of returned shipments is more than 5 per day.
17	C	The subjects are labeled as 1, 2, 3, 4, 5, 6, 7, 8. <u>Ignore repeats</u> because subjects were not used more than once. The random numbers chosen are 0 <u>7</u> <u>1</u> 1 9 9 7 <u>3</u> 3 <u>6</u> resulting in the selection of 7, 1, 3, 6. This corresponds to Klein, Rodriguez, Brown, and Munoz.
18	A	Decreasing the confidence level would make the confidence interval narrower because the critical *z*-value would be smaller. A narrower interval leads to a more precise estimate.
19	D	The number of data points for the two companies would not lend itself to easily using dotplots or stemplots. Because you have only one variable, a scatterplot is inappropriate. Because the companies are quite different in size, a relative-frequency histogram would let you display the <u>percent</u> of workers in each salary group for comparison purposes.
20	C	There are 160 observations in the data set. The median would be the value between the 80th and 81st data points. This clearly falls in the upper end of the "at least 20 but less than 30 minutes" interval. This narrows the choices to (A), (B), or (C). In addition, the distribution of waiting times is skewed toward the higher numbers, causing the mean to be higher than the median. This eliminates choices (A) and (B).
21	C	$$n = \left[\frac{z^*_{0.95}\,\sigma}{ME}\right]^2 = \left[\frac{1.96\sqrt{(0.3)(0.7)}}{0.04}\right]^2 = (22.45)^2 = 504.21 \approx 505$$
22	A	From the *z*-table or by using a calculator, InvNorm(0.20) = –0.84 and InvNorm(0.90) = 1.28 $$z = \frac{x-\mu}{\sigma} \Rightarrow -0.84 = \frac{8.61-\mu}{\sigma} \text{ and } 1.28 = \frac{10.48-\mu}{\sigma}$$ Solving the system: $$\begin{cases} -0.84\sigma = 8.61 - \mu \\ 1.28\sigma = 10.48 - \mu \end{cases}, \ \mu = \$9.35 \text{ and } \sigma = \$0.88$$

23	D	For $n = 10$, there are $n - 2$ degrees of freedom in regression on slope. Therefore, with a 99% confidence level, df = 8 and $t^* = 3.355$. The amount of nitrogen in the fertilizer is the explanatory variable, so the slope coefficient is 1.150.
24	C	The margin of error is defined by $z * \sqrt{\dfrac{\hat{p}(1 - \hat{p})}{n}}$. Assuming that $\hat{p}$ remains the same, a higher level of confidence yields a larger margin of error. A larger sample size yields a smaller margin of error. So, a higher level of confidence and a smaller sample size yields the largest margin of error.
25	C	p_1 = true proportion who claim to be vegetarians at school #1 with sample proportion is 10 / 90 = 0.111. p_2 = true proportion who claim to be vegetarians at school #2 with sample proportion is 12 / 150 = 0.08. CI: $-0.031 \pm 1.645 \left(\sqrt{\dfrac{(0.08)(0.92)}{150} + \dfrac{(0.111)(0.889)}{90}} \right)$
26	B	Predicted resiliency = $-49 + 1.8(110) = 149$. Residual = actual y – predicted y = $140 - 149 = -9$.
27	B	$$P(\text{private} \mid \text{left}) = \frac{P(\text{private} \cap \text{left the company})}{P(\text{left the company})}$$ $$= \frac{(0.3)(0.35)}{(0.3)(0.35) + (0.7)(0.2)}$$ $$= 0.4286$$
28	D	The distribution of hours spent surfing the Web exhibits more variation (has a larger IQR) than does the distribution of hours spent watching TV.
29	B	From the Central Limit Theorem, we know that the larger the sample size, the more normal-like is the approximate sampling distribution. We also know that $\sigma_{\bar{x}} = \dfrac{\sigma}{\sqrt{n}}$, so the distribution of sample means will have less variability than the population distribution, and the larger the sample size, the less variability there will be in the distribution of sample means Histogram B is the original population, Histogram A is sample size 5, and Histogram C is the most normal-like of the three and has the smallest variability.

30	E	The mean (expected value) on each roll is: $$E(\text{winnings}) = (\$5)\left(\frac{1}{3}\right) + (-\$2)\left(\frac{2}{3}\right) = \$\frac{1}{3}$$ with a standard deviation of: $$\sigma(\text{winnings}) = \sqrt{\left(5-\frac{1}{3}\right)^2\left(\frac{1}{3}\right) + \left(-2-\frac{1}{3}\right)^2\left(\frac{2}{3}\right)} = \$3.30$$ For 30 turns, the expected winnings are $E(total) = 30\left(\frac{1}{3}\right) = \$10$. The standard deviation of the 30 turns is $\sigma(\text{total}) = \sqrt{30(3.30)^2} = \$18.07$. $$P(\text{total} > \$15) = P\left(z > \frac{\$15-\$10}{\$18.07}\right) = P(z > 0.277) \approx 0.3910$$
31	B	The standard error of the difference in sample means is given by $$\sqrt{\frac{s_1^2}{n_1} + \frac{s_2^2}{n_2}} = \sqrt{\frac{6.25}{25} + \frac{7.29}{35}}$$
32	B	You are asked to interpret the coefficient of determination, given by r^2. Because $r = 0.7$, $r^2 = 0.49$. The coefficient of determination, r^2, is the percent of variation in the y-variable that can be explained by the regression line, using the x-variable as the predictor. In this case, the y-variable is the amount of hearing loss and the x-variable is the age of the patient.
33	C	This question is asking for an interpretation of the confidence <u>level,</u> not the <u>interval.</u> The 98% level indicates how often, on average, the procedure will produce an interval that will capture the true population parameter of interest
34	D	The expected counts for each cell are determined by $\dfrac{(\text{row total})(\text{column total})}{\text{table total}}$
35	C	The equation is $\widehat{\text{home value}} = 35.70032 + 0.14875(\text{sqfeet})$. The slope is 0.14875. Every increase of one square foot in house size leads to an increase in the predicted home value of $0.14875(\$1000) = \$148.75$.

36	B	Because the superintendent selected a random sample from each type of school to form the overall sample, this sampling method is a stratified random sample. Each type of school is a stratum and individuals within each school may have similar characteristics (i.e., similar opinions about extracurricular activities), making them homogeneous groupings.
37	B	Let X = the number of red wrappers in the Holiday #1 sample and Y = the number of red wrappers in the Holiday #2 sample. X is a binomial random variable with parameters $n_1 = 50$ and $p_1 = 0.5$. Y is a binomial random variable with parameters $n_2 = 50$ and $p_2 = 0.3$. $$E(X+Y) = n_1 p_1 + n_2 p_2 = (50)(0.5) + (50)(0.3) = 40$$ $$\sigma_{X+Y} = \sqrt{50(0.5)(0.5) + 50(0.3)(0.7)} = 4.796$$
38	E	We would reject the null hypothesis if the P-value is less than the significance level α. With a P-value of 0.0760, we would fail to reject H_0 at the 5% level, eliminating choices A, B, and C. The P-value would be sufficient to reject at the 10% level. Choice (D) indicates that there is little difference in income between the current and 2015, which is equivalent to failing to reject H_0 at 10%. Choice (E) rejects H_0 and concludes that a change has occurred exists.
39	D	The treatments are the two types of medication, each at three different dosages, for a total of six treatments. Subjects are blocked into groups of six according to their weight. Because the company is testing which medication is most effective in the least amount of time, time until pain relief is the response variable.
40	C	Because a random sample was selected, the sample mean will be an unbiased estimator, *regardless* of the size of the sample, which eliminates options A, B, and E. A smaller sample size will yield more variability in the estimator; a larger sample size will yield less variability in the estimator. In addition, a larger sample size n (60 > 30) will make the standard deviation of the sample mean decrease, given the formula $\sigma_{\bar{x}} = \dfrac{\sigma}{\sqrt{n}}$.

Answer Key & Textbook Mapping
Multiple Choice Practice Test 1

Multiple Choice Question	Answer	Learning Objective	Skill	College Board Unit	Textbook Section
1	B	DAT-2.A	1.C	1	4.1
2	B	VAR-3.C	1.C	3	4.2
3	B	VAR-4.E	3.A	4	5.2
4	A	DAT-1.A	2.A	2	3.1
5	C	VAR-5.E	3.B	4	6.2
6	A	VAR-5.C	3.B	4	6.1
7	C	DAT-3.E	4.B	7	11.1
8	B	UNC-3.Q	3.B	5	7.3
9	D	UNC-1.K	4.B	1	1.3
10	C	VAR-7.C	1.F	7	11.1
11	D	UNC-5.A	1.B	6	9.1
12	E	VAR-7.B	1.E	7	11.2
13	B	UNC-3.E	3.A	4	6.3
14	A	VAR-2.C	2.D	1	2.1
15	E	UNC-4.AA	4.D	7	10.2
16	E	DAT-3.F	4.E	7	11.1
17	C	VAR-3.C	1.C	3	4.2
18	A	UNC-4.U	4.A	7	10.1
19	D	UNC-1.N	2.D	1	1.2
20	C	UNC-1.M	2.A	1	1.3
21	C	UNC-4.C	3.D	6	8.2

22	A	VAR-2.B	3.A	1	2.2
23	D	UNC-4.AF	3.D	9	12.3
24	C	UNC-4.H	4.A	6	8.2
25	C	UNC-4.K	3.D	6	8.3
26	B	DAT-1.E	2.B	2	3.2
27	B	VAR-4.D	3.A	4	5.3
28	D	UNC-1.N	2.D	1	1.2
29	B	UNC-3.H	3.C	5	7.1
30	E	UNC-5.C	3.B	4	9.2
31	B	UNC-3.T	3.B	5	7.3
32	B	DAT-1.G	2.C	2	3.2
33	C	UNC-4.F	4.B	6	8.1
34	D	VAR-8.H	3.A	8	12.2
35	C	DAT-1.H	4.B	2	3.2
36	B	DAT-2.C	1.C	3	4.1
37	B	UNC-3.C	3.B	4	6.3
38	E	DAT-3.J	4.E	8	12.2
39	D	DAT-2.A, VAR-3.C, VAR-3.A	1.C	3	4.2
40	C	UNC-3.V	4.B	5	7.3

Part II Free-Response Section Solutions

Question 1:

(a) The segmented bar graph illustrates an association between age and movie genre preference. Adults in this sample are more likely to prefer comedy (about 3 times as much as teens), whereas teens are about twice as likely (32%) to prefer horror than adults (15%). Teens also prefer action/adventure slightly more than adults.

(b) The journalist took the sample from 1600 individuals at the movie theater on one day. For a systematic sample, the journalist would pick a random starting point, such as k = 5, and begin with the 5th person that arrives at the movie ticket window and survey that person. Then the journalist could select (for example) every twentieth person for the fixed, periodic interval. This continues until the journalist has a total of 80 survey participants.

(c) Because there were 60 teens and 20 adults that were surveyed, the horizontal widths of the bars will account for this difference in a mosaic plot. The heights of the bars and the percentages for each movie genre preference should be identical to the original segmented bar graph, but the width of the teen bar should be 3 times as large as the adult bar (because 60 is 3 times as large as 20).

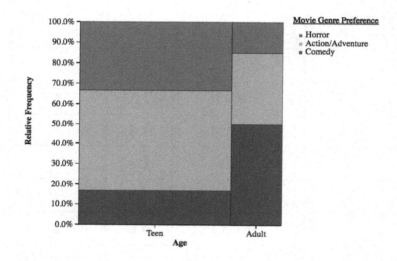

Question 2:

(a) On equally sized slips of paper, write "type I toothbrush" on 20 slips, "type II toothbrush" on 20 slips, and "type III toothbrush" on 20 slips. Put the 60 slips into a hat and mix them well. Have each volunteer select a slip of paper (and not replace it). The slip they select will be the treatment group they are in.

(b) There are a variety of variables that the experimenter may not be able to continue for, such as diet, overall teeth health, genetics, etc. In order to make roughly equivalent treatment groups at the beginning of the experiment, the student will randomly assign subjects into groups. It is hoped that this randomization will distribute the variety of uncontrolled variables equally among the three groups.

(c) Yes, if a statistically significant result is found, the student can infer the toothbrush type caused the reduction in plaque because this was an experiment using random assignment of treatments.

Question 3:

(a) $\mu_W = 4(3) + 5(4) + 1(3) = 35$ ounces

$\sigma_W = \sqrt{4(0.2)^2 + 5(0.3)^2 + 1(0.1)^2} = 0.79$ ounces

(b) $P(W < 34) = P\left(z < \dfrac{34-35}{0.79}\right) = P(z < -1.27) = 0.1020$

The probability that a randomly selected box of candy will weigh less than 34 ounces is 0.102.

(c) $P(\text{a box does } \underline{\text{not}} \text{ weigh} < 34) = 1 - P(W < 34) = 1 - 0.102 = 0.898$

Let $X =$ number of boxes that weigh less than 34 ounces

$P(X \geq 1) = 1 - P(x = 0) = 1 - (0.898)^3 = 0.2758.$

Question 4:
If conditions are met, we will perform a two-sample z test for a difference in proportions whose hypotheses are

$H_0: p_{2010} = p_{2014}$
$H_a: p_{2014} > p_{2010}$

$p_{2010} =$ population proportion of Americans who eat a GF diet in 2010
$p_{2014} =$ population proportion of Americans who eat a GF diet in 2014

Conditions for inference:
1. Independent random samples: The samples in 2010 and in 2014 were independent and selected at random.
2. 10%: Because these samples were selected without replacement, we will check the 10% condition. There were at least 21,050 American adults in 2010 and 17,570 American adults in 2014.
3. Large Counts: The pooled proportion is $\hat{p}_C = \dfrac{(0.005*2105)+(0.02*1757)}{2105+1757}$ which equals 0.011824.

Because $(2105)(0.011824) = 24.9$ and $(2105)(1 - 0.011824) = 2080.1$ are both at least than 10 and $(1757)(0.011824) = 20.8$ and $(1757)(1 - 0.011824) = 1736.2$ are both at least than 10, the sampling distribution of the difference in proportions is approximately Normal, so our sample sizes are large enough.

All conditions are met. We will use a two-sample z test for a difference in proportions.

$z = \dfrac{\hat{p}_1 - \hat{p}_2}{\sqrt{(\hat{p}_c)(1 - \hat{p}_c)\left(\dfrac{1}{n_1} + \dfrac{1}{n_2}\right)}}$

where $\hat{p}_c = 0.011824$

$$z = \frac{0.02 - 0.005}{\sqrt{(0.011824)(0.988176)\left(\frac{1}{2105} + \frac{1}{1757}\right)}} = 4.294$$

P-value $= 2 \cdot P(z > 4.294) = 1.75 \times 10^{-5} \approx 0$

Because $0 < 0.05$, we reject the null hypothesis. There is convincing statistical evidence to conclude that the proportion of Americans who eat GF diets increased from 2010 to 2014.

Question 5:

(a) The analyst will use a prospective observational study, because the recycling contributions of households will be tracked for a 6-week period.

(b) A Type II error is committed when a false null hypothesis is not rejected. The company fails to find convincing evidence that the true mean is greater than 20 pounds, when it really is greater than 20 pounds. Therefore, a consequence of Type II error is that the company decides not to build the collection system even though a sufficient amount of recyclables was available. The company loses an opportunity to make money.

(c) Assuming the significance level of 0.01, sample size of 100, and the true population mean is 25, there is a 72% chance that the company finds convincing evidence that the mean weekly household contribution to recycling is more than 20, when that is the reality of the situation. Thus, there is a 72% chance of avoiding a Type II error described in part (b).

(d) The probability of Type I error is equivalent to the stated significance level of 0.01. So, P(Type I error) = 0.01.

Question 6:

(a) Let $X =$ the number of games in which the team scores the first overtime goal.
P(the team scores first) $= 0.72$

Let the digits 00 through 71 represent scoring the first goal in overtime. Let 72 through 99 represent not scoring the first goal in overtime. Two digits will represent one game and it will take 12 digits to represent the six games played in overtime. Starting at the left, taking two digits at a time, count the number of games in which the team scores first until you have counted six games. In this context, getting the same two-digit number is allowed. For each trial, record the number of games in which the team scored the first goal. Mark the end of each trial with a vertical line. Above each trial write the number of games in which the team scored the first overtime goal.

(b)

 5   5   6   5
8 4 1 7 7 0 6 7 5 7 1 7 |6 1 3 1 5 5 8 2 5 1 5 0| 6 8 1 4 3 5 4 1 0 5 0 9| 2 0 3 1 0 6 4 4 9 0 5 0| 5 9

 4   5   2   5
5 9 8 8 4 3 1 1 8 0| 5 3 1 1 5 8 4 4 6 9 9 4| 8 6 8 5 7 9 6 7 0 5 8 1| 1 8 4 5 1 4 7 5 0 1 1 1| 3 0 0 6

 6   4   4   5
6 3 3 9 5 5 5 0| 4 1 1 5 8 6 6 0 6 5 8 9| 1 3 1 1 9 7 1 0 2 0 8 5| 9 4 0 9 1 9 3 2 0 9 4 8| 8 7 4 9 8 7

# Games	Frequency
0	0
1	0
2	1
3	0
4	3
5	6
6	2

Based on the above simulation:

$$P(\text{win at least 5 games}) = P(x \geq 5) = \frac{8}{12} = 0.667$$

(c) If the teams were fairly evenly matched, then each team would be expected to win approximately 3 out of 6. This situation would best be represented by the histogram in Distribution B. If one team was clearly better than the other, it would be expected to win more games than its opponent and this is represented by Distribution A.

Textbook Mapping
Free Response Practice Test 1

FRQ Part	Learning Objective	Skill	College Board Unit	Textbook Section	SKILL #
1a	UNC-1.P	2.D	2	1.1	2
1b	DAT-2.C	1.C	3	4.1	1
1c	UNC-1.P	2.D	2	1.1	2
2a	VAR-3.C	1.C	3	4.2	1
2b	VAR-3.C	1.C	3	4.2	1
2c	VAR-3.E	4.B	3	4.3	4
3a	VAR-5.E	3.B	4	6.2	3
3b	VAR-2.B	3.A	4	2.2	3
3c	UNC-3.B	3.A	4	6.3	3
4-i	VAR-6.H	1.F	6	9.3	1
4-ii	VAR-6.J	4.C	6	9.3	4
4-iii	VAR-6.K	3.E	6	9.3	3
4-iv	DAT-3.D	4.E	6	9.3	4
5a	DAT-2.A	1.C	3	4.2	1
5b	UNC-5.A	1.B	6	9.1	1
5c	UNC-5.B	3.A	6	9.2	3
6a	UNC-2.A	3.A	4	5.1	3
6b	UNC-2.A	3.A	4	5.1	3
6c	UNC-1.N	2.D	1	1.2	2

PRACTICE TEST #2

SECTION I
Time—1 hour and 30 minutes
Number of questions—40
Percent of total score—50

Directions: Solve each of the following problems, using the available space for scratch work. Decide which is the best of the given choices and fill in the corresponding circle on the answer sheet. No credit will be given for anything written in the test book. Do not spend too much time on any one problem.

1. Which of the following situations would be difficult to explore using a census?

   (A) You wish to know the proportion of teachers in a school district that have a Master's degree.
   (B) You want to know the average amount of time spent on homework by students in your high school.
   (C) You are interested in the difference in performance on the AP Statistics exam for students taught by two different teachers.
   (D) You want to know the proportion of homes in a suburban community that have wireless Internet access.
   (E) You want to know the proportion of trees in a large state forest that are infected with Dutch Elm disease.

2. It is known that 15% of the seniors in a large high school enter military service upon graduation. If a group of 20 seniors are randomly selected from this school, what is the probability of observing at most one senior who will be entering military service?

   (A) $20(0.15)^1(0.85)^{19}$

   (B) $1 - 20(0.15)^1(0.85)^{19}$

   (C) $(0.85)^{20} + 20(0.15)^1(0.85)^{19}$

   (D) $(0.85)^{20}$

   (E) $1 - (0.85)^{20}$

3. A study of two popular sleep-aids measured the mean number of hours slept for 200 individuals. In the group of 200 volunteer subjects, 100 were randomly chosen to be administered Drug 1 and the other 100 were administered Drug 2. A two-sample t test was performed on the difference in the mean sleep times experienced by the subjects. The P-value was 0.12. Which of the following is a correct interpretation of the P-value?

   (A) Approximately 12% of the subjects did not sleep at all.
   (B) There was a 12% difference between the mean sleep times of the two groups.
   (C) We would expect to see a difference in the mean sleep times at least as extreme as the observed difference for 200 subjects 12% of the time.
   (D) Assuming both drugs are equally effective, we would expect to see a difference in the mean sleep times at least as extreme as the observed difference for 200 subjects 12% of the time.
   (E) Assuming both drugs are not equally effective, we would expect to see a difference in the mean sleep times at least as extreme as the observed difference for 200 subjects 12% of the time.

4. Pediatricians were interested in determining if there is an association between how frequently a child snores per week and whether the child has nocturnal coughing, asthma, or neither. The results of a survey of 1048 randomly selected children aged 2 to 5 are given below.

	Snored four or more times per week	Snored three or fewer times per week	Total
Had nocturnal coughing	59	255	314
Had asthma	22	222	244
Did not have asthma or nocturnal coughing	115	375	490
Total	196	852	1048

The hypotheses that the pediatricians used were given as:

H_0: There is no association between frequency of snoring and the prevalence of asthma symptoms and nocturnal coughing among children aged 2 to 5.

H_a: An association does exist between frequency of snoring and the prevalence of asthma symptoms and nocturnal coughing among children aged 2 to 5.

If the test statistic for this procedure is $\chi^2 = 22.38$, which one of the following is a correct conclusion?

(A) Because the P-value is large, an association does exist between frequency of snoring and the prevalence of asthma symptoms and nocturnal coughing among children aged 2 to 5.

(B) Because the P-value is small, there is no association between frequency of snoring and the prevalence of asthma symptoms and nocturnal coughing among children aged 2 to 5.

(C) Because the P-value is large, there is convincing statistical evidence that there is no association between frequency of snoring and the prevalence of asthma symptoms and nocturnal coughing among children aged 2 to 5.

(D) Because the P-value is small, there is convincing statistical evidence of an association between frequency of snoring and the prevalence of asthma symptoms and nocturnal coughing among children aged 2 to 5.

(E) Because the test statistic is large, there is not convincing statistical evidence of an association between frequency of snoring and the prevalence of asthma symptoms and nocturnal coughing among children aged 2 to 5.

5. In order to evaluate the yield per acre of three different varieties of corn, 12 one-acre plots of land will be used. One variety of corn will be randomly assigned to 4 of the plots, the second variety to 4 other plots, and the third variety to the 4 remaining plots of land. At the end of the growing season, the yield per acre will be evaluated. Which one of the following is a TRUE statement?

(A) The type of land is being used as a blocking factor.

(B) The treatments in this experiment are the plots of land.

(C) The experimental units in this situation are the varieties of corn.

(D) Our randomization process will reduce the variation that exists due to the plots of land.

(E) Replication of corn variety on four plots of land allows us to measure variability across plots of land.

6. Biologists have collected data relating the age (in years) of one variety of oak tree to its height (in feet). A scatterplot for 20 of these trees is given below.

If the point labeled A in the above scatterplot were changed to have a height of 40 feet, which one of the following statements would be TRUE?

(A) The slope of the least-squares regression line would decrease, and the correlation would increase.

(B) The slope of the least-squares regression line would decrease, and the correlation would decrease.

(C) The slope of the least-squares regression line would increase, and the correlation would increase.

(D) The slope of the least-squares regression line would increase, and the correlation would decrease.

(E) The slope of the least-squares regression line and the correlation would remain the same.

7. A school principal is interested in calculating a 96% confidence interval for the true mean number of days students are absent during the school year. The attendance office lists the number of days absent for each student during the month of December. Which of the following is the best reason the principal <u>cannot</u> construct the confidence interval?

(A) A confidence interval cannot be constructed unless all data for the population are known.

(B) The critical value for 96% is not listed in the table, therefore it cannot be calculated.

(C) The attendance office should report the average for the month, not the number for each individual student.

(D) Because most students would not miss any days, the average will be too small to construct a confidence interval.

(E) The number of absences in December may not be representative of the rest of the months during the year. Data should be collected from all months.

8. A study of 156 drug addicts in Amsterdam recorded how often each addict had recently injected drugs and whether or not the addict was infected with HIV, the virus that causes AIDS. Here is a two-way table of the number of addicts in each condition:

		HIV Positive	HIV Negative
	Daily	32	45
Injected Drugs?	Less than Daily	20	18
	Never	18	23

If an addict is chosen at random from this group, what is the probability that the addict tests positive for HIV, given that the addict injects daily?

(A)   0.21
(B)   0.42
(C)   0.46
(D)   0.54
(E)   0.58

9. A sports physiologist wants to compare the effects of two different exercise machines, A and B, on the flexibility of gymnasts. There are 20 gymnasts available for the study. All gymnasts have been given a flexibility rating before the experiment starts. A similar ratings test will be given at the end of the experiment. Which one of the following methods of assigning gymnasts to machines would be optimal in order to assess the difference in flexibility due to the machines?

(A)   Randomly assign a number (01 through 20) to each gymnast. Match the gymnasts by consecutive number (i.e., #1 with #2, #3 with #4, etc.). Then assign the odd-numbered gymnast in each pair to machine A and the even-numbered gymnast to machine B.
(B)   Have all the gymnasts use both machines. A coin flip will determine which machine is used first.
(C)   Flip a coin to assign the gymnasts into two groups of 10. Flip the coin again to assign one group to use machine A and the other group to use machine B.
(D)   Match each gymnast with a gymnast who has the same years of experience, training level, and gymnastic ability. Then flip a coin to assign each pair of gymnasts to one of the two machines.
(E)   Match each gymnast with a gymnast who has the same years of experience, training level, and gymnastic ability. Flip a coin to assign one member of the pair to machine A and the other to machine B.

10. According to the Insurance Institute for Highway Safety in 2017, 58% of 18-year-olds admitted to texting while they are driving. In a large city in the Midwest, a random sample of 250 18-year-old drivers found that 160 of them had admitted to texting while driving. If the texting while driving rate of 18-year-old drivers in this Midwestern city is the same as the national rate, which of the following represents the probability of getting a random sample of 250 18-year-old drivers whose texting rate is greater than 64%?

(A) $P\left(z > \dfrac{0.64 - 0.58}{\sqrt{\dfrac{(0.58)(0.42)}{250}}}\right)$

(B) $P\left(z > \dfrac{0.64 - 0.58}{\sqrt{\dfrac{(0.64)(0.36)}{250}}}\right)$

(C) $P\left(z > \dfrac{0.58 - 0.64}{\sqrt{\dfrac{(0.64)(0.36)}{250}}}\right)$

(D) $\dbinom{250}{160}(0.58)^{160}(0.42)^{90}$

(E) $\dbinom{250}{160}(0.64)^{160}(0.36)^{90}$

11. A poll was conducted to determine the level of support within a large suburban school district for the construction of a new football stadium. Of the 655 people who were surveyed, 57% said they would support spending the money to construct the stadium. The poll had a margin of error of 4%. Which is the correct interpretation for this margin of error?

    (A) About 4% of the school district residents polled refused to respond to the question.
    (B) There is most likely less than a 4% difference between the proportion of support in the sample and the true proportion of support in the district.
    (C) There is most likely more than a 4% difference between the proportion of support in the sample and the true proportion of support in the district.
    (D) If we conducted repeated samples from this population, the results would vary by no more than 4% from the current sample result of 57%.
    (E) If the poll had sampled more people, the proportion of district residents who would have said they supported the stadium would have been about 4% higher.

12. A company that ships vitamins claims that 97% of shipments will arrive on time. Let the random variable A represent the number of shipments that arrive on time in 50 randomly selected shipments. Random variable A follows a binomial distribution with a mean of 48.5 and a standard deviation of 1.21. Which of the following is the best interpretation of the mean?

    (A) Every random sample of 50 shipments will have 48.5 shipments that arrive on time.
    (B) Every random sample of 50 shipments will have 48.5 shipments that do not arrive on time.
    (C) On average, the company ships 48.5 shipments until one is late.
    (D) For all possible shipments of size 50, the average number of on time shipments is equal to 48.5.
    (E) For all possible shipments of size 50, the average number of not on time shipments is equal to 48.5.

13. As of August 2017, there were more than 116,000 men, women, and children in the United States who were awaiting transplants of a variety of organs such as livers, hearts, and kidneys. A national organ donor organization is trying to estimate the proportion of all people who would be willing to donate their organs after their death to help transplant recipients. Which one of the following would be the most appropriate sample size required to ensure a margin of error of at most 3 percent for a 98% confidence interval estimate of the proportion of all people in the U.S. who would be willing to donate their organs?

    (A) 1075
    (B) 1180
    (C) 1510
    (D) 1740
    (E) 1845

14. A researcher is interested in the effect of energy drinks on a person's physical actions. The number of times a person can tap on a surface per minute was measured before and after a person consumed a popular energy drink. The results are below:

Subject	1	2	3	4	5	6	7	8	9	10	$\overline{x}$	s_x
Before Drink	105	99	93	96	95	99	94	87	100	89	95.7	5.36
After Drink	103	102	105	102	101	110	95	89	102	98	100.7	5.70
Difference	2	–3	–12	–6	–6	–11	–1	–2	–2	–9	–5	4.59

The conditions for inference were checked and verified. Which one of the following represents the standardized test statistic for a test of $H_0 : \mu_{B-A} = 0$, where μ_{B-A} is the true mean difference (before drink minus after drink) in the number of taps for subjects like the ones in this study?

(A) $\quad t = \dfrac{95.7 - 100.7}{\sqrt{\dfrac{5.36}{10} + \dfrac{5.70}{10}}}$

(B) $\quad t = \dfrac{95.7 - 100.7}{\sqrt{\dfrac{5.36^2}{10} + \dfrac{5.70^2}{10}}}$

(C) $\quad t = \dfrac{95.7 - 100.7}{\sqrt{\dfrac{5.36^2}{9} + \dfrac{5.70^2}{9}}}$

(D) $\quad t = \dfrac{5 - 0}{\dfrac{4.59}{\sqrt{10}}}$

(E) $\quad t = \dfrac{5 - 0}{\dfrac{4.59}{\sqrt{9}}}$

15. The number of goals scored per game in a full season of games for a professional soccer league is strongly skewed to the right with a mean of 2.3 goals. An SRS of size $n = 15$ is selected from the population and the sample mean is computed. This process is repeated a total of 375 times. Which one of the following best describes the shape and center of the resulting distribution of sample means?

(A) Skewed to the right with a mean of 2.3 goals.

(B) Skewed to the right with a mean of $\dfrac{2.3}{\sqrt{15}}$ goals.

(C) Approximately normal with a mean of 2.3 goals.

(D) Approximately normal with a mean of $\dfrac{2.3}{\sqrt{15}}$ goals.

(E) Binomially distributed with a mean of 2.3 goals.

16. The enrollment rate of graduating high school seniors who were accepted into the freshman class of a random selection of public and private colleges and universities was compared. For example, at a highly selective academic institution, only 12% of the applicants to the school may be accepted to the incoming class but 75% of those accepted may choose to enroll at that school. The side-by-side boxplots below summarize the distribution of enrollment rate for the selected colleges and universities.

Percent of accepted students that enroll

Which one of the following statements is TRUE about the distribution of enrollment rate?

(A) The *IQR* of the distribution of private enrollment rate is smaller than the *IQR* of the distribution of public enrollment rate.

(B) The median of the distribution of private enrollment rate is smaller than the median of the distribution of public enrollment rate.

(C) The mean of the distribution of private enrollment rate is larger than the mean of the distribution of public enrollment rate.

(D) The distribution of private enrollment rate is skewed to the left.

(E) The third quartile for the distribution of public enrollment rate is larger than the third quartile of the distribution of private enrollment rate.

17. The Department of Traffic Safety wants to reduce the number of drivers who speed on a certain stretch of road. In an attempt to reduce repeat offenders, the Department of Traffic Safety will randomly select 5 drivers, without replacement, from a population of 50 drivers convicted of speeding in order to assess the effectiveness of a new "safe driving" program. If the drivers are labeled 01, 02, 03, ..., 50 and the following line is from a random number table

22368 46573 25595 85393 30995 89198 27982 53401 93965 34095 52666 19174

Which one of the following represents the sample of 5, starting from the left end of the table?

(A) 22, 36, 8, 46, 32

(B) 22, 36, 84, 65, 73

(C) 22, 36, 25, 30, 27

(D) 22, 36, 46, 32, 39

(E) 22, 23, 36, 46, 32

18. The following frequency table summarizes the final exam scores for 150 students in a statistics class at a large university.

Interval	Frequency
90–99	18
80–89	27
70–79	44
60–69	37
50–59	19
40–49	5

Which of the following is closest to the percentile of a score of 79 in this distribution?
(A)   25
(B)   30
(C)   70
(D)   75
(E)   88

19. A local family owns two pizza restaurants in a town, one located on Valley Parkway and the other one on Grand Avenue. The Valley Parkway store does 70% of the family's business in the town, and the Grand Avenue store does the rest. In the Valley Parkway store, 40% of all pizzas are deep dish. At the Grand Avenue store, 30% of all pizzas are deep dish. If a customer is selected at random, what is the approximate probability that the customer purchased a deep dish?

(A)   0.175
(B)   0.33
(C)   0.35
(D)   0.37
(E)   0.70

20. A car salesperson receives a commission of $300 for each car she sells. The number of cars she sells on a randomly selected day follows the probability distribution given in the table below.

Cars Sold	0	1	2	3	4
Probability	0.15	0.25	0.35	0.20	0.05

Based on this distribution, what are the mean and standard deviation of the daily commission that the salesperson should receive?

(A)   Mean = $525 and standard deviation = $87.46
(B)   Mean = $525 and standard deviation = $326.92
(C)   Mean = $525 and standard deviation = $335.41
(D)   Mean = $600 and standard deviation = $335.41
(E)   Mean = $600 and standard deviation = $474.34

21. An insurance company provides insurance policy coverage for automobile owners at a fixed yearly premium. If an applicant is high-risk, the company is likely to pay out more in damages than it collects in premiums. If an applicant is low-risk, however, the company stands to make a profit, because the company will collect the premium but will likely not have to pay out in damages. Each time a potential customer applies for insurance the company is faced with a decision based on the following hypotheses.

H_0: The applicant is a low-risk.
H_a: The applicant is a high-risk.

Which of the following represents a Type II error and its consequence for the company?

(A)   The company decides that the applicant is a high-risk, but he was, in fact, a low-risk. The company misses an opportunity to make a profit.
(B)   The company decides that the applicant is a high-risk, but he was, in fact, a low-risk. The company loses money.
(C)   The company decides that the applicant is a low-risk, but he was, in fact, a high-risk. The company loses money.
(D)   The company decides that the applicant is a low-risk, but he was, in fact, a high-risk. The company makes a profit.
(E)   The company decides that the applicant is a high-risk and he is a high-risk. The company avoids losing money.

22. A family-run convenience store/gas station in a resort town experiences a lot of variation in sales, depending on whether it is during the summer vacation season or during the off-season. Sales during the off-season do not vary that much, but the sales in the vacation season can be very unpredictable. The family is interested in predicting the total daily sales from the number of customers who buy gas and various other items in the store each day during the summer vacation season. A random sample of 20 days from the past two summer seasons is selected. Some of the summary statistics about the number of customers per day and daily sales (in thousands of dollars) are given below.

Mean number of customers = 721.47   Standard deviation of customers = 182.0
Mean daily sales = 38.778   Standard deviation of daily sales = 7.442
$r = 0.862$

Which one of the following would be <u>closest</u> to the predicted daily sales if there were 800 customers on a given day during the summer season?

(A) $10,820
(B) $14,555
(C) $16,770
(D) $41,135
(E) $41,545

23. A spring-loaded launcher is used to propel a ping pong ball for a game at a school carnival. If the ball lands in a bucket, the participant wins a prize. In testing the launcher to determine where the bucket should be placed, 20 test shots are taken. The mean distance traveled is 64.5 inches with a standard deviation of 2.1 inches. The conditions for inference were checked and verified. Which one of the following is the approximate 98% confidence interval estimate for μ, the true mean distance traveled by the ping pong ball?

   (A) $64.5 \pm 2.539 \left(\dfrac{2.1}{\sqrt{19}} \right)$

   (B) $64.5 \pm 2.539 \left(\dfrac{2.1}{\sqrt{20}} \right)$

   (C) $64.5 \pm 2.528 \left(\sqrt{\dfrac{2.1}{20}} \right)$

   (D) $64.5 \pm 2.528 \left(\dfrac{2.1}{\sqrt{9}} \right)$

   (E) $64.5 \pm 2.528 \left(\dfrac{2.1}{\sqrt{20}} \right)$

24. Automobile engineers wanted to check the effect of a new automatic transmission on mileage. They selected 50 cars of the same make and model. Twenty-five of the cars used the old transmission, while the other 25 cars used the new model of transmission. A hypothesis test on the difference between the means was conducted. Which one of the following is a condition necessary to conduct this test?

   (A) The standard deviation of each group should be different.
   (B) The sampling distribution of the difference between the sample means is bimodal.
   (C) The sample size times the proportion of cars with a large number of miles must be greater than 10.
   (D) Twenty-five cars are randomly selected with the new transmission and 25 with the old transmission.
   (E) The difference between the means was within one standard deviation.

25. Which of the following would be classified as a discrete quantitative variable?

   (A) The heights of 10 randomly selected students in middle school.
   (B) The 40-yard dash times of 50 randomly selected professional athletes.
   (C) The weights of the first five dogs that arrive at a dog park.
   (D) The favorite color of a group of students in an art studio.
   (E) The number of recyclable cans found in trash cans around a local park on a randomly selected day.

26. In which of the following should the random variable X <u>not</u> be modeled with a geometric distribution?

    (A)   According to an Internet search, 68% of American households own a pet. Let X represent the number of randomly selected American households surveyed to find one with a pet.

    (B)   Suppose that at a certain stop light 40% of drivers text while waiting for a green light. Let X represent the number of randomly selected drivers at this light to find one that is texting.

    (C)   Alex struggles to throw a ball into the air and catch it. He catches only about 10% of throws. Let X represent the number of throws Alex makes to catch one.

    (D)   In a classroom of 25 students, 20% are blonde. Students will be selected, one at a time without replacement, and the student's hair color will be recorded. Let X represent the number of students selected to find one blonde.

    (E)   A marketing company claims that 10% of people on a website will click on an ad. Let X represent the number of people that are randomly selected to find one person who clicked on the ad.

27. An insurance salesperson sells an average of 3.1 policies per day with a standard deviation of 1.1 policies. The salesperson is paid $300 a week plus a commission of $250 for each policy sold. What are the mean and standard deviation, respectively, of the salesperson's total weekly pay?

    (A) $1705.00, $605.00
    (B) $1705.00, $275.00
    (C) $1075.00, $775.00
    (D) $1075.00, $302.50
    (E) $1075.00, $275.00

28. A group of friends believe that there is a difference between the popularity of four teachers (1, 2, 3, and 4) at their school. They select a random sample of students and ask who the most popular teacher is from a list of these four teachers. Their results are shown in the table below.

Teacher	1	2	3	4
Votes	12	11	15	18

Which of the following would be the most appropriate inference procedure to test the student's claim?

    (A)   A chi-square test for independence.
    (B)   A chi-square test for goodness of fit.
    (C)   A two-sample t test for a difference in means.
    (D)   A one-sample t test for a mean.
    (E)   A t test for the slope.

29. A large insurance company has 95 agents within a certain state. The histogram below shows the amount of insurance sold (in $100,000) for the period October through December in a recent year. The tallest bar, for example, indicates that 23 agents sold between $7.25 million and $7.75 million of insurance during the three-month period.

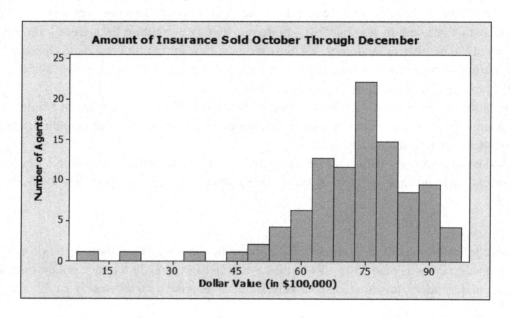

Which one of the following represents a boxplot of the same data?

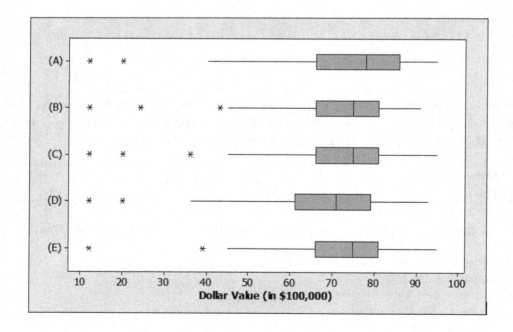

30. A biologist is comparing the lengths of two varieties of bowerbird, the MacGregor's bowerbird and the Vogelkop bowerbird. The length of the MacGregor's bowerbird is approximately Normal with mean 26 cm. The length of the Vogelkop bowerbird is approximately Normal with mean 28 cm. Twelve birds of each variety will be selected at random and the lengths will be recorded. Let $\bar{x}_M$ represent the sample mean length of the 12 MacGregor's bowerbirds, and let $\bar{x}_V$ represent the sample mean length of the 12 Vogelkop bowerbirds.

Which of the following is the best interpretation of $P(\bar{x}_M - \bar{x}_V > 4) = 0.17$?

(A) The probability that the lengths of all 12 MacGregor's bowerbirds will exceed the lengths of all 12 Vogelkop bowerbirds by more than 4 cm is 0.17.

(B) The probability that the lengths of all 12 MacGregor's bowerbirds will exceed the lengths of all 12 Vogelkop bowerbirds by more than 0.17 is 4.

(C) The probability that the average length of all 12 MacGregor's bowerbirds will exceed the average lengths of all 12 Vogelkop bowerbirds by more than 4 cm is 0.17.

(D) The probability that the lengths of all MacGregor's bowerbirds will exceed the lengths of all Vogelkop bowerbirds by more than 4 cm is 0.17.

(E) The probability that the average length of all 12 MacGregor's bowerbirds will exceed the average lengths of all 12 Vogelkop bowerbirds is 0.17.

31. In which of the following distributions is the mean most likely greater than the median?

(A)

(B)

(C)

(D)

(E)

32. At a large university, a random sample of 20 students will be asked, "How many times a week do you eat breakfast?" The sample mean $\bar{x}$ will be computed to estimate the population mean μ. Is $\bar{x}$ an unbiased estimator of μ?

   (A)   No, because the sample mean $\bar{x}$ does not always equal the population mean μ.
   (B)   No, because a sample size of 20 is not large enough to assume the sampling distribution of $\bar{x}$ is approximately Normal.
   (C)   Yes, because the wording of the question is not biased.
   (D)   Yes, because the expected value of $\bar{x}$ based upon a random sample is equal to μ.
   (E)   Yes, because with a sample size of 20 the variability of the sample mean $\bar{x}$ will be small.

33. To determine the effectiveness of speed-boosting a computer by "overclocking" its processor, researchers randomly selected 16 computers of various makes and models and paired each of them with a second identical make and model. For each pair, it was randomly decided which of the two would be "overclocked" and which would be unmodified. The 95% confidence interval for the mean difference in speeds (not modified – "overclocked") was (1.3, 17.3). Assuming the conditions for inference are met, what can we conclude?

   (A)   The difference in mean speeds will be greater than 1.3 MHz approximately 95% of the time.
   (B)   The unmodified computers are anywhere from 1.3 to 17.3 MHz faster than those that were overclocked 95% of the time.
   (C)   Because the interval does not contain 0, there is a significant difference between the mean speeds for the two procedures (not modified and "overclocked").
   (D)   95% of the differences between speeds will be between 1.3 and 17.3 MHz.
   (E)   A two-sample t test should have been used instead of an interval.

34. Suppose the mean rate of return on the common stocks in a large diversified investment portfolio was 12% last year. If the rates of return of the stocks within the portfolio are approximately normally distributed and a rate of return of 15% represents the 80th percentile, what is the approximate standard deviation of the rates of return in the portfolio?

   (A)   1.79%
   (B)   2.8%
   (C)   3.57%
   (D)   3.98%
   (E)   4.1%

35. A newspaper wants to determine the level of support in a large town regarding the establishment of a city-wide residential recycling program. Which one of the following would represent a method of obtaining a stratified random sample?

(A) Randomly select eight residential blocks in the town and ask everyone who lives on those blocks if they would be in favor of a city-wide residential recycling program.

(B) Randomly select one of the first four people who enters City Hall, and every fourth person who enters thereafter until the desired number of people is selected.

(C) Select a random sample of people from the town phone directory.

(D) Select a random sample of residents from each of the northwest, northeast, southwest, and southeast quadrants of the city.

(E) Number the residents of the town using the latest census data. Use a random number generator to pick the sample.

36. A biologist in the Northeast has gathered data on a random sample of 22 white tailed deer in New England and performed a regression analysis on the weight of the white tailed deer and their length. Some of the output is given below.

Regression Analysis: Weight versus Length

```
Predictor      Coef  SE Coef           T          P
Constant    -441.39    29.91      -14.76      0.000
Length      10.3382   0.4825       21.42      0.000

S = 53.7777   R-Sq = 76.5%   R-Sq(adj) = 76.3%
```

Which of the following would represent a 95% confidence interval to estimate the true slope of the regression line relating white tailed deer weight to length? The conditions for inference were checked and verified.

(A) $-441.39 \pm 2.086(29.91)$

(B) $-441.39 \pm 2.080(29.91)$

(C) $10.3382 \pm 2.086(0.4825)$

(D) $10.3382 \pm 2.086 \left(\frac{0.4825}{\sqrt{22}} \right)$

(E) $10.3382 \pm 2.080(0.4825)$

37. A simple random sample of 50 adults is surveyed to estimate the true proportion of adults who visit the dentist at least once per year, and a confidence interval for the proportion is constructed. Suppose the researcher had surveyed a random sample of 450 adults instead and got the same sample proportion. How would the width of the confidence interval for 450 adults compare to the width of the interval for 50 adults?

(A)   The width would be about one-ninth the width of the original interval.
(B)   The width would be about one-third the width of the original interval.
(C)   The width would be the same as the width of the original interval.
(D)   The width would be about three times the width of the original interval.
(E)   The width would be about nine times the width of the original interval.

38. A biologist has gathered sample data about a population of bears in the forests of the northeast. The distribution of the weights (in pounds) of the sample of bears and their sex is given below. Based on the plot, which statement below is TRUE?

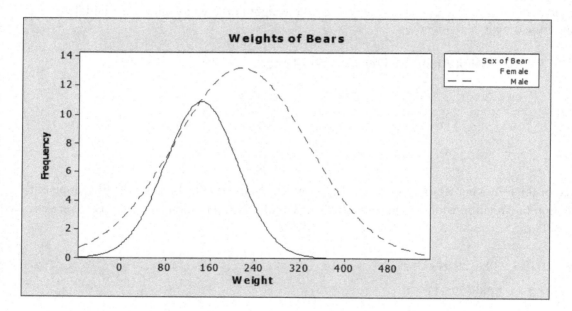

(A)   Because the distributions overlap, there is not much difference between male and female bears.
(B)   The female bears have a greater mean weight than the male bears and also exhibit more variability in those weights.
(C)   The female bears have a greater mean weight than the male bears and also exhibit less variability in those weights.
(D)   The male bears have a greater mean weight than the female bears and also exhibit more variability in those weights.
(E)   The male bears have a greater mean weight than the female bears and also exhibit less variability in those weights.

39. A professional football analyst is using Elo (a measure of the strength of a team) to predict the team's probability at making the playoffs. The analyst selects a random sample of professional football teams and records the team's Elo and the probability that the team will make the playoffs. A scatterplot (not shown) shows a roughly linear form. Below is the output from a least-squares regression analysis examining the linear relationship between Elo and the projected probability the team will make the playoffs. Which one of the following is the correct value and corresponding interpretation for the correlation?

Predictor	Coef	SE Coef	T	P
Constant	-344.5883	40.1511	-8.582	0.000
Elo	0.2543	0.0267	9.540	0.000

S = 14.78   R-Sq = 75.21%   R-Sq(adj) = 74.38%

(A) The correlation is 0.7521, and 75.21% of the variation in a team's probability of making the playoffs can be explained by its Elo.
(B) The correlation is 0.7521. There is a strong, positive, linear relationship between a team's probability of making the playoffs and its Elo.
(C) The correlation is 0.867, and 86.7% of the variation in a team's probability of making the playoffs can be explained by its Elo.
(D) The correlation is –0.867. There is a strong, negative, linear relationship between a team's probability of making the playoffs and its Elo.
(E) The correlation is 0.867. There is a strong, positive, linear relationship between a team's probability of making the playoffs and its Elo.

40. Echinacea is widely used as an herbal remedy for the common cold, and researchers were interested in its effectiveness. In a double-blind experiment, healthy volunteers agreed to be exposed to common-cold-causing rhinovirus type 39 and have their symptoms monitored. The volunteers were randomly assigned to take either a placebo or an echinacea supplement daily for 5 days following the viral exposure. Among the 103 volunteers taking a placebo, 88 developed a cold, whereas 75 of 116 subjects taking echinacea developed a cold. Which of the following represents the 95% confidence interval for the difference in the proportion of individuals like these who would develop a cold after viral exposure when taking echinacea versus when taking a placebo?

(A) $(0.647 - 0.854) \pm 1.645 \sqrt{(0.744)(0.256)\left(\dfrac{1}{116} + \dfrac{1}{103}\right)}$

(B) $(0.647 - 0.854) \pm 1.645 \sqrt{\dfrac{(0.647)(0.353)}{116} + \dfrac{(0.854)(0.146)}{103}}$

(C) $(0.647 - 0.854) \pm 1.960 \sqrt{\left(\dfrac{75}{116}\right)\left(\dfrac{88}{103}\right)\left(\dfrac{1}{116} + \dfrac{1}{103}\right)}$

(D) $(0.647 - 0.854) \pm 1.960 \sqrt{\dfrac{(0.647)(0.353)}{116} + \dfrac{(0.854)(0.146)}{103}}$

(E) $(0.647 - 0.854) \pm 1.960 \sqrt{(0.744)(0.256)\left(\dfrac{1}{116} + \dfrac{1}{103}\right)}$

PRACTICE TEST #2

SECTION II
Part A
Questions 1-5
Spend about 1 hour and 5 minutes on this part of the exam.
Percent of Section II score—75

Directions: Show all your work. Indicate clearly the methods you use, because you will be scored on the correctness of your methods as well as on the accuracy and completeness of your results and explanations.

1. The scatterplot shows the reading and math proficiency test scores for 22 randomly selected high schools in a certain state. The secretary of education of the state wonders if performance on the reading proficiency test is associated with scores on the math proficiency test.

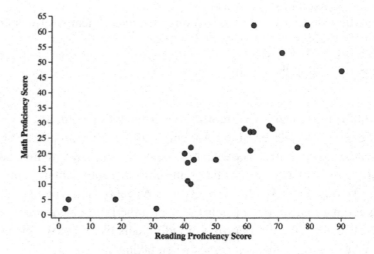

    a)   Describe the association between reading proficiency score and math proficiency score for these high schools.

The original data sets were transformed using natural logarithms in an effort to linearize the form of the relationship. Various logarithmic transformations were implemented. The transformed regression equations, summary statistics, and scatterplots for each transformation are shown below.

Model	Transformed Regression Equation	s	r^2
A	$\widehat{\ln(\text{math})} = 1.0253 + 0.03632(\text{reading})$	0.50	0.74
B	$\widehat{\text{math}} = -16.027 + 10.995\ \ln(\text{reading})$	14.4	0.37
C	$\widehat{\ln(\text{math})} = -0.0121 + 0.7808 \cdot \ln(\text{reading})$	0.62	0.61

b) Which model—A, B, or C—most effectively transforms the original data set of reading proficiency vs. math proficiency among high schools in this area? Justify your choice.

c) Using the model you chose in part (c), predict the math proficiency score for a school with a 70 in reading proficiency.

2. A group of medical researchers believe that swimming regularly lessens the chances of developing depression among college-aged students. To test their conjecture, they recruit a group of 120 college-aged students. The researchers plan to compare three different treatments: swimming 15 minutes a day, swimming 30 minutes a day, or swimming 45 minutes a day. The researchers will have participants take an emotional health inventory before and after the experiment.

    (a) Describe how the researchers could implement random assignment to ensure that the treatment groups are of equal size.

    (b) Explain the benefit of adding a control group in this experiment.

    (c) If researchers found statistically significant evidence for their conjecture, would they be able to infer that the swimming was the cause of the improvement in emotional health? Explain your thinking.

3. A simple random sample of 1012 individuals in a certain state responded to the question, "Have you ever felt pressured to lie on your tax returns?" The location and response for each individual was recorded. The resulting data are summarized in the following table.

LOCATION

		Northeast	Northwest	Southeast	Southwest	Total
	Often	10	6	19	11	56
RESPONSE	**Sometimes**	48	32	56	60	196
	Never	129	248	135	258	760
	Total	187	286	210	329	1012

    (a) What is the probability that a person chosen at random from this sample will be from the Southeast?

    (b) What is the probability that a person chosen at random from this sample will respond "Often" given they are from the Southeast?

    (c) Are being from the Northwest and responding "sometimes" independent?

    (d) For this study, describe one source of potential bias and how it would affect the estimate of the proportion of individuals in this state who would respond "often" to the question.

Answer Key & Textbook Mapping
Multiple Choice Practice Test 2

Multiple Choice Question	Answer	Learning Objective	Skill	College Board Unit	Textbook Section
1	E	DAT-2.C	1.C	3	4.1
2	C	UNC-3.B	3.A	4	6.3
3	D	DAT-3.G	4.B	7	11.2
4	D	DAT-3.L	4.E	8	12.2
5	E	VAR-3.B	1.B	3	4.2
6	C	DAT-1.I	2.A	2	3.2
7	E	UNC-4.P	4.C	7	10.1
8	B	VAR-4.D	3.A	4	5.3
9	E	VAR-3.C	1.C	3	4.2
10	A	VAR-6.G	3.E	6	9.2
11	B	UNC-4.C	3.D	6	8.2
12	D	UNC-3.D	4.B	4	6.3
13	C	UNC-4.C	3.D	6	8.2
14	D	VAR-7.I	3.E	7	11.2
15	A	UNC-3.Q, UNC-3.R	3.B, 3.C	5	7.3
16	C	UNC-1.N	2.D	1	1.2
17	C	DAT-2.C	1.C	3	4.1
18	C	UNC-1.I	2.C	1	1.3
19	D	VAR-4.E	3.A	4	5.3
20	B	VAR-5.C	3.B	4	6.1
21	C	UNC-5.A	1.B	6	9.1

22	E	DAT-1.G	2.C	2	3.2
23	B	UNC-4.Q	3.D	7	10.1
24	D	VAR-7.H	4.C	7	11.2
25	E	UNC.1.F	2.A	1	Intro
26	D	UNC-3.G	4.B	4	6.3
27	E	VAR-5.E	3.B	4	6.2
28	B	VAR-8.C	1.E	8	12.1
29	C	UNC-1.L	2.B	1	1.3
30	C	UNC-3.V	4.B	5	7.3
31	C	UNC-1.M	2.A	1	1.3
32	D	UNC-3.I	4.B	5	7.1
33	C	UNC-4.AA	4.D	7	10.2
34	C	VAR-2.B	3.A	1	2.1
35	D	DAT-2.C	1.C	3	4.1
36	C	UNC-4.AF	3.D	9	12.3
37	B	UNC-4.H	4.A	6	8.2
38	D	UNC-1.N	2.D	1	1.2
39	E	DAT-1.B, DAT-1.G	2.C	2	3.2
40	D	UNC-4.K	3.D	6	8.3

Part II Free-Response Section Solutions

Question 1:

(a) The association between reading proficiency score and math proficiency score among these high schools appears moderately strong, non-linear (curved), and positive with no apparent outliers.

(b) Model A most effectively transforms (or linearizes) the data. Its residual plot shows the most random scatter and its value of r^2 is the largest (74%) among the three models.

(c) $\widehat{\ln(\text{math})} = 1.0253 + 0.03632(70)$

$\widehat{\ln(\text{math})} = 3.5677$

$\widehat{\text{math}} = e^{3.5677} \approx 35.4$

Using Model A, we predict a math proficiency score of 35.4 for the school with a reading proficiency score of 70.

Question 2:

(a) Assign each subject a unique number from 1 through 120. Use a random number generator to generate the numbers from 1 to 120 in a random order. The first 40 of the randomized numbers will be assigned to the 15 minutes a day group, the next 40 numbers will be in the 30 minutes a day group, and the remaining 40 numbers will be in the 45 minutes a day group.

(b) A control group would be useful in that we could get a measure of how emotional health changes depending on external variables not being measured, such as time of year, holidays, etc. For example, suppose we observe subjects from winter into summer. The mere fact that progressively sunnier days might alleviate some of the emotional health issues, could coincide with both exercise groups showing an improvement in emotional health but the improvement isn't attributable to the exercise groups, rather, it is due to the sunnier days. A control group can provide a baseline for comparison to help show whether or not a treatment is effective.

(c) As a well-designed experiment with randomly assigned treatments, we can infer cause and effect.

Question 3:

(a) $P(\text{southeast}) = 210/1012 = 0.2075$

(b) $P(\text{often} \mid \text{southeast}) = 19/210 = 0.0905$

(c) If the response of northwest and the response of sometimes were independent, then the probability of saying sometimes among northwest people, $P(\text{sometimes} \mid \text{northwest})$, should be the same as the probability of saying sometimes among people <u>not</u> from the northwest, $P(\text{sometimes} \mid \text{not northwest})$.

$P(\text{sometimes} \mid \text{northwest}) = 32/286 = 0.112$

$P(\text{sometimes} \mid \text{not northwest}) = (48 + 56 + 60) / (187 + 210 + 329) = 164/726 = 0.226$

Because these probabilities are not equal, these events are <u>not</u> independent.

<u>Other approaches to determine independence:</u>

- If $P(\text{sometimes}) = P(\text{sometimes} \mid \text{northwest})$, then the events are independent.
  $196/1012 = 0.194$ does not equal $32/286 = 0.112$
- If $P(\text{northwest}) = P(\text{northwest} \mid \text{sometimes})$, then the events are independent.
  $286/1012 = 0.283$ does not equal $32/196 = 0.163$
- If $P(\text{northwest and sometimes}) = P(\text{northwest}) \cdot P(\text{sometimes})$, then the events are independent.
  $32/1012 = 0.0316$ does not equal $(286/1012) \cdot (196/1012) = 0.055$

(d) People may be embarrassed to answer that they have felt pressured to lie on their tax returns. Because of this, they may be more likely to deny that they've felt pressured, even though they may "often" feel pressured. This would lead to an underestimate of the proportion of individuals in the state who would respond "often" to this question.

Question 4:
Because we have categorical data in a two-way table based on a random sample from one population, we will use a chi-square test for independence.

H_0: There is no association between the number correct on this economics quiz and the college graduation status for individuals in the US.
H_a: The number correct on this economics quiz and the college graduation status for individuals in the US are associated.

- Random: 2235 randomly selected individuals in the US.
- 10%: $2235 < 10\%$ of the population of all individuals in the US.
- Large Counts: All expected counts are at least 5, as shown in the table:

Number Correct	Did Not Graduate	College Graduate
21 to 24	25.8	36.2
17 to 20	54.5	76.5
13 to 16	146.9	206.1
9 to 12	130.7	183.3
0 to 8	572.2	802.9

$$\chi^2 = \sum \frac{(\text{Obs} - \text{Exp})^2}{\text{Exp}} = \frac{(39 - 25.8)^2}{25.8} + \frac{(23 - 36.2)^2}{36.2} + \cdots + \frac{(827 - 802.9)^2}{802.9} = 14.798$$

P-value $= 0.0051$ and df $= 4$.

Because $0.0051 < 0.05$, we reject the null hypothesis. There is convincing statistical evidence that the number correct on this economics quiz is associated with the college graduation status for individuals in the United States.

Question 5:

(a) We will use a one-sample t interval to estimate the population mean radon level μ for homes within the development boundaries with 95% confidence if the conditions are met.

- Random: The builders selected a random sample of 26 homes.
- 10%: Because the homes were sampled without replacement, we note that 26 is less than 10% of the 300 homes in the development.
- Normal/Large Sample: Although $26 < 30$, the dotplot provided shows no strong skew or outliers, so we assume the population is approximately Normal.

The conditions are met.

Given a 95% confidence level with df $= 26 - 1 = 25$ degrees of freedom, the desired interval is

$$4.3 \pm 2.060 \left(\frac{0.5}{\sqrt{26}} \right) = (4.098, 4.502)$$

We are 95% confident that the interval from 4.098 pCi/L and 4.502 pCi/L captures the population mean radon level μ for homes within the development boundaries.

(b) The team should install radon removal systems in each home because the 95% confidence interval (4.098, 4.502) provides a plausible set of population mean radon levels, and this entire interval exceeds 4 pCi/L.

Question 6:

(a) The researchers have paired data, so the appropriate hypotheses for this test are H_0: $\mu_d = 0$ and H_a: $\mu_d > 0$, where $\mu_d =$ population mean difference (emphasized – not emphasized) in achievement scores between twin pairs where one was raised in a home where academics were emphasized and the other was raised in a home where academics were not emphasized

(b) Based on the boxplot and dotplot below, the condition of Normality appears to be violated because the sample size is small (12) and there is an outlier among the differences in scores. We should not assume the sampling distribution of the sample mean difference is approximately Normal, so it is not appropriate to use a one-sample t test for paired data.

(c) The ranks and ranks with signs are shown in the table below.

Difference = Academic –Nonacademic	Absolute value of difference	Rank	Rank With Sign
15	15	**11**	**11**
6	6	6	6
–2	2	2	–2
9	9	8	8
5	5	5	5
8	8	7	7
0	0	1	1
–3	3	3	–3
4	4	4	4
10	10	**9**	**9**
–20	20	**12**	**–12**
12	12	**10**	**10**

(d) T_- : The sum of all the ranks that have negative signs is $-2 + -3 + -12 = -17$

T_+ : The sum of all the ranks that have positive signs is $1 + 4 + 5 + 6 + 7 + 8 + 9 + 10 + 11 = 61$.

$|-17| < 61$, so the value of the test statistic T is 17.

(e) As indicated in part (d), to find convincing evidence for the alternative hypothesis, we count how often values of T of 17 or less occur by random chance when the null hypothesis is true. For example, the strongest evidence for H_a would be if all differences were positive, which is when $T_- = 0$ and therefore the test statistic $T = 0$. From the histogram, 17 or less occurs $21 + 13 + 18 + 8 + 7 + 7 + 7 + 3 + 5 + 5 + 2 + 2 + 1 + 1 + 2 = 102$. Out of 1000 trials, 17 or less occurred 102 times, giving an approximate P-value of $102/1000 = 0.102$. At the 5% significance level, we fail to reject the null hypothesis. We do not find convincing statistical evidence of a mean difference in academic achievement between twin pairs where one was raised in a home where academics were emphasized and the other was raised in a home where academics were not emphasized.

Textbook Mapping
Free Response Practice Test 2

FRQ Part	Learning Objective	Skill	College Board Unit	Textbook Section	SKILL #
1a	DAT-1.A	2.A	2	3.1	2
1b	DAT-1.J	2.C	2	3.3	2
1c	DAT-1.D	2.C	2	3.2	2
2a	VAR-3.C	1.C	3	4.2	1
2b	VAR-3.C	1.C	3	4.2	1
2c	VAR-3.E	4.B	3	4.3	4
3a	VAR-4.A	3.A	4	5.2	3
3b	VAR-4.D	3.A	4	5.3	3
3c	VAR-4.E	3.A	4	5.3	3
3d	DAT-2.E	1.C	3	4.1	1
4-i	VAR-8.I	1.F	8	12.2	1
4-ii	VAR-8.K	4.C	8	12.2	4
4-iii	VAR-8.L	3.E	8	12.2	3
4-iv	DAT-3.L	4.E	8	12.2	4
5a	UNC-4.P, UNC-4.R, UNC-4.S	4.C, 3.D, 4.B	7	10.1	4
5b	UNC-4.T	4.D	7	10.1	4
6a	VAR-7.C	1.F	7	11.1	1
6b	VAR-7.D	4.C	7	11.1	4
6c		2.C	7		2
6d		3.E	7		3
6e		4.E	7		4